2

Wm Schmidt
ΠΚΑ
G

400
675

HR —
Final — 300
Prob — 100
Lab — 100

Feb 12
Mar 5
Apr 2
Apr 23
May 7

ELEMENTS OF

Mechanics of Materials

ELEMENTS OF

Mechanics of Materials

By

GERNER A. OLSEN

ASSOCIATE PROFESSOR OF CIVIL ENGINEERING
THE CITY COLLEGE OF NEW YORK

PRENTICE-HALL, INC.

Englewood Cliffs, N. J., 1958

Library of Congress Catalog Card Number: 58-6500.

PRINTED IN THE UNITED STATES OF AMERICA
26697

PREFACE

This book has been written with the objective of presenting the fundamentals of mechanics of materials with clarity and thoroughness. To accomplish this objective, frequent reference is made to prerequisite statics. Each topic is discussed from a layman's point of view before rigorous mathematics is applied. Numerous illustrative problems reveal the proper application of theory. No theory is considered fully presented without the establishment of its assumptions and limitations. In the paragraphs which follow, a more detailed attempt will be made to indicate the methods used in the attainment of the initial objective.

Few will disagree that an understanding of the free body forms an important part of a student's background in the study of mechanics of materials. To offset any difficulty which might result from a possible unfamiliarity with this vital subject, a simplified discussion of its development and use has been presented in Chapter 1.

The desire to produce clear concepts of the material discussed is not only portrayed at the introduction of each subject, but is also revealed when considering possible modifications of the simple theory to advanced problems. For instance, in the study of thin cylinders in Chapter 4, a graph is used to illustrate the effect of an increasing wall thickness. A graph is also used in Chapter 15, to illustrate the effect of curvature in beams on the application of the flexure formula. Chapter 5, devoted mainly to the action of circular shafts under stress, alxo includes a discussion of the membrane analogy, to illustrate the method of obtaining experimentally the torsional resistance and stress developed in non-circular sections. In Chapter 7, special consideration is given to explaining why non-symmetrical beams bend differently than symmetrical beams. The discussion of beam design in the same chapter proceeds with beams of increasing degrees of dissymmetry, to discourage the erroneous and flippant use of the flexure formula in non-symmetrical beam design.

Another method used in the text, to provide a realistic approach to the subject, is its reference to practical applications. Frequent use is made of the AISC tables of properties (found in the appendix) in selecting economical sections. On occasion, practical procedures are explained in the light of theory. The moment distribution method, a practical method for finding restraining moments, is presented in Chapter 9, using the moment area principles previously studied.

Practical considerations also directed the author in his presentation of methods for finding slopes and deflections in statically determinate beams (Chapter 8). At its outset he recognizes the double integration method as the basic and classical method for this purpose. Use of this method, however, proceeds only to the point where calculations of slopes and deflections become excessively laborious and time consuming. Thereafter the moment area method is introduced to provide simpler solutions for determinate beams of any complex loading and to statically indeterminate beams as well.

On occasion, the fundamentals of a course in mechanics of materials must be expanded to provide a basic understanding of new techniques and concepts injected into engineering design. One development which has gained increasing favor in recent years is the application of the plastic or inelastic theory to design. It appears to have much to offer from the point of view of economy of materials. For this reason, there is included at pertinent points throughout the text the fundamental relative to its application. Particular attention is given to this subject in Chapter 9, where comparisons are made between statically indeterminate beams designed and investigated by the elastic and plastic theories. Another development which has gained much attention is prestressed concrete. The fundamentals pertaining to its use are explained in Chapter 15.

The study of combined strains, made necessary by the extraordinary development and use of the electric strain gage, is discussed as a complementary subject to combined stresses in Chapter 12. Here the discussion is presented in a gradual manner, starting with the most elemental type and proceeding to the most complex. The Mohr's circle is used throughout to visualize better the variation of stresses and strains from plane to plane. The direction of the maximum and minimum principal stresses and strains are related to similarly directed lines on the Mohr diagram.

The presentation of the subject matter in this text has been influenced by many factors. Chief among these have been the students, faculty, and practicing engineers with whom the author has had the privilege of working for about a quarter of a century. Their mere contact has been instrumental in molding many of the author's viewpoints. Some students and faculty

PREFACE vii

have had a greater degree of influence than others, contributing much to the overall pattern of the text through extended discussion and advice. In this regard the courtesies extended by Professor Lathrop C. Pope and Dr. David Chang of the Civil Engineering Department and Professor Frederick Kuhlen (retired) and Harold A. Rothbart of the Mechanical Engineering Department, all of The City College of New York are gratefully acknowledged.

Although the aforementioned influences have been instrumental in the presentation of the subject material, the most important influence in the final consummation of this text has been the encouragement and the extra curricula typing of his wife.

G.A.O.

CONTENTS

13. Fatigue Strength — Stress Concentrations   437

14. The Application of Energy Relationships   451

Energy Developed by Gradually Applied Loads

Impact Loads

15. Miscellaneous Topics 469

Curved Beams

Non-Homogeneous Beams

Reinforced Concrete Beams

Prestressed Concrete

Appendices 495

Center of Gravity

Moment of Inertia of Areas

CONTENTS

LIST OF SYMBOLS

a partial area, let of fillet weld, a dimension

A total area

b width of beam, a dimension

c distance from neutral axis to outside fiber

c_1, c_2, etc.   constants of integration

C compressive force, slope of straight line column formula

d diameter, depth of beam, distance

D diameter

e total axial deformation, eccentricity

e_s total shear deformation

E modulus of elasticity in tension or compression

f factor of safety

f_c, f_s unit stress in compression and tension (for concrete)

F force

g acceleration of gravity

G shear, modulus of elasticity

h a distance, height

I moment of inertia of cross sectional area

I_x, I_y moments of inertia about x and y axes

I_Z, I_W principal moments of inertia

I_{xy} product of inertia

I/c section modulus

J polar moment of inertia

k proportionality factor, stress concentration factor

K timber column constant

l length, unsupported length of column

L total length

m spring index

M bending moment

n coefficient of linear expansion, number, revolutions per min., ratio of moduli of elasticity

N number of completely reversed stress cycles

O origin of axes

p rivet pitch, intensity of fluid pressure, torque arm

P force, concentrated load

P_H, P_V component forces

P_R resisting force

q number of revolutions

Q central load

r radius of shaft, radius of gyration

R reaction

R_H, R_V component reactions

s unit stress

s_b bearing unit stress

s_n normal unit stress

s_p principal stress

s_r modulus of rupture

s_s shearing unit stress

s_t tensile unit stress

s_u ultimate stress

s_w working unit stress

s_y yield stress

S section modulus

t thickness, tangential deviation

T tensile force, torque

T_R resisting torque

U strain energy

v shearing unit stress (concrete)

V volume, total shear force

w load per unit length

W total weight

x, y, z coordinate distances

$\bar{x}, \bar{y},$ centroidal distances

y displacements of elastic curve

Greek Letter Symbols

α an angle

β an angle

Δ maximum deflection, change of any designated function

ϵ unit normal strain

ϵ_s unit shear strain

θ an angle, angle of twist of a shaft

μ Poisson's ratio

ρ radial distance, radius of curvature

Σ summation of (finite)

ϕ an angle

ω angular velocity

Chapter One

INTRODUCTION

1-1. *The purpose of the study of mechanics of materials*

The study of mechanics of materials concerns the theory involved in either the selection or investigation of members subjected to various loading conditions. To illustrate the use of such theory in the selection of members, consider a man who is about to choose a plank on which to walk across a ravine. It must be both safe and economical. Two methods of selection present themselves. First, he could try planks of different thicknesses until, by trial and error, he obtained one capable of sustaining his weight with a minimum of material. This method would undoubtedly prove time-consuming and expensive, both of material and limb, should one of the planks fail during the experiment. On the other hand, even before touching a plank, he could compute, from the basic theoretical laws of design, the exact dimensions required. Such an analysis could also include a determination of the maximum deflection, the effect of using different materials, their cost, and their resistance to impact loading and temperature change. The latter approach provides a safe, economical design, eliminating costly experimentation and delay.

A closely allied function of mechanics of materials, and a very important one, is the investigation of internal conditions of existing members. To illustrate, suppose a member is to be subjected to a revised system of loads. To insure its continued safety, the basic relationships of mechanics of materials are applied to prevent the occurrence of any dangerous internal conditions. Sometimes investigations are conducted on members to explain their persistent failure when subjected to operating loads. Whatever the reasons for an investigation, the fundamentals involved in the study of mechanics of materials will assume a major role in providing a proper solution to the problem.

1

1-2. Classification of loads

Concentrated loads, distributed loads, uniform loads. Loads applied to engineering members may be of various types. They may be *concentrated loads*, which act at one point, such as loads produced by a cable tied to a beam. Or they may be *distributed loads*, such as those produced by grain spread over the floor of a granary or by wind applied to the side of a building. If a distributed load is applied evenly, it is called a *uniform load*.

In the design of load-resisting members, such as tension and compression bars, beams, and so forth, uniform loads are often considered advantageously as concentrated loads acting at their centers of gravity. However, a note of warning is in order. When replacing a uniform load with a concentrated load one must remember that such a concentrated load is hypothetical and can be used only when the effect of the concentration is similar to that of the uniform load which it replaces. This can be illustrated in the following manner: A man carrying a beam on his shoulder would feel its entire weight concentrated at the point of contact. No difference would be felt in the amount of load carried if the board were cut into several pieces and piled upon the man's shoulder. Therefore, when the magnitude of the thrust on the shoulder is desired, it is permissible to concentrate the load. However, if the deflection of the ends of the beam were to be determined, the weight of the beam could not be concentrated because any attempt to reduce its length would reduce the deflection.

1-3. Dead load; live load; impact

In the study of statics, the probability of a force being applied continuously or intermittently was not considered. In the study of mechanics of materials, however, we must distinguish between permanent and occasional loads. Those loads that are continuously applied and never change position or magnitude are called *dead loads*. The weight of a structure or any piece of permanent equipment is such a load. Dead loads always act vertically downwards.

Temporarily applied loads are called *live loads*. Live loads can be subdivided into two types — movable and moving. *Movable loads*, such as the lumber placed in a warehouse, the furniture in an office, and the wheat placed in a bin are considered as steady loads and offer no difficulty in computation. *Moving loads*, such as trains on bridges, falling weights, and so forth, may involve considerable difficulty, especially when the movement is fast. Loads of this type will generally produce a much greater effect than that obtained by the same loads considered fixed in position. An even more quickly applied load, such as that produced by hitting a ball with a baseball bat, is further qualified as an *impact load* and will always require an investigation based on energy relationships.

FREE-BODY DIAGRAMS

1-4. *Introduction*

In the analysis of engineering problems much use is made of the free-body diagram. Such a diagram represents a whole body, or a portion thereof, separated from its adjacent supporting bodies. The forces produced by these supporting bodies, as well as any other external forces, are shown on the free-body diagram at their exact points of application and along their given lines of action. Because the free-body diagrams used in this text are derived from engineering members considered at rest or traveling at constant speed, the laws of equilibrium are applicable to them.

1-5. *General principles of constructing free-body diagrams*

In the study of mechanics, the free-body diagrams used generally concern an entire body. In the study of strength of materials, free-body diagrams are more often drawn using only a portion of a body, because of the desire to find internal forces acting on interior sections. The portion of a complete body selected for the free-body diagram is obtained by passing an imaginary plane through the body at the section where the force or forces are desired. The diagram will consist of that portion of the member to either side of the section, including the external forces in their exact location and those forces acting in the exposed section which are necessary for equilibrium.* Which of the two portions of the complete body is to be used for the free-body diagram depends on its convenience in determining the solution.

The basis upon which a free-body diagram is constructed for the solution of engineering problems is the premise that because the complete body is in equilibrium, any portion of it drawn as a free body is also in equilibrium. Second, after the free body is cut, it is deprived of the restraining forces furnished by adjacent parts of the body, and in order to reproduce the former state of equilibrium, the same forces that existed in the member before cutting must be placed on the exposed surfaces. Only one particular force system is possible on any section of a loaded member for the establishment of equilibrium. Consequently, the forces acting on an exposed surface of a free body are identical to the forces acting on the corresponding section of the loaded member before the free body was formed. The determination of these forces by the use of the laws of equilibrium forms the basis upon which further strength computations are made.

---

* If a body is in equilibrium, the summation of the forces in any direction and the summation of the moments in any plane equal zero. Expressed theoretically, this condition exists when $\Sigma F_x = 0$, $\Sigma F_y = 0$, $\Sigma F_z = 0$, $\Sigma M_x = 0$, $\Sigma M_y = 0$ and $\Sigma M_z = 0$. For a coplanar force system, equilibrium exists when $\Sigma F_x = 0$, $\Sigma F_y = 0$ and $\Sigma M = 0$.

To help clarify this discussion, let us solve the following two problems.

Illustrative Problem 1. Two tug-of-war teams are pulling valiantly, but neither side is able to budge the other. If each team consists of six men, each pulling with a force of 200 lb, find the tension in the rope at the two sections, *A-A* and *B-B* (Fig. 1-1).

Figure 1-1

SOLUTIONS. *Section A-A.* To follow the principles laid down in our discussion, let us first obtain our free body. Inasmuch as the tensile force on section *A-A* is required first, let us pass a plane through the rope at this section, cutting the rope into two parts. Instantly, the two grunting teams fall backward. The rope recoils with tremendous force and the 200-lb forces are immediately reduced to zero. Certainly there is very definite evidence that some restraining force must have existed on section *A-A* before severance took place.

To find this force on section *A-A*, we must first re-establish equilibrium for one of the two portions of the rope adjoining this section. Let us choose the left-hand portion (Fig. 1-2).

Figure 1-2

Since each 200-lb force acted on the axis of the member, the restraining force acting on section *A-A* must also have acted at the center of gravity of that section. To restore the left-hand section of rope to its original loading condition with 200 lb at each loading point, let us grasp the rope at section *A-A* and supply an axial load at that section. Assuming that the men never released their grasp on the rope, their restraining force will increase in proportion to our increasing pull. At the very moment our pull requires each man to restrain with his capacity 200-lb force, we have restored the rope to its exact condition prior to severance. Let us now proceed to determine the force on section A-A. Since all the forces acting on the rope act along its axis, only one law of equilibrium ($\Sigma H = 0$) need be used to establish equilibrium. Hence, we can write:

$$200 \times 6 - P = 0, \qquad P = 1200 \text{ lb}$$

This force of 1200 lb was the exact force acting on the fibers of the rope's cross section before cutting took place, because the equilibrium condition was identical in both the free body and uncut rope.

Section B-B. To analyze the force on section B-B, let us choose the simplest free body adjoining this section:

Here again all the 200-lb forces are acting axially. The restraining force on section B-B must, therefore, also be axial. As the force on section B-B is restored, the three men increase their resisting power. At the exact moment they attain 200 lb of restraining force, the conditions previously main-

Figure 1-3

tained in the uncut rope will have been realized, and the force P must be such that

$$200 \times 3 - P_1 = 0, \qquad P_1 = 600 \text{ lb}$$

The forces P and P_1 found in this illustrative problem are further designated as *internal forces*, since they act *within* the body of the rope.

Illustrative Problem 2. Determine the resisting forces acting on a vertical section 3 ft from the free end of a cantilever beam 10 ft long, loaded as shown in Fig. 1-4. Both the load and beam are in the same plane.

Figure 1-4

SOLUTION. As before, our first job must be· to obtain the simplest free body that will enable us to obtain the required resisting forces. Such a free body must adjoin the section in which we are interested. Furthermore, it should have the least number of external forces to provide for the most simple solution. If a body is subject to too many unknown external forces, it might better be discarded for some other free body. Sometimes a very simple free body is impossible to obtain, but nevertheless it should be looked for.

Our free-body diagram will be drawn for that portion of the beam to the left of the 3-ft section, thereby eliminating the necessity for analyzing and computing the reaction at the right end (Fig. 1-5).

Since our exposed section is vertical, let us resolve the 1000-lb force into components P_H and P_V. P_V will then be equal to 1000 × sin 60°, or 866 lb, and P_H will be equal to 1000 × cos 60°, or 500 lb.

Figure 1-5

Obviously, the body was no longer at rest the instant the section was passed through the beam. The three laws of equilibrium $\Sigma V = 0$, $\Sigma H = 0$, and $\Sigma M = 0$, which are symbolic of equilibrium, must have been broken. To restore this condition of equilibrium, those forces which had been acting on the section and were released when the cut was made will have to be restored. When applied to the severed section, the forces will then cause the beam to obey the three laws of equilibrium, or, revising the thought slightly, the forces obtained by the three laws of equilibrium will restore the initial condition of the beam.

Let us apply these three laws of equilibrium to the free body and put it in balance.

Consider first the horizontal forces. If their summation must equal zero, there must have been a horizontal force acting on the cut section in opposition to the P_H force of 500 lb.

Our equation of horizontal forces will then read:

$$\Sigma H = 500 - R_H = 0, \qquad R_H = 500 \text{ lb}$$

If R_H were to be exactly equal to, opposite in direction to, and coaxial with P_H, balance would be completely restored in the horizontal direction. But for complete equilibrium the vertical forces and rotating moments remain to be balanced.

When balancing either horizontal or vertical forces, it is well to imagine the free body acting in parallel guides placed in the direction of the equalizing operation under consideration. Thus, forces or components of forces acting perpendicular to the guides will have no effect on the motion of the free body acting in the guides. This aid is especially valuable in dealing with the vertical forces in this illustrative problem.

Let us balance the vertical forces of the free body. You will note, as before, only one effective external force necessary for consideration — that is, component P_V. Since all the balancing forces must act on the exposed section, there must exist an equal and opposite parallel force, R_V, acting in the plane.

Writing the equation, we obtain:

$$\Sigma V = 866 - R_V = 0, \qquad R_V = 866 \text{ lb}$$

Notice that the active and resistive forces are not coaxial. Because of the hypothetical guides, only vertical motion is permitted. To be sure, a tendency to rotate exists, but it is restrained by the guides.

With the horizontal and vertical forces balanced and all guides removed, an examination of the free body (Fig. 1-6) shows that a possibility of

Figure 1-6

rotation still exists. It will be noted that the two forces, P_V and R_V, which are equal, parallel, and opposite in direction, constitute a couple. Since an unbalanced couple produces rotation, it is necessary to place a restraining couple on the exposed surface to balance the P_V and R_V forces. This couple must act in a clockwise direction to oppose the counterclockwise P_V-R_V couple.

By taking moments about any point B in the plane,

$$\Sigma M = 866 \times 3 - M_R = 0$$
$$M_R = +2600 \text{ ft-lb}$$

The plus sign before our numerical value indicates that the clockwise direction of the restraining couple was assumed correctly.

Observe that the two forces constituting the restraining couple were designated by the letters T and C. Owing to the applied moment, the

Figure 1-7

beam bent downward, thereby placing the top fibers of the beam in tension and the bottom fibers in compression. Thus the reason for making this particular designation becomes clear.

As far as the results are concerned, it makes no difference which of the above equations is used first. But whenever possible, it is more advantageous to begin with a force equation that has only one unknown.

Now that we have obtained the forces to complete our free body (Fig. 1-7), the perfectly balanced free body duplicates its original state as a portion of the whole beam.

PROBLEMS

1-1. Draw the free-body diagrams of joints G, C, and E of the truss shown in Fig. 1-8, assuming the unknown forces in the members to be in tension.

Figure 1-8

1-2. A bolt 12 in. long has one end held in a vise. Assuming the other end to be twisted by a monkey wrench with a 1000 in.-lb torque, draw a free body of that half of the bolt including the monkey wrench. Draw in contrast the free body of the other half. The wrench is 20 in. long.

1-3. Draw the free-body diagrams for those portions of the beams shown in Fig. 1-9, both to the left and right of section A-A. Disregard the weight of the beam.

Figure 1-9

1-4. The free-body diagram shown in Fig. 1-10 is not complete. What must be added to the figure? *Answer:* 1000 lb acting vertically downwards, 3 ft from R_1.

Figure 1-10

1-5. Draw the free body diagram for those portions of the beams shown in Fig. 1-11, both to left and right of section A-A. Disregard the weights of the beams. One kip = 1000 lb. *Answers:* (a) $V_A = -1$ kip, $M_A = +33.5$ ft-kips. (b) $V_A = +6.4$ kips, $M_A = +7.7$ ft-kips.

1-6. In the beams shown in Fig. 1-11, consider additional sections B-B to be

Figure 1-11

drawn 3 ft from the right end. Draw the free body diagram of those portions of the beams between sections A-A and B-B. Disregard weights of beams. *Hint:* Use the forces acting on section A-A as obtained from Problem 1-5 to find those acting on section B-B. *Answers:* (a) $V_B = -4$ kips, $M_B = +22$ ft-kips. (b) $V_B = -3.6$ kips, $M_B = +13.3$ ft-kips.

1-7. In Fig. 1-12, beams AB and CD are in contact with one another at point E. Draw the free body diagram of each beam. Consider the beams to be weightless.

Figure 1-12

1-8. In the wavelike member of Fig. 1-13, draw the free body diagrams of those portions to the left of vertical sections A-A, B-B, and C-C. The entire member lies in a vertical plane.

Figure 1-13

1-9. Draw the free-body diagram of that portion of the axially loaded spring

Figure 1-14

shown in Fig. 1-14 above the enlarged vertical section. The mean diameter of the spring is 3 in. *Answers:* $V_A = 100$ lb, $T_A = 150$ in.-lb.

1-10. Two points are 6 ft apart horizontally and 3 ft apart vertically. A flexible cord 10 ft long is tied between the two points and a weight is hooked over the cord so it can slide until equilibrium is reached. Disregarding the weight and stretch of the cord, what is the location of the low point of the cord with respect to its ends? *Answer:* 2.50 ft below, and 1.88 ft horizontally from the lowest point.

Chapter Two

MEMBERS SUBJECTED TO AXIAL AND
CENTRAL LOADS

2-1. Introduction

Much of the fundamental theory of engineering design concerns the action of axial or central loads on simple engineering members. The development of these fundamental theoretical principles, as well as their use and importance in design, are discussed in this chapter.

2-2. Central loads; axial loads

Figure 2-1

If the action line of a concentrated load were to pass through the centroid of a cross section of any solid body (Fig. 2-1), it would be called a *central load* of that cross section. Its line of action would not need to be perpendicular to the section or coincident with the longitudinal axis of the body. Q is a central load for section AB.

However, if the line of action of the load acted through the center of gravity of *every* cross section in the member, it would be called an *axial load* and would be said to act axially upon the member. Force P is an axial load acting on the body shown in Fig. 2-1.

2-3. Two- and three-force members

Let us consider a steel tie rod acted upon by two forces, one at each end. If equilibrium is desired, our studies in mechanics have revealed that these two forces must be equal, collinear, and of opposite direction.

If the loads are applied axially, the member is either a tension member or a compression member, and no bending is produced.* Such a member is called a *two-force member*. Should distributed loads be placed at each end, the resultants of which act axially, the member would also fill the qualifications of a two-force member.

If, to another steel rod acted upon by forces at either end, we add a non-axially directed third force somewhere along its length, *bending is inevitable* if equilibrium is still to be maintained. The action lines of the three forces will adjust themselves and, by previously considered laws of mechanics, will pass through a common point of intersection and be completely balanced. Such a member is known as a *three-force member*.

NORMAL STRESS—SHEAR STRESS

2-4. Stress on sections perpendicular to the longitudinal axis of axially loaded members

Consider a *short* compression member with a 2 by 2 in. cross section (Fig. 2-2a) to be loaded with a 40,000-lb axial force. It is desired to find

Figure 2-2

the distribution and intensity of the resistance developed on section A-A perpendicular to the longitudinal axis.

Let us first pass a plane through section A-A, and consider the top

---

* Theoretically, a homogeneous column acted upon by axial loads at either end could not bend. Practically, however, no column is perfectly homogeneous and some bending would, of course, occur.

portion as our free body (Fig. 2-2b). Since the load is axial, balance can be restored only by placing an equal, opposite and collinear resisting force of 40,000 lb *at the center of gravity* of section A-A. This force, however, is not concentrated but is the *resultant* of the distributed internal resistance offered by that section.

The question which then arises is whether this internal resistance is uniformly or non-uniformly distributed. Under the circumstances presented, where the body is homogeneous and of constant cross section, it is customary to assume a uniformly distributed resistance.* Thus the load distributed equally to each of the 4 sq in. in our cross section is 40,000/4 or 10,000 psi. The intensity of this resistive force per unit area (an average intensity) is commonly called a *unit stress*† and is defined mathematically by

$$s = \frac{P}{A} \tag{2.1}$$

where s = unit stress in psi, P = central load in lb, and A = cross-sectional area in sq in. It is also a *normal unit stress* in that it acts perpendicularly to the section A-A.

Had the resisting forces on section A-A been unevenly distributed, the amount of force per unit area would have varied. The variation of resistance in each unit area could also vary. Therefore the value of $s = P/A$ would not be the exact stress for every point within area A but an average for all points. To increase the accuracy of the stress calculation at any point would require the use of a smaller and smaller area enclosing that point. The use of an infinitesimally small area would provide the exact stress. Expressed mathematically, this stress would equal

$$s = \lim_{\Delta A \to 0} \frac{\Delta P_R}{\Delta A} = \frac{dP_R}{dA} \tag{2.1a}$$

To return to our previous illustration, the resultant resisting force of 40,000 lb acting on the exposed section is called a *total stress*. In this case, the unit stress is further defined as being a *compressive unit stress* owing to the crushing action of the applied force. If the applied force had acted

---

* The study of photoelasticity has revealed that the degree of uniformity of stress distribution due to axial load depends somewhat on the shape and length of the member and the magnitude of the load applied. The stress will become more uniformly distributed as (1) the cross sections become more uniform, (2) the length of the member increases, and (3) the magnitude of the load decreases. Although the unit stress directly under a concentrated load is greatly intensified, this intensification is rapidly reduced as the distance from the load increases. In elementary studies, such as ours, the stress on any cross section of an axially loaded, two-force member is considered to be uniformly distributed unless otherwise noted.

† The term *unit stress* is often used in its shortened form *stress*. The phrase *strength of a material* refers to the ultimate or *limiting unit* stress at rupture.

in the opposite direction to tear the member apart, the stress induced on the section would have been a *tensile unit stress.*

Except for axially loaded members, unit stresses are not uniformly distributed over each cross section, but vary from point to point. It is the study of these variations of stress that occupies such a great portion of the study of mechanics of materials.

Notes on the use of the $s = P/A$ formula. Figure 2-3 shows a curved compression member with a rectangular cross section. Suppose the stress

Figure 2-3   **Figure 2-4**

on section A-A were desired and the suggestion was made to use the formula $s = P/A$. Would the suggestion have been correct?

For our investigation, let us draw a free body of the upper portion of the member (Fig. 2-4). The only way to balance force P would be to add P_R, equal, opposite, and collinear to force P. Since P_R is the resultant internal force acting on section A-A and does not pass through the centroid of the section, the stress cannot be uniformly distributed. Any attempt at determining the stress on section A-A by the $s = P/A$ formula would, therefore, yield an incorrect result, since dividing the load P by the number of units of area in section A-A would erroneously apportion the load to each of them equally, or, in other words, assume a constant unit stress.

To use the formula $s = P/A$ correctly, it is well to bear the following points in mind:

1. The applied load P must pass through the centroid of the section under investigation.

2. If the maximum tensile or compressive unit stress is desired in a prismatic axially loaded member, area A must be the smallest cross section obtainable. The area to be a minimum must, therefore, be per-

pendicular to the action line of the applied force.

3. Area A must be that area on which the stress is desired.

PROBLEMS

2-1. A square steel plate, 12 in. on a side and 1 in. thick, is placed symmetrically over the end of a hollow vertical cylinder with an 8-in. outside diameter and walls 1 in. thick. If a uniform load of 1000 psi is applied in the downward direction on the steel plate, what maximum compressive unit stress is acting in the walls of the hollow cylinder? Disregard the bending action in the plate.

2-2. If three 1 by 3 in. steel bars are used to restrain a tensile load of 180,000 lb, what maximum tensile unit stress is developed?

2-3. How high can a chimney be built before the compressive unit stress in the brick from which it is made exceeds 300 psi? Brick weighs 150 lb per cu ft. *Answer:* 288 ft.

2-4. A load of 50,000 lb is to be supported axially by a short hollow cylinder made of cast iron. If the outside diameter is 10 in. and the compressive unit stress is not to exceed 2000 psi, what must the inside diameter be?

2-5. How many steel rods $\frac{3}{4}$ in. in diameter will be required to resist a load of 50,000 lb in tension? Allowable tensile stress = 20,000 psi. *Answer:* 6.

2-6. A 1-in. bolt runs vertically through an oak beam. If the unit stress in the bolt is 12,000 psi, what will the minimum diameter of the washer under the head of the bolt have to be if the bearing stress in the oak is not to exceed 500 psi? *Answer:* 5 in.

2-7. Determine the maximum tensile unit stress in bar AB of Fig. 2-5 when $P = 500$ lb. The cross-sectional dimensions of AB are $1\frac{1}{4}$ in. wide by $\frac{1}{4}$ in. thick.

Figure 2-5

2-5. Shear stress

Consider the block shown in Fig. 2-6(a) acted upon by the horizontal force P located in a vertical plane which is perpendicular to section *abcd* and passes through its centroid. Now if that portion of the block above section *abcd* were cut free, it would move under the action of force P. To restore its equilibrium condition necessitates, first, the application of a hori-

Figure 2-6

zontal force P_R in the plane *abcd* (Fig. 2-6b) and second, a couple T-C acting perpendicular to that plane to balance couple P-P_R (Fig. 2-7).

Figure 2-7

Because P_R acts *in the plane abcd* to prevent a sliding action between free bodies I and II, it is known as an *internal shearing force*. Of course it is not a concentrated force, but is the resultant of a distributed resistance acting on plane *abcd*. Assuming that the resistance is *uniformly* distributed, P_R, its equal, must pass through the centroid of area *abcd* and is therefore a central load. Under this assumption, the resistance per unit area or *shearing unit stress* is equal to

$$s_s = \frac{P}{A} \tag{2.2}$$

Since the applied and resisting forces P and P_R are parallel, all horizontal planes located between them have the same tendency to slide with respect to one another and incur the same intensity of shearing unit stress.

Had the distribution been uneven, the exact determination of shear stress at any point, like the normal stress determination in the previous article, could have been obtained by considering the shear force acting on a differential area dA:

$$s_s = \lim_{\Delta A \to 0} \frac{\Delta P_R}{\Delta A} = \frac{dP_R}{dA} \qquad (2.2a)$$

Bending stresses accompanying shear stresses. The couple T-C produced by couple P-P_R acts in the same plane as P and P_R and on the exposed section to produce tension and compression bending stresses (Fig. 2-7b).

To better visualize the inducement of these bending stresses, consider Fig. 2-8, with a much taller block I than is shown in Fig. 2-7. If block I

Figure 2-8

were separated from block II, it is not difficult to see that block I would tilt about line bc upon the application of force P. This tilting tendency would still be evident if blocks I and II were integrally bonded, tension forces being developed on the left-hand side of the block and compression forces on the right-hand side (Fig. 2-8b). Owing to the greater distance between the P and P_R forces, the magnitude of the P-P_R couple would be increased. To balance this increase, couple T-C would have to be made larger by the same amount. With no increase in distance between the T-C forces possible, the only other alternative would be that the T and C forces must themselves increase, with a corresponding intensification of the stresses they produce.

Should it be desirable to eliminate the tensile and compressive stresses from the desired shearing unit stress, the distance between forces P and P_R would have to be made infinitesimally small. That plane immediately below the top plane of block I in Fig. 2-6 would be such a plane. The distortion of the affected solid material during the stressing operation produces practical difficulties which make the production of absolutely *pure shear* by this method an impossibility. Whenever this method is used to produce so-called *pure shear*, care must be taken to make sure the distance between the applied force and the remotest resistance plane is so small as to be of insignificant importance in the results.

Shear stresses may be produced by still other means, such as by loading beams, twisting shafts, by combining twisting, bending and direct forces, and so forth. Some of these more familiar methods will be handled in detail in subsequent chapters.

PROBLEMS

2-8. A certain kind of steel has a shearing strength of 60,000 psi. What force will be required to drive a punch $\frac{3}{4}$ in. in diameter through a plate of this material $\frac{1}{2}$ in. thick? *Answer:* 70,700 lb.

2-9. A small clip angle (Fig. 2-9) is used to support a load of 8,000 lb. If two $\frac{7}{8}$-in. diameter rivets are used to resist this load, what shearing unit stress is developed in the rivets?

2-10. Two $\frac{1}{2}$ by 4 in. steel plates are held together by two $\frac{7}{8}$-in. diameter rivets.

Figure 2-9   Figure 2-10

If the load applied to the joint is 12,000 lb, what is the shearing unit stress developed in the rivets? *Answer:* 10,000 psi.

2-11. A heavy underslung trailer (Fig. 2-10) is used to carry a large steam shovel weighing 40 tons. If 2 in. diameter axles support the 4 wheels, what shearing unit stress is developed in the axles? *Answer:* 3180 psi.

2-12. A 20-in. pulley is turned by means of a leather belt whose opposite tensions are 2000 and 1600 lb, respectively. If the pulley is keyed to a 2-in. shaft with a single rectangular key $\frac{1}{4}$ by $\frac{1}{2}$ by 4 in., what is the shearing unit stress developed on the cross section of the key (Fig. 2-11)? *Answer:* 4000 psi.

2-13. In Fig. 2-12 is shown the lower joint of a single timber truss. If the reaction is 6000 lb and the members are 8 by 10 in., determine the shearing unit stress on the horizontal plane *abc*.

Figure 2-11

Figure 2-12

2-14. A plywood fabricator uses the arrangement shown in Fig. 2-13 to find the shear strength of a glued joint. If P at failure is 4000 lb, what is the shearing unit stress at this load? *Answer:* 2000 psi.

2-15. A specification on plywood construction offers the arrangement shown in Fig. 2-14 to test the shear strength of a glued joint. What is the shearing unit stress obtained at a failure load of 1500 lb? Compare the advantages or disadvantages of this joint with that of Problem 2-14. Do these two joints present conditions of pure shear?

STRESSES ON DIAGONAL PLANES
OF AXIALLY LOADED MEMBERS

2-6. Normal and shearing unit stresses

An axial load applied to a compression block will be held in equilibrium only if the material on *all* planes passing through the block is capable of

Figure 2-13

Figure 2-14 (right)

resisting the load. Suppose section A-A is passed diagonally through the compression block of Fig. 2-15(a), ·reducing the resistance on this plane to zero. Obviously, the top portion would slide. The question then arises: What resisting stresses must have been present on plane A-A to have overcome the tendency to slide before the block was cut in two?

To answer this question, let us use the top portion of Fig. 2-15(a) as our free body. To balance the effect of the applied 40,000-lb. load requires a 40,000-lb. resistive force acting on section A-A placed opposite to, and collinear with, the applied load. This requirement also locates the force

(a)   (b)

Figure 2-15

at the center of gravity of the exposed section, making it a central load producing uniform stresses.

Because load P_R is diagonal to the plane, it is expedient to resolve it into its components, $(P_R)_s$ and $(P_R)_n$, both of which are also central loads. Component $(P_R)_n$, which acts normal to the plane, will produce a uniformly distributed compressive unit stress, or generally speaking a normal unit stress. On the other hand, component $(P_R)_s$ which acts *in the plane* to prevent any sliding action produces a uniformly distributed *shearing unit stress*. The component forces $(P_R)_s$ and $(P_R)_n$ may be expressed mathematically as

$$(P_R)_s = P_R \sin \theta = P \sin \theta$$
$$(P_R)_n = P_R \cos \theta = P \cos \theta$$

If the minimum cross-sectional area of the block is A, the area on which these component forces act is

$$A' = \frac{A}{\cos \theta}$$

Dividing the component forces by this area, we obtain the following unit stresses.

Shearing unit stress:

$$s_s = \frac{(P_R)_s}{A'} = \frac{P \sin \theta}{A/\cos \theta}$$

$$s_s = \frac{P}{A} \sin \theta \cos \theta = \frac{P}{2A} \sin 2\theta \qquad (2.3)$$

Normal unit stress

$$s_n = \frac{(P_R)_n}{A'} = \frac{P \cos \theta}{A/\cos \theta}$$

$$s_n = \frac{P}{A} \cos^2 \theta \qquad (2.4)$$

The normal and shearing stresses on the plane for which $\theta = 30°$, would therefore be:

$$s_s = \frac{40,000}{2 \text{ in.} \times 2 \text{ in.}} \times \frac{\sin 60°}{2} = 4330 \text{ psi}$$

$$s_n = \frac{40,000}{2 \text{ in.} \times 2 \text{ in.}} \times \cos^2 30° = 10,000 \times (0.866)^2 = 7500 \text{ psi}$$

Interestingly enough, the normal stress computed is less than the stress previously obtained for the section perpendicular to the longitudinal axis. The relationship of the magnitude of the shearing and normal unit stresses to the variation of angle θ now to be formulated will provide a clearer insight into this and other problems concerning axially loaded members.

To assist in this analysis, since $\cos^2 \theta$ is equal to $\frac{1}{2} + \frac{1}{2} \cos 2\theta$, we can write Eq. 2.4 as

$$s_n = \frac{P}{2A} + \frac{P}{2A} \cos 2\theta \qquad (2.5)$$

2-7. Analysis of equation of normal stress on diagonal planes of axially loaded members

Analyzing the variation in normal stresses from Eq. 2.5, we note that when $\theta = 0°$, the normal stress equals

$$s_n = \frac{P}{2A} + \frac{P \times 1}{2A} \quad \text{or} \quad (s_n) = \frac{P}{A}$$

This analysis not only corroborates the statements made in the beginning of this chapter, but emphasizes the fact that the normal stress in an axially loaded member will be equal to P/A only if the plane under investigation is perpendicular to the longitudinal axis of the member. It also reveals that the *maximum normal stress* is obtained only on a plane perpendicular to the axis, since the value of $\cos \theta$ will then have its highest value.

As θ increases to 45°, the value of $\cos 2\theta$ becomes equal to zero, giving the normal stress a value of only half the maximum.

On a plane parallel to the direction of the axial load ($\theta = 90°$), there will theoretically be no normal stress, since the latter term of the equation becomes $-P/2A$ and cancels the first term.

2-8. Analysis of equation for shear stress on diagonal planes of axially loaded members

The equation $s_s = (P/2A) \sin 2\theta$ indicates that the value of the shearing unit stress for any one loading condition varies in accordance with magnitude of θ. Since $\sin 2\theta$ attains its greatest value of 1 when $2\theta = 90°$ or $\theta = 45,°$ the maximum value of the shearing unit stress will be

$$(s_s)_{\text{max.}} = \frac{P}{2A} \sin (2 \times 45°) = \frac{P}{2A} \qquad (2.6)$$

Note that the maximum shearing unit stress equals only half the maximum normal unit stress:

$$(s_s)_{\text{max.}} = \tfrac{1}{2}(s_n)_{\text{max.}}$$

If the value of θ were to be 0° or 90°, the shearing unit stress calculated would be zero. Recalling the fact that the normal stress is a maximum when $\theta = 0°$, it is interesting to note in contrast that the shearing unit stress on this same plane equals zero. This is a recurring truth which will be established as a fundamental fact in a later chapter. Going to the other extreme, when θ is 90° we note that both the shearing and normal unit stresses theoretically equal zero.

2-9. Mohr's circle diagram

To assist in remembering the foregoing analysis of normal and shearing unit stresses in axially loaded members, the use of Mohr's circle is invaluable.

Using a pair of rectangular axes, draw a circle on the x axis, tangent to the y axis, with a radius equal to $P/2A$ (Fig. 2-16). Turn off angle 2θ

Figure 2-16

counterclockwise from that portion of the horizontal diameter to the right of center O, the turning radius intersecting the circumference of the circle at D.

Note. Angle θ is always to be taken as the angle between the plane perpendicular to the longitudinal axis of the member and the plane under consideration.

Observation reveals that the abscissa and ordinate of point D as it travels about the circle are equal, respectively, to the normal and shearing unit stresses for the particular value of 2θ used.

Illustrative Problem 1. A compression block 2 by 4 by 8 in. long is axially loaded on one of its ends by a force of 16,000 lb. (a) What are the normal and shearing unit stresses acting on a plane making 60° to the vertical (Fig. 2-17a)? (b) Compute the value of the maximum shearing unit stress and indicate on what plane it acts.

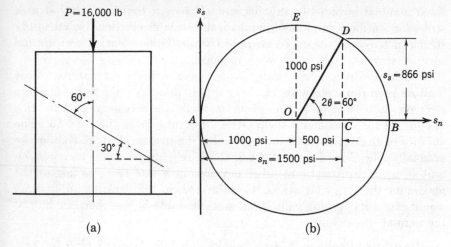

Figure 2-17

SOLUTION. (a) From previous comments, θ, the angle between the plane perpendicular to the axis and the plane upon which the desired stresses act, must be equal to 30°.

The values necessary for the construction of Mohr's circle are

$$(s_n)_{\text{max.}} = \frac{P}{A} = \frac{16,000}{8} = 2000 \text{ psi}$$

$$\frac{1}{2}\frac{P}{A} = 1000 \text{ psi}$$

The Mohr's circle is shown plotted in Fig. 2-17(b), with a radius of 1000 psi. Laying off an angle of $2\theta = 60°$, compute the abscissa and ordinate to point D.

$$AC = s_n = 1000 + 1000 \times \cos 60° = 1000 + 500 = 1500 \text{ psi}$$
$$DC = s_s = 1000 \times \sin 60° = 866 \text{ psi}$$

(b) The maximum shearing stress always occurs on a plane making 45° with the longitudinal axis. If, therefore, an angle of 2θ of 90° is laid off on Mohr's circle, we obtain line OE which, by inspection, is the longest ordinate possible of construction within the circle. The ordinate to point E is, of course, 1000 psi.

2-10. *Importance of determining diagonal stresses*

The materials available in the design of load-resisting members are relatively numerous. Included among these are the various kinds of steel, aluminum, brass, bronze, wood, concrete, brick, porcelain, and so forth.

Each material included in this list has a different limiting value of unit stress for tension, compression, and shear. Some members are particularly strong in tension, but not so strong in shear. Others, again, are just the reverse: strong in shear and weak in tension.

Should the design of an axially loaded member involve a material whose limiting or rupture strength in shear is less than half the corresponding strength in tension or compression, it would be necessary to base this design on the maximum shear stress formula given in Eq. 2.5. The validity of this statement is understood when it is recalled that upon the gradual application of an axial load, the maximum tensile or compression unit stress in a prismatic member develops at a rate twice as fast as the maximum shearing unit stress. Certainly, then, the shearing unit stress would attain its limiting value first, since it would be less than one half of the normal stress value.

Illustrative Problem 2. How would an axially loaded 2 by 2 by 8-in. compression block fail if it had the following rupture strengths: compression, 10,000 psi; shear, 4000 psi?

SOLUTION. The increase of the maximum normal and shearing unit stresses with increase in applied load is given in the following tabulation:

APPLIED LOAD (lb)	MAX NORMAL UNIT STRESS P/A (psi)	MAX SHEARING UNIT STRESS $\frac{1}{2} (P/A)$ (psi)
0	0	0
10,000	2500	1250
20,000	5000	2500
30,000	7500	3750
31,992	7998	3999

None of the loads so far applied has created a normal or shearing unit stress above its respective rupture level. However, the 31,992-lb load has produced a shear stress that is dangerously near this rupture point. In fact, there are only 8 lb of load needed to raise the shear stress to the 4000-psi point where rupture theoretically will take place. On the other hand, the induced maximum normal unit stress is well below its rupture strength.

The compression block used in this problem would, therefore, fail in shear by an applied load of 32,000 lb. Its design would of necessity be based upon shear.

The conditions requiring a design based upon shear stresses are not so frequent as may have been intimated. The majority of engineering materials used today have shear strengths above one half of the tensile strength. Designs for these materials are based on their maximum normal stress.

However, when materials with low shear strengths, such as cast iron, wood, concrete, powder iron, tile, and so forth are to be designed, it is well to investigate the rupture strengths carefully to determine what stress will determine the basis of design.

PROBLEMS

2-16. A porcelain test specimen 1 in. in diameter and 1.25 in. high fails on a plane making 45° to its longitudinal axis when subjected to a load of 60,000 lb. What was the magnitude of the shearing and normal unit stresses acting on the plane at the time of failure? *Answer:* $s_s = s_n = 38,200$ psi.

2-17. During one phase of the tensile test of a piece of structural steel, there appears on its surface diagonal lines (Leuder lines) roughly 45° to its longitudinal axis. What is the magnitude of the shearing and normal stresses in the plane of these lines if the load at their occurrence is 21,000 lb and the cross section of the bar is 1.5 in. wide by 0.375 in. thick?

2-18. In Problem 3-17 what are the normal and shearing unit stresses acting on a plane making 60° with the axis? *Answer:* $s_s = 16,150$ psi, $s_n = 27,980$ psi.

2-19. A short cylindrical compression member, $d = 6$ in., is to be made of a new material whose compressive and shearing rupture strengths are 12,000 psi and 5000 psi, respectively. What axial load can be placed on this member before failure will take place? *Answer:* $P = 283,000$ lb.

2-20. A short square column 6 in. on a side carries an axial load of 14,400 lb. Find the normal and shearing unit stresses on planes making angles of 30°, 45°, and 60° to the vertical (*side view*). Use Mohr's circle, indicating clearly thereon those lines representative of the stresses required.

2-21. A steel bar whose diameter equals $\frac{3}{4}$ in. is loaded with 10,000 lb in tension. Compute the normal and shearing unit stresses on planes making angles of 30°, 45°, and 75° with the cross section of the bar. Use Mohr's circle, indicating clearly thereon those lines representative of the stresses required. *Answer:* (30°) $s_s = 9830$ psi, $s_n = 17,030$ psi; (45°) $s_s = s_n = 11,350$ psi; (75°) $s_s = 5680$ psi, $s_n = 1520$ psi.

NORMAL STRAINS — SHEAR STRAINS
IN AXIALLY LOADED MEMBERS

2-11. *Unit strain—total strain*

Deformation, more commonly referred to as *strain*, is the inevitable result of stress. All materials are deformable by load. Some materials are elastic within a certain range of stress (i.e., up to their *elastic limit* — see Chapter 3) and are able to recover their original size and shape; others show no elasticity whatsoever. But of one thing we are absolutely sure: a stress, no matter how small, incurs a strain.

Referring to Fig. 2-2(a), suppose the load of 40,000 lb applied to the end of the 2 by 2 by 8-in. compression block shortened its length to 7.92 in.

Figure 2-18

The *total strain* in the direction of the load would then be equal to 0.08 in. (Fig. 2-18). Assuming the deformation to have been spread evenly over its entire length, the *unit strain* would be equal to 0.08/8 in., or 0.01. In all problems of elongation or contraction the longitudinal or normal unit strain is defined as

$$\epsilon = \frac{e}{l} \qquad (2.7)$$

where ϵ is the strain per unit of length, e is the total strain, and l is the original length of the member. This value would have been called a *unit elongation* had the load applied been tensile, creating a lengthening of the member. The sidewise expansion or contraction taking place during the application of axial load will generally be about 25 to 35 per cent of the longitudinal deformation within the design range of any engineering material. This *ratio of lateral unit strain to longitudinal unit strain* is known as *Poisson's ratio* and is of great importance in the design of members subjected to combinations of various stresses. (See chapter 3 for further discussion.)

Discussion of units. Note that the value of unit strain is obtained by dividing a length by a length, and if both are in feet or inches, the result is an abstract number or a ratio. Thus, if a bar is 100 in. long and has a unit strain of 0.01 imposed upon it, its total deformation would be equal to 1 in. If the bar had a length of 100 ft, with the same amount of unit strain imposed, the total strain would be equal to 1 ft.

Illustrative Problem 3. A bridge tie rod has dimensions as given in Fig. 2-19. Upon tightening, it is found that an elongation of 0.400 in. was created. If the unit strain on the interior portion equaled 0.0026, what was the unit strain on the two end portions?

Figure 2-19

SOLUTION. The interior portion elongated a total of

$$e_i = \epsilon l = 0.0026 \times 120 = 0.312 \text{ in.}$$

Subtracting this value from the total elongation gives the total elongation of the end portions:

$$e_e = 0.400 \text{ in.} - 0.312 \text{ in.} = 0.088 \text{ in.}$$

Since the total length of the end sections is 4 ft, or 48 in., the unit strain in those sections is

$$\epsilon_e = \frac{e_e}{l} = \frac{0.088}{48} = 0.00183$$

PROBLEMS

2-22. A bar, 10 ft long and 2 in. in diameter, is elongated 0.48 in. (a) What is the unit strain in the bar? (b) If its lateral deformation equals 0.0024 in., what is Poisson's ratio?

2-23. The unit strain in the tensile member BC (Fig. 2-20) is to be set at 0.0005. Considering the bar AB to be so heavy as to produce an insignificant amount of bending, how far will point A have to be moved to give the desired strain? Give answer in inches.

2-24. The unit strain in a 1-in. diameter, 100-ft rod, suspended from one end, varies in direct proportion to the distance from its free end. If the total elongation is 0.800 in., what is the maximum unit strain in the rod? *Answer:* 0.00133.

Figure 2-20

Figure 2-21

2-12. *Shear strains*

When block I was acted upon by force P in Fig. 2-6, it was deformed. Magnified, its distortion appears as shown in Fig. 2-21, and can be explained if block I is considered as made up of several thin layers, each layer sliding a small amount over the layer below.

It has been indicated that a unit strain is always equal to the magnitude of the total strain divided by the length over which the deformation takes place. This is true regardless of whether the stress be tensile, compressive, or shear. Therefore, to evaluate the unit strain in shear we must divide e_s by the depth of block I. Thus,

$$\epsilon_s = \frac{e_s}{l}$$

Since the deformation and length are at right angles to one another, the above ratio is also equal to the tan ϕ, where ϕ is the angular change in the edge of block I.

Inasmuch as ϕ is generally very small, tan ϕ may be expressed as the angle ϕ expressed in radians. Hence,

$$\epsilon_s = \frac{e_s}{l} = \tan \phi = \phi \tag{2.8}$$

Illustrative Problem 4. Suppose in Fig. 2-6, force P displaces the top of block I a horizontal distance of 0.0026 in. with respect to section *abcd*. What is the average shear strain, assuming the height of the block I to be 1.3 in.?

SOLUTION. $\epsilon_s = \dfrac{0.0026}{1.3} = 0.0020$

STRESS-STRAIN RELATIONSHIPS
AXIAL AND SHEAR LOADS

2-13. *Tensile or compressive modulus of elasticity*

In 1678, Sir Robert Hooke observed that when rolled materials were subjected to equal increments of stress, they suffered equal increments of strain. The ratio formed by dividing a unit stress by its corresponding value of unit strain is called the *modulus of elasticity*, and is here represented by the capital letter E. It is written as

$$E = \frac{s}{\epsilon} \tag{2.9}$$

where E = psi (lb per sq in.), s = unit stress in psi, and ϵ = unit strain in in. per in. This ratio of stress to strain remains constant for all steels and many other structural materials within their useful range. The maximum stress at which the proportionality of stress to strain remains a constant is known as the *proportional limit*.

The above expression may also be written in a very useful expanded form whenever the stress and deformation are caused by axial loads.

$$E = \frac{P/A}{e/l} = \frac{Pl}{Ae} \quad \text{or} \quad e = \frac{Pl}{AE} \tag{2.10}$$

One characteristic of steel that allows it to predominate as a structural material is its high modulus of elasticity. In contrast to aluminum, its modulus is about three times as great. This means that steel will allow about three times as much load as aluminum on a given area for a given deformation. However, the lightness of aluminum, in addition to its other advantages, has created many new markets — notably in the aircraft industry — in spite of its higher cost and lower modulus.

2-14. Shear modulus of elasticity

The shear modulus of elasticity is similar to the tension and compression modulus of elasticity insofar as it is a ratio of unit stress to unit strain. Expressed mathematically,

$$G = \frac{s_s}{\epsilon_s} \qquad (2.11)$$

where s_s is the shearing unit stress in psi and ϵ_s is the shearing unit strain. It is different in that the total strain e_s is measured perpendicular to the height of the shear zone, making the value of ϵ_s equal to e_s/l or $\tan \phi$. Values of shear moduli of elasticity will be found in Table 2 (p. 52).

PROBLEMS

2-25. A flat steel bar of rectangular cross section, 3 by $\frac{1}{2}$ in., is subjected to an axial pull of 20,000 lb. Determine the elongation of the bar in inches if its unloaded length is 16 ft. *Answer:* 0.0853 in.

2-26. Determine the total elongation of a bronze bar 48 in. long when subjected to a unit stress of 10,000 psi. What would the elongation be if the bar were made of steel? Duralumin? Copper?

2-27. How much will the hollow cast-iron column shown in Fig. 2-22 be shortened by an axial load of 80,000 lb? *Answer:* 0.00905 in.

2-28. Two bars of exactly the same size, one of steel and the other of copper, are elongated the same amount. How do the stresses in the bars compare?

2-29. A steel ring, having an inside diameter of 9.995 in. and a 1 by $\frac{1}{4}$-in. cross section at room temperature, is to be heated and, in its expanded state, placed over a cast-iron cylinder 10 in. in diameter. What will be the unit stress developed in the steel ring upon cooling, assuming the cast-iron cylinder will not deform? *Answer:* $s = 15,000$ psi.

2-30. A brass ring 1 by $\frac{1}{4}$ in. in cross section is to be shrunk onto a cylinder 24 in. in diameter. What should the inside diameter of this ring be if the unit stress in the ring when cool is to be 10,000 psi?

$P - 80,000$ lb

10″ diam

8″ diam

48″

Figure 2-22

2-31. Find the expression for the total elongation of a bar of constant cross-sectional area A and length L due to its own weight W when suspended from one end. *Answer: WL/2AE.*

2-32. Determine the expression for the total axial elongation of a vertically hung right circular cone of weight W, suspended from its base. The cone has a base area A, length L, density W, and modulus of elasticity E. *Hint:* Consider the origin of the X and Y axes at the vertex of the cone. Assume uniformly distributed tensile stress on each cross section and each disk element to be cylindrical. *Answer: WL/2AE.*

2-33. What is the elongation of a steel rod $\frac{3}{4}$ in. in diameter, 100 ft long, carrying a suspended load of 8000 lb? Include the elongation of the rod due to its own weight. *Hint:* The elongation of the rod due to its own weight and the 8000-lb load are found separately and added together. *Answer:* 0.734 in.

2-34. Three steel tie rods, 3 in. wide and $\frac{1}{2}$ in. thick are to be placed side by side and used as a composite tensile member in a Pratt truss. The rods were each supposed to be 20 ft long, but through an error in fabrication the middle bar was made 0.02 in. short. What will the stresses be in the rods if rigid pins are to be placed in the holes located at the ends of each rod? *Answers:* Outside rods 833 psi (C); inside rods 1667 psi (T).

2-35. What will the stresses be in the tie rods of Problem 2-34 if the center bar is 0.03 in. too long?

2-36. Compute the total elongation of the bar shown in Fig. 2-23 if $E = 10 \times 10^6$ psi. *Answer:* 0.1368 in.

A = 1.0 sq in.   A = 0.5 sq in.   A = 1.0 sq in.

8000 lb   I   7000 lb 9000 lb   III   10,000 lb
                                        II

|← 6' →|← 3' →|← 6' →|

Figure 2-23

2-37. A horizontal beam 6 ft long is suspended by two vertical rods, one placed at each end of the beam. One of the rods is steel $\frac{1}{2}$ in. in diameter and 3 ft long; the other is of bronze, $\frac{5}{8}$ in. in diameter and 8 ft long. Where must a load of 8000 lb be placed for the beam to retain its horizontal position after application of the load? Disregard the weight of the beam.

2-38. In analyzing a possible oil field, a geologist estimates the location of oil at 8000 ft below the level of the earth. If a $1\frac{1}{2}$-in. steel rod is to be used by the well driller, how much will the rod elongate due to its own weight if the entire length of 8000 ft is required? *Hint:* The unit stress in the rod varies directly with the distance from the free end. *Answer:* 43.5 in.

2-39. Determine the magnitude of the total load P which will produce an axial compressive stress of 1000 psi in member C, if the clearance between the rigid member and C is 0.002 in. when P is zero (Fig. 2-24).

Member A: $1\frac{1}{2}$-in. $\times$ 2-in. brass rod, $E = 15 \times 10^6$ psi.
Member B: 2-in. $\times$ 1-in. Duralumin rod, $E = 10.5 \times 10^6$ psi.
Member C: 3-in. $\times$ 4-in. concrete block, $E = 3.6 \times 10^6$ psi. *Answer:* 15,290 lb.

| Figure 2-24 | Figure 2-25 |

2-40. Beam OA (Fig. 2-25) is supported on a pin joint at O, and by bronze rods AB and CD, each rod having a cross-sectional area of 0.75 sq. in. When load W is applied, a strain gage placed on AB shows that the longitudinal strain in that member is 0.000167 in./in. Determine the magnitude of load W, assuming that beam OA does not bend. $E = 12 \times 10^6$ psi. *Answer:* 10,000 lb.

2-41. A homogeneous bar (area = 1 sq in.) is rigidly fixed to D (Fig. 2-26). If $P_1 = 20,000$ lb and $P_2 = 10,000$ lb, what will the stress be in BC if the gap between A and the wall equals 0.040 in. before the loads are applied? *Answer:* 11,480 psi.

| Figure 2-26 | Figure 2-27 |

2-42. Three wires connect two rings as shown in Fig. 2-27. Their characteristics are as follows:

WIRE	AREA (sq in.)	E (psi)	LENGTH BEFORE LOAD APPLIED (ft)
a	0.06	30×10^6	100.000
b	0.06	15×10^6	99.930
c	0.06	10×10^6	99.900

Determine the unit stress in, and the final length of wire a after a load of $W = 1500$ lb is applied at the lower ring.

TEMPERATURE STRESSES

2-15. Effect of temperature on engineering design

Almost all structural materials increase in volume when subjected to heat and decrease in volume when cooled. Whenever a design prevents the change in length of a member subjected to temperature variation, the stresses which develop may be sufficiently high to exceed the elastic limit and cause serious damage. For example, it is common practice to allow one end of a bridge to move over rollers. On very long bridges, where the expansion might measure several feet, the bridge is built in sections, each having a roller at one end. To prevent the action of free expansion on a hot day would undoubtedly cause severe buckling and probable failure. Cooling effects may be equally dangerous.

2-16. Coefficient of linear expansion—dimensional changes due to temperature

To facilitate the calculation of dimensional changes owing to temperature variations, the *coefficient of linear expansion* has been determined for all engineering materials (see Table 1). This coefficient is defined as the change in length, per unit of length per one degree Fahrenheit change in temperature. For example, if we raised the temperature of a 1-ft bar of steel through 1°F, we would find that the bar elongated 0.0000065 ft. Or, if it had been only 1 in. in length, the elongation would have been just one-twelfth of this amount, or 0.0000065 in.

TABLE 1
COEFFICIENTS OF LINEAR EXPANSION (per °F)

Steel	0.0000065	Concrete	0.0000062
Cast iron	0.0000062	Bronze	0.0000100
Brass	0.0000092	Invar	0.0000006
Duralumin	0.0000128	Copper	0.0000093

Had the bar previously used been 100 ft long, each foot length in this bar would have expanded 0.0000065 ft, giving a total expansion of 0.00065 ft.

Since the coefficient of linear expansion remains constant over a considerable range of the solid state of the material, a rod subjected to a temperature change of 100°F will expand 100 times that obtained for a 1°F temperature change. Thus, the 100-ft bar previously mentioned would, if it were increased in temperature 100°F, expand 0.065 ft.

To summarize the calculations necessary to obtain a change in length of a bar, we may write the following expression.

$$e = nl \, \Delta t \tag{2.12}$$

where e = the total change in length of bar l (values of e and l must have same units), n = the coefficient of linear expansion, Δt = the change in temperature in degrees Fahrenheit.

2-17. Stresses caused by temperature variations

Of perhaps even greater importance in engineering design are the stresses developed by restraining the free expansion and contraction of members subjected to temperature variations. To calculate these temperature stresses, it is well to determine first the free expansion or contraction of the member involved, and second, the force and unit stress developed in forcing the member to attain its original length. The problem from this point on is exactly the same as those solved in the earlier portions of this chapter dealing with axial stresses and strains. The formula used to determine the amount of stress developed by restoring a bar to its original length l is

$$s = \epsilon E = \frac{e}{l} E = \frac{nl \, \Delta t \, E}{l} = n \, \Delta t \, E \tag{2.13}$$

Illustrative Problem 5. A steel I beam 10 ft long is placed between two immovable walls when the temperature is 60°F. What compressive unit stress will be developed in the I beam if the temperature rises to 120°F ($n = 0.0000065$)?

SOLUTION. Had no restraints been placed at the ends of the I beam, the beam would have elongated

$$e = nl \, \Delta t = 0.0000065 \times 120 \text{ in.} \times 60°F = 0.0468 \text{ in.}$$

The stress developed by compressing the beam to its original length is, therefore,

$$s = \epsilon E = \frac{e}{l} E = \frac{0.0000065 \times 120 \times 60 \times 30 \times 10^6}{120} = 11{,}700 \text{ psi}$$

Although the computation performed here in finding the stress in the beam may be somewhat lengthy, the procedure is safer and eliminates the necessity of memorizing Eq. 2.13.

PROBLEMS*

2-43. A stress of 10,000 psi is to be placed in a horizontal steel cable tied between two immovable points by heating the cable during its installation and then

---

* The coefficients of linear expansion for various materials will be found in Table 1. The moduli of elasticity are found in Table 2.

allowing it to cool to room temperature of 68°F. If the cable is 10 ft long, to what temperature must it be heated to attain the desired stress upon cooling?

2-44. A thin steel hoop of 21.95-in. inside diameter is to be shrunk over a cylinder 22 in. in diameter. To what temperature must the hoop be raised so that it will just slip over the cylinder, assuming the room temperature to be 70°F? What average stress will be induced in the ring when it cools to room temperature, assuming that the cylinder does not contract during cooling? *Answer:* 421°F; 68,000 psi.

2-45. A steel measuring tape measures exactly 100 ft at 70°F when subjected to a pull of 20 lb. If the tape is $\frac{1}{32}$ in. thick and $\frac{1}{2}$ in. wide, what correction should be made in the reading of the tape if it is subjected to a temperature of 120°F and a pull of 30 lb?

2-46. A wood stave penstock 10 ft in diameter is held together by $\frac{3}{4}$-in. diameter steel hoops tightened to a tension of 9000 psi when the temperature was 80°F. What will be the unit stress in the hoops at 0°F? at 120°F? Assume the penstock to be rigid during these temperature changes. *Answer:* 24,600 psi, 1200 psi.

2-47. Three vertical steel wires A, B, and C are loaded through a horizontal yoke. Wires A and C are 60 in. long and have a cross section of 0.1 sq in. Wire B is 30 in. long and has a cross section of 0.2 sq in. At the normal temperature of 68°F, the bottom ends of the wires were at the same elevation with no application of load. If load P of 5000 lb was then applied and the temperature increased by 100°F, what load is carried by each wire? (Fig. 2-28.)

$P = 5000$ lb

Figure 2-28

2-48. If in the previous problem the same load is applied, to what temperature must the wires be heated before the load is entirely taken by wire B? *Answer:* 196.1°F.

2-49. A weight is supported by two taut steel wires, 3 ft and 4 ft long, which form a triangle with a level ceiling to which they are fastened at points 5 ft apart. If the wires are subjected to a temperature rise of 60°F, how much will the weight be lowered? Ceiling expansion is negligible. *Answer:* 0.0224 in.

2-50. Two rods are joined together and the ends attached to supports as shown in Fig. 2-29. If initially there is no stress in the rods, what is the unit stress developed in the steel bar if the temperature drops 100°F and the supports do not yield?

Figure 2-29

2-51. In Fig. 2-30, the left bar is copper, the right bar is steel, and the area of each bar is 4 sq in. $\Delta = 0.010$ in. (a) Determine the total force in each bar when the temperature is raised 70°F; (b) determine the deformation in each bar. The distance between walls remains constant. *Answer:* (a) 26,000 lb, (b) $e_{st.} = 0.00433$ in., (c) $e_{cu.} = 0.00764$ in.

Figure 2-30   Figure 2-31

2-52. A bar of Invar steel and a bar of copper are placed end to end at an initial temperature of 32°F, and the temperature is raised to 232°F (Fig. 2-31). If the end supports are unyielding, determine the total force on the end of each bar. Cross-sectional area of each bar = 5.0 sq in. Invar $E = 21 \times 10^6$ psi. *Answer:* 116,000 lb.

2-53. A Duralumin band (Fig. 2-32) is placed on an Invar steel core 12 in. in diameter, and a nut on the band is then tightened until the unit stress in the band is 12,000 psi. Determine the rise in temperature in the Duralumin band in order to just slip it off the core. The core is incompressible. *Answer:* 98.4°F.

2-54. A copper hoop is 1 in. wide, 1 in. thick, and has a 20 in. inside diameter. This hoop fits over a steel hoop 1 in. wide, 1.5 in. thick and 20 in. outside diameter, with zero clearance at room temperature (70°F). When the temperature is lowered to 0°F, determine the circumferential unit stress in each material. *Answer:* $s_{cu.} = 2420$ psi (T), $s_{st.} = 1610$ psi (C).

2-55. In Fig. 2-33 compression blocks A and B have been placed between two immovable surfaces and develop a compression force between them of 100 kips. It is desired to free block A. Two 20-kip forces are available for this purpose, to be applied at C and D as shown. What minimum temperature change is also required to permit A to be removed without any frictional resistance on its end surfaces? $E_A = 30 \times 10^6$ psi, $n_A = 0.0000065/°F$, $E_B = 10 \times 10^6$ psi, $n_B = 0.0000100/°F$. Disregard weights of members. *Answer:* 35.2°F.

Figure 2-32   Figure 2-33

2-56. What will the unit stress be in block C (Fig. 2-24) if P equals zero and the temperature increases $50°F$? $n_A = 0.0000912$, $n_B = 0.000012$, $n_C = 0.000006$.

2-57. Assuming FG to be initially horizontal (Fig. 2-34), what variation of temperature could be tolerated so that point F would not sag more than 0.075 in. when subjected also to $P = 20$ kips? Load and temperature change applied simultaneously. Consider bar BC inflexible. *Answer:* $100°F$.

	CHARACTERISTICS	
	I	II
A (sq in.)	0.5	2
E (psi)	30 x 10^6	15 x 10^6
n (per °F)	0.0000065	0.0000092

Figure 2-34

STATICALLY INDETERMINATE
AXIALLY LOADED MEMBERS

2-18. *Stresses due to loads and temperature variations*

When a load produces axial stress on two or more members simultaneously, it may not be possible to find the stresses in each of the component members through use of the simple $s = P/A$ formula. In other words, the problem may be a statically indeterminate one, necessitating the incorporation of additional equations for a solution. These equations are usually based upon a relationship of the deformations in the component members.

Illustrative Problem 6. A short, hollow cast-iron cylinder is filled with concrete. If the outside diameter of the cylinder is 10 in. and the wall thickness is 1 in., find the unit stress transmitted to the cast iron and concrete by an axial load of 150,000 lb uniformly distributed over the cross section by means of a thick steel plate. $E_{c.i.} = 15 \times 10^6$ psi and $E_c = 3 \times 10^6$ psi.

SOLUTION. That portion of the total 150,000-lb load acting on either the cast iron or concrete is impossible to find directly. Because the loads are unattainable, the stresses can not be found by substitution in $s = P/A$. The problem is therefore *statically indeterminate.*

However, an investigation of the deformations produced may provide the necessary information to find the loads and stresses.

Because the cast iron is five times as rigid as the concrete, it must have a unit stress five times as great. This is shown by equating the total deformation of the cast iron to the total deformation of the concrete (see Eq. 2.10).

$$e_c = e_{c.i.}$$

$$\left(\frac{Pl}{AE}\right)_c = \left(\frac{Pl}{AE}\right)_{c.i.}$$

In the foregoing equation, the values of P_c and $P_{c.i.}$ are the only unknowns. Since $s = P/A$, and the problem asks for the unit stresses in the two materials, and the length of each material is the same, we may rewrite the equation as:

$$\frac{s_c}{E_c} = \frac{s_{c.i.}}{E_{c.i.}}$$

or

$$\frac{s_{c.i.}}{s_c} = \frac{E_{c.i.}}{E_c} = \frac{15 \times 10^6}{3 \times 10^6} = 5$$

Thus, in an axially loaded member of two materials *of the same length* the unit stress in each is directly proportional to their moduli of elasticity.

Obviously, the stresses cannot be found without the assistance of another equation. This we may obtain from equating the partial loads P_c and $P_{c.i.}$.

$$P_c + P_{c.i.} = 150,000$$

$$A_c \times s_c + A_{c.i.} \times s_{c.i.} = 150,000$$

But

$$s_{c.i.} = 5s_c$$

Hence

$$A_c s_c + A_{c.i.} \times 5s_c = 150,000$$

$$\frac{\pi 8^2}{4} \times s_{c.} + \frac{\pi}{4}(\overline{10^2 - 8^2})5s_{c.} = 150,000$$

$$50.2s_{c.} + 141.5s_{c.} = 150,000$$

$$191.7s_{c.} = 150,000$$

$$s_{c.} = 783 \text{ psi}$$

$$s_{c.i.} = 5s_{c.} = 3915 \text{ psi}$$

The loads acting on the concrete and cast iron are, therefore,

$$P_{c.} = \frac{\pi 8^2}{4} \times 783 = 39,200 \text{ lb}$$

$$P_{c.i.} = \frac{\pi}{4}(\overline{10^2 - 8^2}) \times 3915 = 110,800$$

$$P = P_{c.} + P_{c.i.} = 150,000 \text{ lb.}$$

Illustrative Problem 7. In Fig. 2-35, the weight W of 40,000 lb is being held in a horizontal position by three rods, A, B, and C. Rods A and C are 42 in. long, 1 in. in diameter, and are made of steel. Rod B is 20 in. long, $1\frac{1}{2}$ in. in diameter, and is made of brass. If the nuts on the three bolts were in the same horizontal plane before the loading took place, determine the load placed on each rod. $E_{st.} = 30 \times 10^6$ psi, $E_b = 14 \times 10^6$ psi.

Figure 2-35

SOLUTION. Upon the application of weight W, all three rods elongated the same amount, Δ. The relationship between the elongations of the rods is

$$e_{st.} = e_{b.}$$

or

$$\left(\frac{Pl}{AE}\right)_{st.} = \left(\frac{Pl}{AE}\right)_{b.}$$

Substituting, we obtain

$$\frac{P_{st.} \times 42}{0.785 \times 30 \times 10^6} = \frac{P_{b.} \times 20}{1.76 \times 14 \times 10^6}$$

$$1.785P_{st.} = 0.812P_{b.}$$

$$P_{st.} = 0.455P_{b.}$$

The relationship of the loads provides the second equation necessary for the solution. Since

$$2P_{st.} + P_{b.} = 40,000 \quad \text{and} \quad P_{st.} = 0.455 P_{b.}$$

we may write

$$0.91P_{b.} + P_{b.} = 40,000$$

whence

$$P_{b.} = \frac{40,000}{1.91} = 21,000 \text{ lb}$$

Also,

$$P_{st.} = \frac{40,000 - 21,000}{2} = 9500 \text{ lb}$$

Illustrative Problem 8. If in Illustrative Problem 7 the temperature were to increase 50°F, what would the distribution of the loads be? $n_{st.} = 0.0000065$, $n_b. = 0.0000092$.

SOLUTION. In those statically indeterminate problems involving temperature changes, it is well to determine first the change in length of the rods with no load applied.

Since at the original temperature the nuts on the rods were in a horizontal plane, the difference in the elongations due to the temperature rise would equal the difference in elevation of the nuts.

$$e_{st.} = 0.0000065 \times 42 \times 50 = 0.0136 \text{ in.}$$
$$e_b. = 0.0000092 \times 20 \times 50 = 0.0092 \text{ in.}$$
$$e_{st.} - e_b. = 0.0044 \text{ in.}$$

Thus we note that the steel rods elongate more than the brass by 0.0044 in. This means that resistance to the entire load of 40,000 lb will be taken by the brass rod alone until it has stretched 0.0044 in.

The load that is necessary for a stretch of 0.0044 in. in the brass rod is

$$P'_b. = as = a\epsilon E = a \frac{e}{l} E = 1.76 \times \frac{0.0044}{20} \times 14 \times 10^6 = 5420 \text{ lb}$$

Upon the application of this load, contact is made with the nuts on the steel rods. Thereafter, the load distribution is obtained by the method given in Illustrative Problem 7. Since the elongation from this point will be the same for the three rods,

$$\left(\frac{Pl}{AE}\right)_{st} = \left(\frac{P''l}{AE}\right)_b.$$

$$\frac{P_{st.} \times 42}{0.785 \times 30 \times 10^6} = \frac{P''_b. \times 20}{1.76 \times 14 \times 10^6}$$

$$P_{st.} = 0.455 P''_b.$$

Also, $$2P_{st.} + P''_b. = 40,000 - 5420 \text{ lb}$$

$$0.91 P''_b. + P''_b. = 34,580$$

$$P''_b. = \frac{34,580}{1.91} = 18,100$$

$$P_{st} = 0.455 \times 18,100 = 8240 \text{ lb}$$

To obtain the total load on the brass rod $P_b.$, we must add the 5420 lb force required to stretch it prior to contacting the steel to the 18,100-lb load applied as its proportional part of the load when acting with the steel.

Thus, $P_b. = P'_b. + P''_b. = 5420 + 18,100 = 23,520$ lb.

Illustrative Problem 9. If, in Illustrative Problem 7, the point of attachment of the brass rod to the ceiling could be heightened or lowered, what length of brass rod would be required to create no difference in load between the rods as the temperature varied?

SOLUTION. To cause no change in the loads applied to the three rods during temperature variations would require the temperature elongations of the rods to remain equal under all conditions. Hence

$$e_{\text{st.}} = e_{\text{b.}}$$

or

$$0.0000065 \times 42 \times \Delta T = 0.0000092 \times l \times \Delta T$$

$$l = \frac{0.0000065}{0.0000092} \times 42 = 29.7 \text{ in.}$$

PROBLEMS

2-58. A steel bolt 1 in. in diameter is passed through a bronze tube 40 in. long, $1\frac{1}{2}$-in. outside diameter and 1-in. inside diameter. If the pitch of the bolt threads is $\frac{5}{8}$ in., what stresses will be induced in the bronze tube and steel bolt by tightening the nut one quarter of a turn, assuming contact of nut to bolt just before tightening? *Answer:* $s_{\text{b.}} = 6240$ psi, $s_{\text{st.}} = 7840$ psi.

2-59. Two steel plates $\frac{1}{4}$ in. thick by 8 in. wide are placed on either side of a block of oak 4 in. thick by 8 in. wide, as shown in Fig. 2-36. If the allowable stress in the steel is 20,000 psi and in the oak is 1000 psi, what total load may be applied?

2-60. If in the previous problem, both plates were placed on one side of the oak block, what total load creating equal deformation in the steel and oak could be applied if the unit stress in the steel were limited to 20,000 psi? How far from the center line of the block must P be applied? *Answer:* 122,700 lb acting 3.47 in. from outside of oak block.

Figure 2-36   Figure 2-37

2-61. A horizontal beam carrying a uniformly-distributed load of 50,000 lb is supported by three rods, A, B, and C (Fig. 2-37). Rods A and C are of steel, each 1 sq in. in cross section and 40 in. long. Rod B is of bronze, 1.2 sq in. in cross section and 60 in. long. Before the load was applied, the nuts on the rods were at the same elevation. Determine the load carried by each bar immediately after loading and also after the temperature had increased 100°F. Assume beam to slide freely over rods A, B, and C, and to be inflexible.

2-62. What change in temperature would be necessary to decrease the stress in the steel bolt of Problem 2-58 to zero? Indicate whether the temperature must increase or decrease. *Answer: 223°F decrease.*

2-63. A close-fitting bronze sleeve $1\frac{1}{2}$ in. in diameter fits over a steel bolt 1 in. in diameter. If at 40°F the shoulder of the nut fits snugly against the sleeve, what will be the intensity of stress in the sleeve and bolt when the temperature rises to 160°F?

2-64. A horizontal beam 10 ft long is suspended by two vertical rods, one at each end of the beam (Fig. 2-38). One of the rods is steel $\frac{1}{2}$ in. in diameter and 4 ft long; the other of brass $\frac{7}{8}$ in. in diameter and 8 ft long. If a load of 6000 lb is applied to the beam, where must it be placed in order that the beam remain absolutely horizontal? $E_b. = 14 \times 10^6$ psi. $E_{st.} = 30 \times 10$ psi. Disregard the weight of the beam. *Answer:* 49.9 in. from steel rod.

2-65. The cables of a power line are copper-coated steel wire. The over-all diameter of the wire is $\frac{3}{4}$ inch. The steel core has a diameter of $\frac{5}{8}$ inch. If the maximum tension in a wire is 10,000 lb, what are the unit stresses in the steel and in the copper?

Figure 2-38

2-19. Effect of changing the cross section of an axially loaded member

In order to ascertain qualitatively the effect of changing the cross section of an axially loaded member, let us consider its ntral portion, 1 in. by 5 in. in cross section, to be represented by a uniformly distributed, cross-linked family of rubber bands arranged parallel to the applied load (Fig. 2-39). The cross-linkage may be considered to be provided by small helical springs having stress-strain characteristics similar to the rubber bands. Because of the uniform distribution of the rubber bands, the ΔA areas on which they act are equal. If these ΔA areas are projected vertically onto the top and bottom loading blocks, they will present a duplicate set of areas at the centers of which the rubber bands act as concentrated forces.

If a tensile force P is now applied to the member through the loading blocks, each rubber band will stretch the same amount and will apply the same load to each ΔA area. This condition is representative of uniformly distributed stress in the end pieces as well as in the rubber band assembly inasmuch as the equal forces are equally spaced.

Figure 2-39

It is to be noted that any *lateral* strain of the end pieces is reflected in a slightly contracted position of the rubber bands.

Now suppose we taper the central portion of our member to a cross section of 1 in. by $2\frac{1}{2}$ in. at its lower end (Fig. 2-40). The concentric areas on the lower end will be half their previous value, or $\Delta A/2$. Because the density of the rubber bands on the lower area is twice that on the top area, the stress produced on the lower area will be twice that on the top area. If now the rubber bands are adjusted to zero stress with no slack and load P is reapplied, the rubber bands will stretch through approximately the same vertical distance. However, their unit strain will vary because of (1) their different initial length and (2) the lessened effect of the vertical displacement on rubber bands with increased slope (Fig. 2-41). Thus the strain, i.e. load, in the outer inclined rubber bands will be less than on the shorter vertical rubber bands. Furthermore, the normal stress placed on the horizontal concentric areas will reflect an even greater variation due to their inclination to the outer rubber bands. Thus the variation of normal stress on the top and bottom cross sections will appear as shown in Fig. 2-41.

Let us now consider the previously discussed straight tensile member with a $2\frac{1}{2}$-in. diameter hole in it. Its rubber band system is arranged around the hole as though a circular bar of the same diameter had been forced through it. The diameter of the hole is elastically maintained by

Figure 2-40 (left)

Figure 2-41

a readjustment of the cross-linkage system. The entire imaginary system of rubber bands and springs is at zero stress.

With the application of force P, another previously unencountered phenomenon occurs. Those bands that have been curved around the hole attempt to straighten. In so doing, they apply lateral force against the cross-linkage springs, crowd themselves toward the side of the hole and attempt to make it egg-shaped. This crowding action does two things:

Figure 2-42

(1) it decreases the size of the concentric areas on which the rubber bands act, and (2) it prevents the free extension of the rubber bands. The latter effect causes a greater strain in the rubber bands around the hole, which coupled with the effect of decreased concentric areas, increases the stress at the hole to a value much greater than the average stress. The normal stress distribution on sections A-A and B-B will therefore be somewhat as shown in Fig. 2-42. The ratio of the maximum stress at the hole to the average stress on cross section obtained as $s = P/A_2$ is equal to the *stress concentration factor*

The effect of other variations of cross sections on axially loaded members can be analyzed in a manner similar to that already shown. As indicated from the beginning, this study is intended for qualitative reasoning alone. In order for the analogy between the actual member and the rubber band assembly to be exact, their ratios of lateral to longitudinal unit strain would have to be the same. Actual stress concentrations for various types of discontinuities and the method of including them in design will be considered in Chapter 13. Up to that point, no consideration will be given to stress concentration unless otherwise directed.

Chapter Three

DESIGN DATA OBTAINED BY EXPERIMENTATION

STRESS-STRAIN CURVES

3-1. *General discussion*

The numerical data required for the design of engineering members are obtained from standard tests performed in a materials-testing laboratory. These tests include tension, compression, torsion, bending, etc., and are performed on the materials from which the members are to be made. During the course of each test, corresponding readings of load and deformation can be plotted directly to give *load-deformation curves,* or, in the case of axial loading, can be converted to unit stresses and unit strains and plotted to form *stress-strain curves.* In either case, the information obtained is invaluable to efficient and economical design.

The stress-strain curves obtained from tension or compression tests conducted on various materials reveal several characteristic patterns (Fig. 3-1). Ductile* rolled steels, such as ordinary structural steel, stretch considerably after following a straight-line variation of stress and strain. For steels alloyed with increasing amounts of carbon and other strengthening material, such as chromium, nickel, silicon, manganese, and so forth, the tendency to produce such an intermediate stretching point becomes increasingly remote. The stress-strain curves for heavily alloyed steels are generally straight to a point a short distance from the rupture point.

In contrast to the straight-line stress-strain curves mentioned above, are those obtained for materials such as cast iron, brass, concrete, wood, and so forth, which are often curved throughout most of their length.

If the slope of the initial portion of a stress-strain curve is constant, a constant modulus of elasticity is obtained. Indeed, the slope of the initial portion of the curve is equal to the modulus. This important fact

---

* Ductile materials are defined as materials that can undergo considerable deformation before actual rupture.

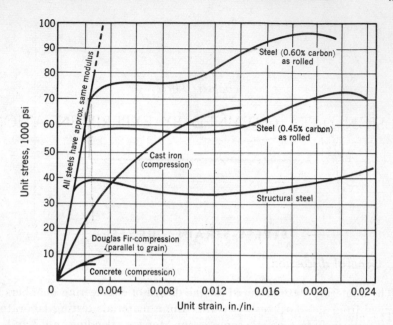

Figure 3-1. Stress-strain diagram for various materials.

allows us to obtain with a glance at the graph a knowledge of the comparative *rigidity* of the material tested, since the steeper the slope, the more
stress required to produce a given deformation. A knowledge of the
curvature of the initial portion of the curve also permits some estimate of
the accuracy of deformation computations. If the initial portion of the
curve is straight, the possibility of obtaining accurate deformations is
excellent. If the curve is rounded, the possibility of obtaining accuracy is
more remote, since the modulus of elasticity for such a material is usually an
average for its working range.

3-2. Important strength values

The stress-strain curve for low-carbon steel (Fig. 3-2) will form the basis
for the ensuing remarks concerning several familiar strength values. Low-
carbon steel is the most commonly used steel for structural purposes.

The proportional limit. The *proportional limit* is a strength value often
used in technical literature and discussion and, as such, has a specific
meaning. The proportional limit is *that unit stress beyond which the ratio
of stress to strain no longer remains constant.* Its exact location on a stress-
strain graph is not easily determined, because it often depends upon the
judgment of the draftsman as to where the curve starts to bend. The
location of the proportional limit in Fig. 3-2 is at point *PL*.

Figure 3-2. Detailed stress-strain diagram for structural steel.

The elastic limit. Located close to the proportional limit, yet entirely different in meaning, is the *elastic limit*. The elastic limit (point *EL* in Fig. 3-2) is *that maximum unit stress that can be developed in a material without causing a permanent set.* In other words, a specimen stressed to a point below its elastic limit will assume its original dimensions when the stress is released. If the stress should exceed its elastic limit, the specimen will deform *plastically* and will no longer attain its original dimensions when unloaded. It is then said to have incurred *a permanent set.*

The elastic limit is found by placing increasing loads on a specimen and noting the presence of any permanent deformation after the release of each load. That maximum unit stress, produced by the increasing loads, which causes no permanent set will be *the elastic limit.*

The determination of the elastic limit stress is seldom made since the time consumed for the test is prohibitive. This stress is usually limited to academic discussions where its concept plays an important part in comparing the relative merits of the various materials.

Yield point. Soon after the stress passes the elastic limit, the low-carbon steel attains its yield-point stress. *The yield point of a material is defined as that unit stress that will cause an increase of deformation without an increase in load.* Upon the arrival of the yield point, a ductile material such as low-carbon steel stretches an almost unbelievable amount, frequently 10 per cent of the original length. During the yielding period, there is usually a slight relaxation of stress to a *lower yield point* (point *LYP* in Fig. 3-2). This is differentiated from the more familiar *upper yield point*, which has already been mentioned (point *UYP* in Fig. 3-2).

In contrast to the two previous strength values, the yield point is very easily determined by a tension test. For this reason, it is one of the critical strength values used in writing the specifications for steel and is, consequently, a much-discussed term.

Ultimate strength. An easily obtainable and very important strength value is the *ultimate unit stress*, frequently called the *ultimate strength*. It is defined as being the maximum unit stress which the material is capable of withstanding (point *US* in Fig. 3-2). The load creating this stress is readily indicated by the testing machine (Fig. 3-3).

Figure 3-3. Universal testing machine. (Courtesy of Baldwin-Lima-Hamilton Corp.)

Rupture strength. In a ductile material, rupture does not usually occur at the ultmate unit stress. After the ultimate unit stress has been obtained, the material will generally *neck down* and its rapidly increasing elongation will be accompanied by a decrease in load. This decrease becomes more rapid as the rupture point is approached. As its name implies, the *rupture strength* is the unit stress at the moment of failure and is of little or no value in the design of members made of ductile materials.

STRESS-STRAIN CURVES — MATERIALS WITH
NO YIELD POINT

3-3. General discussion

Judicious engineering design never permits a member to have a general stress condition approaching its yield point. To the contrary, elastic analyses of members are generally based on stresses considerably lower than the yield-point stress, even though at times this stress may be exceeded at points of high stress concentration.

In the light of these statements, no difficulties in determining design stresses would be encountered if all stress-strain curves had a yield point. Unfortunately, not all structural materials show this phenomenon. Some are of the type whose characteristic stress-strain curve is shown in Fig. 3-4.

Figure 3-4. Stress-strain diagram for cast iron (compression).

It has, therefore, been necessary to adopt two arbitrary methods of locating on the stress-strain curve a point that would designate the beginning of the plastic range and serve as an *upper limit of usefulness*. The values obtained are useful not only for comparative purposes, but also as ceiling values of stress in determining allowable working stresses. They are the *Johnson's Apparent Elastic Limit (JAEL)* and the *yield strength* or *offset stress*.

Johnson's apparent elastic limit. This limiting stress value, supposedly indicative of a general plastic yielding, was proposed by Professor J. B. Johnson and is defined as *that unit stress at which the unit strain increases at a rate of 50 per cent greater than shown by the initial tangent*

TABLE 2

AVERAGE STRENGTH VALUES FOR COMMON ENGINEERING MATERIALS

Materials	Proportional Limit (psi)			Ultimate Strength (psi)			Modulus of Elasticity (psi)	
	Tension	Compress.	Shear	Tension	Compress.	Shear	Tension or Compress.	Shear
Steel								
Structural, hot-rolled, 0.3% carbon	35,000	35,000	21,000	66,000	*	45,000	30,000,000	12,000,000
High carbon, 0.7% carbon	65,000	65,000	42,000	110,000	*	80,000	30,000,000	12,000,000
Nickel steel, 3.5% carbon	50,000	50,000	38,000	100,000	*	75,000	30,000,000	12,000,000
Iron								
Grey cast	†	25,000	‡	20,000	80,000	20,000	15,000,000	6,000,000
Malleable	25,000	25,000	12,000	50,000	*	40,000	24,000,000	11,000,000
Wrought	30,000	30,000	18,000	58,000	*	38,000	25,000,000	10,000,000
Duralumin, rolled, 2017-T3	32,000		21,000	56,000	*	32,000	10,000,000	4,000,000
Brass, rolled, 70% copper, 30% zinc	25,000		15,000	55,000	*	48,000	14,000,000	6,000,000
Bronze, cast heat-treated	55,000		37,000	75,000	*	56,000	12,000,000	5,000,000
Copper, drawn	40,000		24,000	52,000	*	36,000	17,000,000	6,000,000
Timber, Air-dry								
Yellow pine		6,200			8,400	1,000	1,600,000	
White oak		5,000			7,400	1,300	2,000,000	
Douglas fir		5,400			6,800	800	1,600,000	
Spruce		4,000			5,000	750	1,200,000	
Concrete, 1:2:4 mix, 28 days old					2,500			

* Slightly greater than compressive proportional limit.
† Not well defined.
‡ Greater than tensile strength.

to the stress-strain curve. The construction necessary for the procurement of this value is shown in Fig. 3-5.

Yield strength or offset stress. When a test specimen is stressed beyond its elastic limit and then has its load released, it is revealed that during the load-reducing stage, the stress-strain curve parallels the initial portion of the curve, as shown in Fig. 3-6. The horizontal intercept on the *x* axis is the permanent set.

Figure 3-5   Figure 3-6

The previous discussion does not imply that a material is necessarily damaged if the imposed stress exceeds the elastic limit. On the contrary, the material may be benefited. True, its ductility may be lowered, but the hardness and elastic limit stress of the material will generally increase. The large amount of ductility possessed by some materials is not always essential to good service.

To derive the maximum efficient use of a material exhibiting no yield-point stress, an upper useful limit of the material is frequently obtained by locating the unit stress that will produce an arbitrarily assigned permanent set. This unit stress is called the *yield strength* or *offset stress.* Yield strengths are now universally employed for materials without yield points. The permanent set values range from about 0.1 to 0.3 per cent of the original gage length. The construction necessary for locating the yield strength is shown in Fig. 3-7.

3-4. Tangent and secant modulus of elasticity

As already discussed, some stress-strain graphs are continuous sweeping curves, whereas others contain an initial straight-line portion. In the latter type, the slope of the initial portion is equal to the modulus of elasticity.

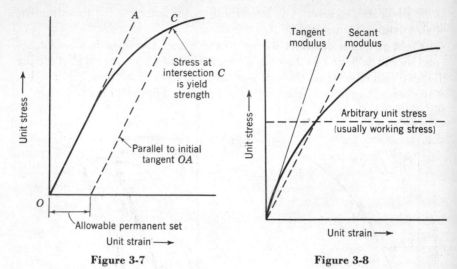

Figure 3-7   Figure 3-8

In the curved type, however, the question arises as to what slope can be used to ascertain the modulus. The stress developed in a material having a curved stress-strain diagram is often high enough on the curve to create at that point a much flatter slope than found at the origin. To offset this condition, a secant modulus of elasticity is frequently used in addition to the already discussed tangent modulus. The secant modulus (Fig. 3-8) is the slope of a line joining the point of zero stress to that point on the curve whose ordinate equals the allowable working stress, or some other arbitrarily selected stress. Its use is an attempt to average the variation in the obtainable moduli.

OTHER IMPORTANT PROPERTIES
OF STRUCTURAL MATERIALS

3-5. Behavior of materials under repetition of stress: Fatigue

Most of our information concerning the strength of structural materials is obtained from a simple tension or compression test. Considering the extended life of many of our structural members, and the hard usage which they endure, it is of great importance to know the behavior of the material under many repetitions of stress. If the properties were to change, the characteristics indicated by a single pull test would be of little value.

Fortunately, most structural members do not encounter enough repetitions of stress to warrant any special attention to their design. Those structural and machine members that do undergo many thousands of repetitions of stress in their lifetime are subject to *fatigue* and require special care in their design, as will be described in Chapter 13. We shall concern ourselves at this point with a comparatively few, rather than millions, of stress cycles as applied to the ordinary ductile engineering materials.

When a specimen of ductile steel is stressed a short distance above its elastic limit and then has its load released, the return stress-strain graph, as already explained, travels toward the zero-stress axis on a line parallel to the initial stress-strain curve shown in Fig. 3-6. Subsequent repetitions of stress above the elastic limit will duplicate the previous action. After the stress has passed beyond the lower yield point, as obtained from a single pull test, the stress-strain graph is identical to that of a cold-rolled steel. This process of continued repetition of stress above the elastic limit of a material is called *cold working*.

3-6. Behavior of materials under sustained stress: Creep

The deformation which most structural materials undergo when stressed up to their allowable limit at room temperature is a completed deformation and will not increase no matter how long the stress is applied. At some higher temperature, however, these same materials will reveal a continuing deformation or *creep* which, if permitted to continue, will ultimately lead to excessive displacements or rupture (Fig. 3-9). The length of time that elapses before failure or unsatisfactory performance occurs, may extend beyond the ordinary useful life of the member, causing no concern. On the other hand, if the temperature at this maximum stress condition is increased, failure due to creep is hastened and may occur before the termination of its expected normal life.

Figure 3-9

When such a possibility exists, the maximum allowable stress must be reduced in order to establish a rate of creep that will insure satisfactory performance at the desired temperature over a specified length of time. This reduced maximum stress is known as the *creep limit*. In this design of machine parts, the creep limit is generally set at that stress which will produce a total elongation of 1 per cent in 100,000 hours (11.4 years). Curves showing the reduction of the creep limit with temperature are given for three steels in Fig. 3-10.

3-7. Ductility

Ductility is that property of a material that allows a load to develop large plastic deformations without rupture. There are two general methods used

Figure 3-10

for the determination of ductility. The first is based upon the percentage of elongation in a specified length. If e equals the total deformation in length l, the percentage of elongation would be

$$Q = \frac{e}{l} \times 100 \tag{3.1}$$

The second method used in determining ductility employs the percentage of reduction in area (sometimes called *contraction*). If A is the original cross section, and A' the cross section of the ruptured area, the percentage of reduction of area is

$$R = \frac{A - A'}{A} \times 100 \tag{3.2}$$

It is generally true that if the figures for percentage of elongation and reduction of area are large, the material has the ability to stand abuse in fabrication and service. It is also true that in many instances ductility is necessary to relieve localized and initial stresses and to act as insurance against destruction and complete collapse due to excessive loads.

3-8. Resilience

When a tension member is acted on by an axial load P and undergoes a corresponding axial deformation Δ, an amount of external work equal to

$\frac{1}{2}P\Delta$ is performed *on the member.** This external work as dictated by the Conservation of Energy theorem, is captured or transformed into an equivalent amount of internal energy created by the elastic or semi-elastic distortion of the interior elements and is equal to the area under the stress-strain curve.

The ability of a member to release this captured energy quickly as the load is removed is a measure of its *resilience.* It is measured as the area under the released stress-strain curve. For purposes of comparison and design, the value of *modulus of resilience* is used. It is equal to the area under the stress-strain curve up to the elastic limit. For materials having a straight-line variation of stress to strain up to the elastic limit, and whose released stress-strain curve is almost identical to it, (Fig. 3-6) the modulus of resilience is equal to $\frac{1}{2} s_E \epsilon_E$ or $s_E^2/2E$ where s_E is the elastic limit stress of the material. It might also be thought of as the amount of energy stored in each cubic inch of material at the elastic limit.

3-9. Toughness

The total energy absorbed by a material before failure is known as its toughness, and although mostly unrecoverable, is important in determining the maximum resistance of a material to impact. The unit measure of this maximum resistance (toughness) is called the *modulus of toughness* and is defined as *the amount of energy absorbed per unit volume up to the breaking point.* It is equal to the area under the stress-strain curve to rupture.

3-10. Poisson's ratio

Poisson, a French engineer of the early 19th century, found that the lateral unit strain of structural materials bore an almost constant ratio to the longitudinal unit strain when subjected to either tension or compression stress within the elastic limit. The Poisson ratios for metals vary from about 0.25 to 0.36 and are denoted by the letter μ.

The relationship between G and E. A convenient relationship between the torsional and axial rigidities of a material and its Poisson's ratio can be shown theoretically to be

$$G = \frac{E}{2(1 + \mu)} \tag{3.3}$$

Therefore, the value of μ also can be determined by computation from a knowledge of the experimental values of G and E. The equation also reveals that structural steel having a value of μ equal to 0.25 provides a theoretical ratio of $G/E = \frac{2}{5}$, which agrees with its experimental determination.

---

* The work equals $\frac{1}{2} P\Delta$ rather than $P\Delta$ because the maximum deformation Δ was obtained only after P had increased from zero to its full value.

Another stress-strain relationship. Because of the presence of lateral strain, a cubical element (Fig. 3-11a) stressed in tension in the y direction produces strains along the three axes equal to

$$\epsilon'_y = \frac{s_y}{E}, \quad \epsilon'_x = -\mu\epsilon'_y, \quad \epsilon'_z = -\mu\epsilon'_y \tag{3.4}$$

the negative sign indicating a contraction.

Figure 3-11

Similarly, were a tensile stress acting along the x direction (Fig. 3-11b), the strains would be

$$\epsilon''_x = \frac{s_x}{E}, \quad \epsilon''_y = -\mu\epsilon''_x, \quad \epsilon''_z = -\mu\epsilon''_x \tag{3.5}$$

However, should there be tensile stresses acting in *both* the x and y directions (Fig. 3-11c), their corresponding strains would have an additive effect on one another, so that

$$\epsilon_x = \epsilon''_x - \mu\epsilon'_y \tag{3.6}$$

$$\epsilon_y = \epsilon'_y - \mu\epsilon''_x \tag{3.7}$$

$$\epsilon_z = -\mu\epsilon'_y - \mu\epsilon''_x \tag{3.8}$$

where the values of ϵ_x, ϵ_y, and ϵ_z are the actual experimental strains measured in the x, y and z directions. If the biaxial strain equations above are placed in terms of the stresses in the x and y directions, they will read as follows:

$$\epsilon_x = \frac{s_x}{E} - \frac{\mu s_y}{E}, \quad \epsilon_y = \frac{s_y}{E} - \frac{\mu s_x}{E}, \quad \epsilon_z = -\frac{\mu s_y}{E} - \frac{\mu s_x}{E} \qquad (3.9)$$

Simultaneous solution for s_x and s_y obtains

$$s_x = \frac{(\epsilon_x + \mu \epsilon_y)E}{1 - \mu^2}, \quad s_y = \frac{(\epsilon_y + \mu \epsilon_x)E}{1 - \mu^2} \qquad (3.10)$$

These equations are used in the experimental determination of stresses and will be discussed in more detail in a later chapter.

Illustrative Problem 1. An engine housing is to be tested under load. Two strain gages placed at a certain point on its surface perpendicular to one another and in directions parallel to applied stresses s_x and s_y record unit strains of $\epsilon_x = +0.00080$ and $\epsilon_y = -0.00050$. If Poisson's ratio equals 0.3 and $E = 15,000,000$ psi, what are the stresses in the directions of the gages? No shear stresses accompany s_x and s_y.

SOLUTION. Substituting the given data in Eq. 3.10 gives

$$s_x = \frac{(0.00080 - 3 \times 0.00050)}{1 - 0.09} 15 \times 10^6$$

$$= \frac{0.00065 \times 15 \times 10^6}{0.91} = 10,700 \text{ psi}$$

$$s_y = \frac{(-0.00050 + .3 \times 0.00080)}{0.91} 15 \times 10^6$$

$$= \frac{-0.00026 \times 15 \times 10^6}{0.91} = -4280 \text{ psi}$$

PROBLEMS

3-1. A 2-in. Duralumin test specimen ($d = 0.505$ in.), when subjected to tensile load, elongates in accordance with the following data:

Unit Stress	Unit Strain	Unit Stress	Unit Strain	Unit Stress	Unit Strain
5,000	0.0005	30,000	0.003	50,000	0.125
10,000	0.0010	32,500	0.00325	54,000	0.300
15,000	0.0015	35,000	0.00375	45,000	0.480
					(Ruptured)
20,000	0.0020	40,000	0.0065	Reduced diameter	
25,000	0.0025	45,000	0.0110	= 0.320 in.	

Plot the stress-strain curve and determine the proportional limit, the modulus of elasticity, the yield strength (offset = 0.1 per cent strain), the percentage of elongation, and the percentage of reduction of area.

3-2. From the tension test on a piece of structural steel, the following data are obtained: original diameter, 0.505 in.; diameter of ruptured area, 0.346 in.; original test length, 2 in.; elongated test length, 2.88. Determine the ductility of the steel based on percentage of elongation and percentage of reduction in area. *Answer:* 44.0 per cent, 53.0 per cent.

3-3. In the tension test of a cellulose-acetate butyrate plastic, the following stress-strain readings were obtained:

Unit Stress (psi)	Unit Strain	Unit Stress (psi)	Unit Strain	Unit Stress (psi)	Unit Strain
0	0.00	2800	0.035	3720	0.310
400	0.005	3200	0.040	3780	0.370
800	0.010	3600	0.048	3950	0.440
1,200	0.015	3900	0.060	4150	0.500
1,600	0.020	4380	0.120	4450	0.560
2,000	0.025	3750	0.185	4800	0.620
2,400	0.030	3700	0.250	5100	0.000

Determine the following: (a) proportional limit, (b) upper yield point stress, (c) lower yield point stress, (d) modulus of elasticity, (e) modulus of resilience, (f) modulus of toughness, (g) ultimate strength. *Answers:* (a) 3200 psi, (b) 4380 psi, (c) 3700 psi, (d) 80,000 psi, (e) 64 psi, (f) 2580 psi, (g) 5100 psi.

3-4. A gray cast-iron specimen, with a 2 in. gage length tested in tension, gave the following stress-strain readings:

UNIT STRESS	UNIT STRAIN
5,000	0.0003
10,000	0.0007
15,000	0.0012
20,000	0.0020
25,000	0.0032
30,000	0.0055
32,500	0.008 (failure)

Determine the following: (a) tangent modulus of elasticity, (b) secant modulus of elasticity (use stress = 15,000 psi), (c) Johnson's apparent elastic limit, (d) yield strength (offset equal to 0.001 in.^{2}), (e) modulus of toughness. *Answers:* (a) 16.67 $\times$ 10^6 psi, (b) 12.50 $\times$ 10^6 psi, (c) 7500 psi, (d) 21,000 psi, (e) 172 in.-lb per in.^{3}

3-5. In a tensile test of an alloy steel specimen 1 in. in diameter, the total elongation in 8 in. recorded at a load of 46,000 lb is 0.01560 in. At the same moment, the diameter measures 0.9995 in. Compute the modulus of elasticity and Poisson's ratio, assuming the applied stress to be below the elastic limit. *Answers:* 30 $\times$ 10^6 psi, 0.256.

3-6. If Poisson's ratio is equal to 0.33 for the specimen of Problem 3-1, determine the lateral contraction of the diameter at a unit stress of 25,000 psi. *Answer:* 0.000417 in.

3-7. If in Illustrative Problem 3-1, the strains recorded were $\epsilon_x = -0.00080$ and $\epsilon_y = +0.00050$ what would the corresponding stresses be?

3-8. Assume $\epsilon_x = +0.00080$ and $\epsilon_y = +0.00050$ in Illustrative Problem 3-1 and solve for the corresponding stresses. *Answers:* $s_x = 15,650$ psi, $s_y = 12,200$ psi.

ALLOWABLE WORKING STRESS — FACTOR OF SAFETY

3-11. *Allowable working stress*

An allowable working unit stress is that maximum unit stress that can be safely applied to a material subjected to a particular loading condition. It is a unit stress derived from the results of many tests and the accumulated experience obtained from many years of first-hand observation in the performance of members in actual service. The magnitude of the allowable working unit stress will control the cross-sectional area and, consequently, the weight and cost of the members designed.

3-12. *Factor of safety*

Owing to the possible inconsistency of structural strengths, the variance in calculated and exact stress and the difficulty of ascertaining the magnitude of the applied loads, a reduction of stress from the ultimate, or yield-point, stresses is necessary for design purposes. The ratio of the ultimate unit stress (or yield-point stress) to the allowable working unit stress is called the *factor of safety*.

The actual determination of the value of the factor of safety to be used, say, for structural steel for buildings, is usually delegated to a group of engineers appointed by some of the larger national engineering societies or by a large city for use in its building code. These engineers, in addition to determining the uncertainties of structural properties, stresses, and applied loads, consider such matters as the depreciation or useful life of the structure, the loss in life and property should the structure collapse, the effectiveness of regular painting, and so forth. Building contracts often specify the maximum stresses that may be employed.

The specifications for machine members are perhaps even more rigid than those for structural steel. Impact, fatigue, and creep are items generally to be encountered. In each case, a reduction of the allowable working unit stress is required.

Values of allowable working unit stress for various materials under static load and normal working conditions are given in Table 3. This table should be committed to memory.

TABLE 3
ALLOWABLE UNIT STRESSES FOR VARIOUS ENGINEERING MATERIALS

	Tension (psi)	Compression (psi)	Shear (psi)
Structural steel.....................	20,000	20,000	15,000
Wrought iron.......................	12,000	12,000	8,000
Duralumin..........................	15,000	15,000	10,000
Cast iron..........................	3,000	15,000	3,000
Yellow pine, air dry.................	...	1,200*	150†
White oak, air dry..................	...	1,000*	200†
Douglas fir, air dry.................	...	1,200*	150†
Spruce, air dry.....................	...	700*	100†

* Parallel to grain.
† Shear, with the grain.

Illustrative Problem 2. The clevis joint shown in Fig. 3-12 has a capacity load of 6 tons. (a) If the material has a yield point in tension of 40,000 psi and 0.6 of that amount in shear, what are the factors of safety, based upon the yield points of the tensile stress in the clevis on section *A-A* and the shear stress in the pin? (b) If the allowable working unit stresses were increased to 14,000 psi in tension and 9000 psi in shear, what percentage of material would be saved? (c) Determine the factors of safety of the allowable working unit stresses given in (b) with the ultimate

Figure 3-12

tensile unit stress of 66,000 psi and the ultimate shearing unit stress of 40,000 psi.

SOLUTION. (a) Factor of safety on section A-A of clevis:

$$\text{Tensile unit stress used in design} = \frac{P}{A} = \frac{12,000}{2 \times (3-1) \times \frac{1}{4}} = 12,000 \text{ psi}$$

$$\text{Factor of safety} = \frac{40,000}{12,000} = 3.33$$

Factor of safety on pin:

$$\text{Shearing unit stress used in design} = \frac{P_s}{A_s} = \frac{12,000}{2 \times \pi 1^2/4} = 7640 \text{ psi}$$

$$\text{Factor of safety} = \frac{24,000}{7640} = 3.14$$

(b) The percentage of material saved on section A-A would equal

$$\frac{\text{present cross section} - \text{new cross section}}{\text{present cross section}}$$

$$\frac{2 \times \frac{1}{4} \times (3-1) - \dfrac{12,000}{14,000}}{2 \times \frac{1}{4} \times (3-1)} = \frac{1 - 0.833}{1} \times 100 - 16.7 \text{ per cent}$$

The percentage of material saved on the pin would be equal to the reduction of the cross-sectional area:

$$\frac{2 \times 0.7854 - \dfrac{12,000}{9000}}{2 \times 0.7854} = \frac{1.571 - 1.333}{1.571} \times 100 = 15.1 \text{ per cent}$$

Further computation would reveal that the amount of material used in the design of tension and shear members is inversely proportional to the allowable working unit stresses. When, at the beginning of World War II, the shortage of steel was felt in all channels of industry, the allowable working stress in steel was increased up to 50 per cent. This resulted in a substantial saving of this precious material.

(c) The new factors of safety with respect to the given ultimate unit stresses are:

For tension, $\dfrac{66,000}{14,000} = 4.71$

For shear, $\dfrac{40,000}{9000} = 4.44$

These values are considerably higher than those used for steel under conditions of steady load and normal temperatures (factor of safety = 3 to 4). However, should impact, fatigue, high temperatures, or combinations of two or three of these items be involved in the design of a member, the factor of safety could easily reach the values obtained above.

PROBLEMS

3-9. The allowable soil-bearing pressure at the site of a contemplated foundation is 4 tons per sq ft. What size of square footing would be required to resist a load of 273,000 lb? The weight of the footing is 15,000 lb. *Answer:* 6 by 6 ft.

3-10. A certain building code requires that an allowable stress of 16,000 psi be used in the design of a certain member. If the material of which this member is made has an ultimate strength of 70,000 psi and a yield-point strength of 38,000 psi, what will be the factor of safety (a) based on the ultimate strength, (b) based on the yield-point strength?

3-11. If the allowable stress for steel eyebars is 24,000 psi, how many bars 1 by 4 in. will be required to resist a load 384,000 lb? *Answer:* 4.

3-12. A pulley 20 in. in diameter (Fig. 3-13) is fastened to a 2-in. shaft with a $\frac{1}{4}$ by $\frac{1}{2}$-in. key, 4 in. long. While operating at constant speed, the belt driving the pulley has opposite tensions of 300 and 200 lb. What factor of safety is obtained in the key if the ultimate shearing unit stress is 45,000 psi?

Figure 3-13   Figure 3-14

3-13. A roll of paper weighing 6000 lb has passed through its center a 2-in. steel shaft supported by 2 angle frames, one on each end (Fig. 3-14). (a) If the shearing ultimate strength of the steel is 40,000 psi, what is the factor of safety of the shaft based on shear? (b) The end supports rest on timber bearing blocks. If the contact surface between one metal frame and its bearing block is 20 sq in., what factor of safety is obtained if the timber has a bearing ultimate strength of 900 psi? *Answer:* (a) 41.9, (b) 6.0.

3-14. A hotel canopy is 25 ft by 20 ft, the 25-ft dimension being parallel to the wall. The canopy is held by two round tie-bars fastened to the canopy 12 feet from the wall and making an angle of 45° with the horizontal. The maximum total load is 100 lb. per sq ft. What diameter tie-bar is required at an allowable tensile stress of

10,000 psi, assuming 25 per cent of the section to be lost because of rivet holes? Consider the canopy to be free to rotate at the wall. *Answer: 2.24 in.*

3-13. *Plastic yielding at stress concentrations*

In the analysis of the axially loaded tensile member made of rubber bands (§ 2-19), it was shown that the insertion of a hole produced a non-uniform stress distribution on the transverse section passing through its center (Fig. 3-15(a). More specifically, the stress at the edge of the hole was substantially higher than the average normal stress on the section. Forming the basis of this analysis was the assumption that stress

Figure 3-15

and strain were proportional; in other words, that all deformations were perfectly elastic.

Let us now assume that the material from which the member is made has a stress-strain diagram shown in Fig. 3-15(b) and that the stress at the edge of the hole has just attained the yield point. If the load is now removed, the stresses would reduce to zero, elastically restoring the hole to its original shape. If, on the other hand, the load is increased, the fibers near the edge of the hole will find it impossible to increase their resistance and will yield instead in accordance with line YF on Fig. 3-15(b). Because of the restraint offered by other fibers on the section, such as B, C, and D, still stressed below the yield point and deformed elastically, yielding at the edge of the hole continues to a point R instead of F, Fig. 3-15(c). Were the load now removed, all fibers on the section would try to resume their original position. Fiber A, however, stretched through a portion of the yield range, has undergone a permanent set OR' and cannot return completely. Fiber B, still elastic, tries to assume its normal zero strain position but, because adjacent fiber A has a permanent set, finds it impossible to do so. Fiber B is therefore still under tension compressing fiber A. The approximate stress distribution curve after this last removal of load is shown in Fig. 3-15(d).

Subsequent static tensile loadings of the same member would find its resistance improved rather than lessened. This apparent inconsistency is substantiated when stress diagrams 3-15(c) and 3-15(d) are superimposed on one another, revealing a decrease of stress concentration and perfect elastic action of all fibers (Fig. 3-15e). Compression loadings, however, are therefore more critical while repeated tension and compression loads reveal the inelastic stretch to have weakened the material considerably.

Chapter Four

STRESSES IN THIN-WALLED CYLINDERS AND
SPHERES, RIVETED AND WELDED JOINTS

4-1. *Stresses in thin-walled cylinders and spheres — general discussion*

The formulas of stresses in the walls of thin-walled cylinders and spheres subjected to uniform internal pressure are based upon the assumption of a uniform stress distribution over the thickness of the wall (Fig. 4-1). The close

Figure 4-1

agreement of this assumption with the actual stress distribution in such vessels permits the application of these formulas to the design of all common types of cylinders and spheres, such as storage tanks, water tanks, steam boilers, and so forth.

Because the modifier *thin-walled* is a relative term, care must be taken not to use the following stress formulas for all cylinders and spheres. The effect of wall thickness on stress variation will be discussed in § 4-3.

4-2. Derivation of formula for stress on longitudinal section of thin-walled cylinders subjected to uniform interior pressure

The longitudinal section on which the maximum stress will occur is found by passing a plane through the cylinder that will expose a minimum cross section of wall and provide a maximum thrust. Such a combination is

Figure 4-2

obtained when the cutting plane passes through the longitudinal axis (see Fig. 4-2b).

In Fig. 4-2(a) is shown a section of a thin-walled cylinder subjected to a uniform interior pressure. An end view of one half of this section is shown in Fig. 4-2(b) and will serve as the free body for this discussion.

Since the internal pressure acting on the interior of our circular-sectioned free body is uniformly distributed and symmetrical about the horizontal center line, it produces a perfect balance in the vertical direction. The resultant must, consequently, be horizontal and act to the left of the figure along the center line.

To balance this resultant internal pressure, forces must act on the two exposed vertical surfaces. Since these two forces are equidistant from the resultant, they must be equal and horizontal to retain the circular shape of the shell. In fact, Fig. 4-2d, a free body of a very small portion of the cylinder wall, shows that the effect of the internal pressure is to change the direction of the resisting force in the shell so that it is tangent at all points on the circumference. Assuming these resisting forces to act at the centroids, they will develop uniformly distributed tensile unit stresses over the wall sections. If the average unit stress thus developed is s_t, each resisting force will be equal to

$$P = s_t \times t \times l \tag{4.1}$$

To ascertain the magnitude of the force created by the internal pressure p psi, let us refer to Figs. 4-2(a) and (b). Directing our attention more specifically to dA, one of the many very small areas of ds width and length l shown on Fig. 4-2(a), we may write the following:

The force on dA equals

$$p \times dA = p \times ds \times l$$

The horizontal component of force acting on dA equals

$$p \times ds \times l \times \cos \theta$$

To obtain the total horizontal effect R, we must add all the horizontal components acting on the various dA's.

$$R = \int pl \cos \theta \, ds$$

But since p and l are constant quantities appearing in every horizontal component, we may write the above as

$$R = pl \int \cos \theta \, ds$$

The value of $\cos \theta \, ds$ is, however, equal to the vertical projection of the arc distance ds or dh (Fig. 4-2c). Thus

$$R = pl \int dh$$

But the summation of all the vertical projections equals the inside diameter d. So the previous expression can be written

$$R = pld \qquad (4.2)$$

Since the horizontal forces must balance,

$$P + P = R, \qquad 2P = pld$$

But $p = s_t tl$; therefore,

$$t = \frac{pd}{2s_t} \quad \text{or} \quad s_t = \frac{pd}{2t} \qquad (4.3)$$

where s_t = unit stress on longitudinal section of wall in psi, p = internal uniform fluid pressure in psi, d = inside diameter of cylinder in inches, and t = wall thickness in inches.

Illustrative Problem 1. A boiler 6 ft in diameter and 12 ft long is subjected to an internal steam pressure of 125 psi. If the thickness of the plates is $\frac{1}{2}$ in., what unit stress is developed on a longitudinal section of the shell?

SOLUTION. By substituting the above values in formula 4.3 we obtain

$$s_t = \frac{pd}{2t} = \frac{125 \times 72}{2 \times \frac{1}{2}} = 9000 \text{ psi}$$

4-3. Effect of cylinder wall thickness on stress variation

The graph shown in Fig. 4-3 reveals the variation of the maximum stress to the uniform stress assumed in the thin-cylinder formula as the thickness of the wall increases. To illustrate its use, let us determine the ratio of the maximum unit stress to the assumed uniform stress in a cylinder wall whose ratio of inside to outside radius is equal to 0.7. The value of the ordinate at the 0.7 abscissa is 1.25, indicating that this is the ratio of the maximum stress to the uniform stress assumed in the thin-cylinder formula. The dash line has been added to show the actual stress distribution over the cross section of the shell.

An analysis of this graph further reveals that when the wall thickness is 20 per cent of the internal radius, the maximum stress computed by exact theory is only 10 per cent greater than the uniform stress assumed in the thin-wall formula. Reducing the wall thickness to 10 per cent of the internal radius reduces the difference between the stresses to about 4 per cent.

The thin-cylinder formula, consequently, has a field of application as wide as that allowed by the permissible stress variation. If the ratio of the radii, r_1/r_2, becomes so large as to increase the stress variation above

Figure 4-3

the allowable, the constant found in the graph of Fig. 4-3 when multiplied by the stress obtained from the formula will give the theoretical maximum stress.

4-4. Stress on transverse section of cylinders and spheres

Cylinders. In addition to the tendency of a cylinder to burst open along a longitudinal section when subjected to an internal pressure, there is also the tendency for the ends to be blown off. To combat this latter tendency, tensile stresses are developed along every transverse section of the cylinder. Significantly enough, the cylinder, owing to the pressure acting on each end plate, is in reality *an axially loaded tension member*. To determine these tensile stresses, therefore, we need only apply the now familiar $P = As$ formula.

Derivation. In Fig. 4-4, a free body of the end portion of a cylinder is shown exposing a section perpendicular to the longitudinal axis. The resultant of the uniformly distributed internal pressure acting on the inside of the end bulkhead

Figure 4-4

is an axial force equal to

$$R = \frac{\pi d^2}{4} \times p$$

Opposing this internal pressure, and of necessity equal to R, is the restraining force on the cross section of the cylinder wall whose diameter is taken equal to d. Equating both in the $P = As$ formula, there is obtained

$$\frac{\pi d^2}{4} \times p = (t \times \pi d) s'_t$$

from which

$$s'_t = \frac{pd}{4t} \qquad (4.4)$$

A comparison of the stresses on the longitudinal and transverse sections reveals that the stress on the longitudinal section is just twice the value of the stress on the transverse section. This observation leads to an important conclusion in that *if joints are required in a cylinder, twice the amount of reinforcement in either rivets or weld material is required for a longitudinal joint as compared to that for a transverse joint.*

Illustrative Problem 2. What is the tensile unit stress developed on a transverse section of the boiler discussed in Illustrative Problem 1? SOLUTION.

$$s'_t = \frac{pd}{4t} = \frac{125 \times 72}{4 \times \frac{1}{2}} = 4500 \text{ psi}$$

Figure 4-5

Spherical shells. The hemisphere shown in Fig. 4-5 is used as a free body in the determination of the maximum tensile stresses occurring in spherical shells. The ratio of the internal force acting on this free body to the area of its metallic cross section, being greater than for any other possible free body, makes the stresses on the section a maximum. Because an infinite number of different pairs of hemispherical free bodies can be formed·by bisecting a sphere, it follows that every point in the spherical shell is subjected to the same maximum tensile unit stress. Furthermore, since the number of great circles passing through any point on the sphere is unlimited, each point has impressed upon it equal maximum tensile stresses occurring in all tangential directions.

Derivation. From Pascal's law, we know that the internal pressure acts normal to the surface. In an endeavor to obtain the resultant of this pressure, let us first obtain a general relationship of the force acting on an elementary circular strip dA, shown in Fig. 4-5. Inasmuch as

$$dA = 2\pi y \, ds$$

the force on $dA = 2\pi y \, ds \times p$.

From the symmetry of the hemisphere about the horizontal axis, we are assured that the components of forces perpendicular to the axis annul one another. It is only those components acting parallel to the axis that produce tensile stress on the exposed section.

The horizontal component of force acting on dA equals

$$dR = 2\pi y \, ds \times p \times \cos \theta$$

The sum of all such horizontal components,

$$R = \int 2\pi y \, ds \times p \times \cos \theta$$

But $ds \cos \theta$ or dh is equal to the vertical projection of the intercepted arc ds, making $2\pi y \, dh$ the vertical projection of area dA. The value of R may, therefore, be further simplified as

$$R = p \int 2\pi y \, dh$$

To project every possible dA area on the vertical cutting plane would completely cover the circular section, and the value of R may be written as

$$R = p \times \frac{\pi d^2}{4} \tag{4.5}$$

Note that this resultant force is equal to that found for a flat-ended cylinder. Thus, as a further development of these studies, we may conclude that *the resultant pressure on any irregular enclosure is equal to the pressure contact area of the sectioning plane used to separate it as a free body, multiplied by the uniform internal pressure.*

Referring again to the sphere (Fig. 4-5), it is shown that the resultant of the internal pressure must be balanced by the internal tensile forces created on the exposed circumferential section. Writing the equation for horizontal forces, there is obtained

$$\pi d \times t \times s'_t = \frac{\pi d^2}{4} \times p$$

from which

$$s'_t = \frac{pd}{4t} \tag{4.6}$$

Thus, the tensile unit stress developed on a diametral section of a sphere is exactly the same as that developed on the transverse section of a cylinder of equal diameter.

Illustrative Problem 3. A 50-ft diameter sphere is to be used to contain helium gas under 100 psi pressure. If the joints in the sphere reduce the carrying capacity of the plates by 80 per cent, what thickness of plate will be required? Allowable tensile unit stress is 20,000 psi.

SOLUTION.

$$20,000 = \frac{50 \times 12 \times 100}{4t \times \frac{4}{5}}, \quad t = \frac{5000 \times 12 \times 5}{4 \times 20,000 \times 4}, \quad t = \frac{15}{16} \text{ in.}$$

4-5. Weight of fluid

In all our discussions on stresses in cylinders and spheres, no consideration was taken of the weight of the fluid producing the internal pressure. This factor may become very important, especially if the cylinder is lying horizontal and carries a heavy fluid. However, if the fluid creating the pressure is light, such as steam or air, its weight may be disregarded because its effect is of little or no consequence.

PROBLEMS

4-1. If the boiler in Fig. 4-2 is 60 in. in diameter and 8 ft long, and is subjected to an internal pressure of 125 psi, determine (a) the total stress acting on the two exposed longitudinal cross sections of the free body ($l = 4$ in.), and (b) the unit stress acting on these sections if their thickness is $\frac{1}{2}$ in.

4-2. A water supply pipe is 6 ft in diameter and built of longitudinal wood staves held by hoops of 1-in. round steel rod. What spacing of hoops is required when the pressure is 50 psi? Allowable unit stress in steel rod is 20,000 psi. *Answer:* 8.73 in.

4-3. A wood stave pipe, four feet in diameter, is wrapped spirally with a flat steel band $\frac{1}{2}$ in. wide by $\frac{1}{8}$ in. thick. If the maximum allowable unit tensile stress in the steel band is 50,000 psi and the maximum allowable unit crushing pressure on the wood under the band is 250 psi, what actual unit tensile stress may safely be used in the steel band? *Answer:* 48,000 psi.

4-4. If over the end of a 6-in. diameter steel pipe there is placed a rubber diaphragm which expands to a radius of 2 ft upon the application of 20-psi pressure, what is the tensile stress in the rubber if its expanded thickness is equal to 0.1 in? What is the tensile unit stress in the rubber if it is deflated to a 1-ft radius with one half of the above pressure, and if the thickness increases to 0.12 in? What is the resultant pressure acting on the diaphragm in each case? *Answer:* 2400 psi, 500 psi, 566 lb, 283 lb.

4-5. A hydroelectric plant has a welded surge tank connected to its penstocks that is 10 ft in diameter and 50 ft high. What is the maximum tensile unit stress in the bottom vertical plate if the plate thickness is $\frac{3}{8}$ in. and the tank is completely filled? Water weighs 62.5 lb per cu ft.

4-6. A spherical shell 40 ft in diameter is subjected to an internal pressure of 3 atmospheres. Find the tensile stress in the shell if its thickness is equal to $\frac{3}{8}$ in. One atmosphere is 14.7 psi. *Answer:* 14,100 psi.

4-7. A steam boiler is to have a 12-in. diameter hand hole placed on one end. If the maximum internal pressure is to be 200 psi, how many $\frac{5}{8}$-in. bolts will be required to keep the cover plate in position? Root diameter of a $\frac{5}{8}$-in. bolt is $\frac{1}{2}$ in. Allowable tensile unit stress is 8000 psi. *Answer:* 15 bolts.

4-8. A bronze hoop $\frac{1}{2}$ in. thick and with an inside diameter of 25 in. fits snugly over a steel hoop $\frac{3}{4}$ in. thick when the two hoops are at an initial temperature of 370°F. Both hoops are of width 4 in. $n_{st} = 0.0000065$, $n_{br} = 0.0000100$.

Compute the contact pressure between the hoops when the temperature drops to 70°F. *Answer:* 398 psi.

RIVETED JOINTS

4-6. Types of joints — definitions

Structural members are joined together by either rivets, bolts* or welds. If riveting is chosen as the method of fabrication, the following two types of joints are generally used:

(1) The lap joint (Fig. 4-6a) in which the members to be joined are overlapped and secured with rivets placed in holes that are punched or drilled through the overlapped portion of both members.

(2) The butt joint (Fig. 4-6b) in which the edges to be joined are butted one against the other and held rigidly by means of rivets passed through the edges of the main plate and one or two butt straps placed over the seam.

* Because riveted and bolted joints are almost identical in design, reference will be made in this book to the design of riveted joints only.

Figure 4-6

Lap and butt joints are further identified by their complexity of structure. If, for instance, a lap joint has but one row of rivets, it is called a *single-riveted lap joint* (Fig. 4-6a). If a lap joint has two rows of rivets, it is called a *double-riveted lap'joint* (Fig. 4-7a). If it has four rows, a *quadruple-riveted lap joint*, and so forth. Butt joints are similarly identified by the number of rows located on one side of the joint. In Fig. 4-6b is shown a single-riveted butt joint. A triple-riveted butt joint is shown in

Figure 4-7

Fig. 4-7b. In some instances, such as shown in Fig. 4-7a, adjoining rows of rivets may be staggered.

Another important classification of riveted joints is that based upon their use. Those joints used for structural purposes are called *structural joints*. Those used for boilers are called *boiler joints*. Although these joints may look and act alike, the assumption and specifications used in their design are somewhat different. Both methods of design will be illustrated.

Pitch. The distance between two adjacent rivets on any row is called the *pitch*. It is not necessary that the pitch be the same for every row, as is shown in Fig. 4-7b.

The distance between adjacent rows is called the *transverse pitch* p_t. If the rivets are staggered, the diagonal distance between adjacent rivets on adjoining rows is called the *diagonal pitch* p_d.

Repeating section. Important in the analysis of every long riveted joint is the selection of the repeating section (Fig. 4-7). This section is the smallest symmetrical grouping of rivets that repeats itself along the length of a joint. It is customary to use the repeating section rather than the entire length of a joint when determining its strength characteristics.

4-7. Assumptions in the design of riveted joints

Load distribution, structural joints. One of the major assumptions made in the design of most riveted structural joints is that the load transfer of the rivets is proportioned directly on the basis of their resisting cross-sectional areas. In other words, each resisting cross section of equal size transfers the same amount of load. Based on this assumption, the resultant of the resisting forces passes through the centroid of the rivet cross sections. If the applied load also passes through the centroid of the rivets, no eccentricity is experienced.

Unfortunately, this assumption, which would provide a uniform distribution of stress, is an approximation. However, it should not be construed as meaning to eliminate all rigor from the usual stress calculations, because the approximation approaches the assumed condition after the rivets have been loaded and the stresses at the critical points have been relieved by exceeding their yield points. The present method of calculating rivet stresses is a simple and practical one which, in the light of past experience, might better be continued than modified.

Load distribution, boiler joints. Boiler joints are designed on the basis that each rivet will carry its maximum permissible load. This assumption, used only in the design i.e. the determination of the load carrying capacity of the joint, permits a step by step evaluation of the resistance offered by the rivets and the cross sections passing through the rivet holes.

Friction. After a joint has been riveted and the heated rivets allowed to cool, the various members located between the heads of these rivets are drawn tightly together. This shrinking action in the rivets causes a good deal of friction between the riveted members, and in most instances of first loading is appreciable. This is particularly true when rivets having

Figure 4-8

long grips are used. The friction, however, has been known to decrease after repeated heavy loadings. The unpredictability of the action of friction has precluded its inclusion as a design feature.

Bending stresses in rivets. If a riveted joint is loaded sufficiently, the various members of the joint slip relative to one another (Fig. 4-8). Accompanying this slipping action is a bending action in the rivets. The stresses developed due to the bending may be considerable, especially if several thick plates are joined together, necessitating the use of rivets having relatively long grips.

However, the danger of producing excessive bending stresses is averted by the use of ductile material and by increasing the number of rivets whenever the grip exceeds $4\frac{1}{2}$ to 5 times the rivet diameter.*

4-8. Modes of failure

To design a riveted joint properly, one must anticipate and control the maximum stresses developed at critical sections. Since it is to be expected that failure will occur at one of these critical sections, any knowledge as to where these sections may be located provides information for a successful design. Several common critical stress conditions developed in all joints, each of which is capable of producing failure, form the basis of our study of the double-riveted lap joint shown in Fig. 4-9.

Three basic types of failure present themselves in our study of this joint:

(1) The net section through a row of rivets may fail in *tension*.

(2) The rivets may fail in *shear* along the plane of sliding.

(3) The material immediately in back of the joint may wrinkle because of an intensive compressive unit stress and cause failure of the joint in *bearing*.

Other methods of joint failure may be possible but are not likely to occur owing to imposed design specifications. The possibility of a rivet

* Four and a half is required by the American Railway Engineering Association. Five is required by the American Institute of Steel Construction.

Figure 4-9

causing a joint to fail by excessive bending has been eliminated in the manner previously described in § 4-7. The possibility of a joint failing by the opening up of a rivet hole in back of the rivet (Fig. 4-10) has been

Figure 4-10

eliminated by requiring a minimum edge distance, whose width depends on the size of the rivet.

In larger riveted joints, failure may be produced by the simultaneous action of two or more basic modes of failure acting at adjoining critical sections. In Fig. 4-11, it is possible to obtain failure by simultaneous shear of rivet on line 1-1 and tension of main plate on line 2-2. To insure a

Figure 4-11

safe design, other combinations on this and other joints should be analyzed carefully for every possibility of failure.

4-9. Efficiency of a riveted joint

The efficiency of a riveted joint is defined as its effectiveness in transferring load across the joint. It is measured by the percentage of the allowable load that may be applied to the unriveted plate. Thus

$$\text{Per cent efficiency} = \frac{\text{maximum allowable load on joint}}{\text{allowable load on main plate with no joint}} \times 100$$

(4.7)

In some instances, notably in connection with pressure vessel design, the percent efficiency is obtained on the basis of ultimate loads. Generally little difference is realized in changing from one method to the other.

4-10. Codes and allowable stresses

It has been the purpose of several of our technical agencies and municipalities to formulate, during the past years, the specific and detailed rules for the design and fabrication of riveted joints. These rules have been included in so-called codes governing the design and manufacture of structural frameworks and pressure vessels. The most familiar codes are (1) the Boiler Construction Code of the American Society of Mechanical Engineers, (2) the American Institute of Steel Construction Code for Buildings, (3) the American Railway Engineering Association Code for Railway Bridges, and (4) the American Association of Highway Officials Standard Specifications for Highway Bridges. It is recommended that these codes be consulted for those details of riveted joints that are omitted from this book because of space limitations.

In a partial analysis of the first three of these codes, several differences appear that emphasize the degree of safety deemed necessary for the particular riveted joints to which the codes apply. Table 4 shows the allowable unit stresses in shear, bearing, and tension given in each of these three codes. As might be expected, the Boiler Code, which governs the design of pressure vessels, is the most conservative.

The A.I.S.C. Code for Buildings permits rivet holes to be punched in material not thicker than the rivet diameter plus $\frac{1}{8}$ in., whereas in the A.R.E.A. Code for Bridges, no punching is allowed for material over $\frac{5}{8}$ in. in thickness. When the thickness of the material exceeds these maximum limitations, the holes must either be drilled or subpunched and reamed. Since the punching operation leaves a ragged hole, both codes require that all punched rivet holes shall be considered $\frac{1}{8}$ in. larger than the nominal diameter of the rivet when computing the tensile stress on the net section.

The more conservative Boiler Code of the A.S.M.E. permits punching only when the holes are afterwards reamed to size. It also stipulates that rivet diameters are to be taken equal to the diameter of the reamed hole. The expansion of the rivet diameter while it is being driven eliminates the $\frac{1}{16}$-in. difference required between rivet and hole diameters to insure easy insertion.

TABLE 4

ALLOWABLE STRESSES FOR THE DESIGN OF AXIALLY STRESSED
RIVETED JOINTS

	Shear Stress (psi) s_s	Tensile Stress (psi) s_t	Bearing Stress (psi) s_b
A.S.M.E. Boiler Code..............	8,800	11,000*	19,000
A.R.E.A. Code for Railway Bridges			
Power-driven rivets..............	13,500	18,000	27,000
Hand-driven rivets................	11,000	18,000	20,000
A.I.S.C. Code for Buildings..........	15,000	20,000	32,000† (single shear) 40,000 (double shear)

* Varies with design conditions. Read text material.

† A surface is in single or double shear bearing depending on whether one or two shear resisting surfaces bound the bearing area. If there is one, the area is in single shear bearing. If there are two, it is in double shear bearing.

In the fabrication of railway bridges, a major portion of the assembly work may be completed in the shop. Here are available large pneumatically or electrically operated power riveters. Such tools are much more efficient and produce greater uniformity than the hand-operated pneumatic hammer that is used in the field or in the shop when rivets are inaccessible to the larger power riveter. Owing to their better operational control, rivets driven by the power riveter are accorded greater allowable stresses.

The value of allowable tensile unit stress is not a constant in the A.S.M.E. Boiler Code, but varies with the kind of steel and the conditions under which the steel is to be used. The value given in Table 4 pertains to steel having an ultimate tensile unit stress of 55,000 psi subjected to a maximum temperature of 700°F. This allowable stress value is used in all problems included in this book. Reference should be made to the A.S.M.E. Code for Unfired Pressure Vessels for further information.

When subjected to load, lap joints will invariably bend into alignment with the impressed force (Fig. 4-12). This action places the rivets in a

Figure 4-12

combined state of stress, including some bending and tension with a predominant amount of shear. The A.I.S.C. Code for Buildings specifies a reduction in the allowable bearing stress for rivets in single shear to eliminate any possible danger of earlier failure. No reduction is specified in the other codes.

4-11. Resume of design details: codes for riveted joints

In bearing. A.I.S.C. and A.R.E.A. use the nominal size of the rivet; A.S.M.E. uses a rivet hole diameter equivalent to the expanded diameter of the rivet, i.e., rivet diameter plus $\frac{1}{16}$ in. A.I.S.C. requires a reduction in the allowable unit stress for single shear bearing. The other codes do not specify such a reduction.

In shear. A.I.S.C. and A.R.E.A. use the nominal size of the rivet to obtain the cross section. A.S.M.E. uses the diameter of the rivet hole as the expanded rivet diameter after driving.

In tension. A.I.S.C. and A.R.E.A. deduct the rivet diameter plus $\frac{1}{8}$ in. for punched holes, and the rivet diameter plus $\frac{1}{16}$ in. for punched and reamed holes. A.S.M.E. deducts the diameter of the rivet hole.

Rivet holes. All codes require rivet holes to be made $\frac{1}{16}$ in. larger in diameter than the rivet, for easy insertion.

4-12. Design and investigation of riveted structural joints

Illustrative Problem 4. In the double-riveted butt joint shown in Fig. 4-13, determine the shearing unit stress in the rivets, the bearing

Figure 4-13

unit stress between the rivets and the plate, and the maximum tensile unit stress on the net sections passing through the rows of rivets when the applied load is 60,000 lb. Calculate also the efficiency of the joint assuming the rivets are power-driven. Use the A.I.S.C. Code for Buildings for this investigation. Rivet holes are to be punched.

Shearing unit stress. As discussed in § 4-7, structural riveted joints are designed on the basis of equal distribution of stress to all resisting rivet cross sections. The 60,000-lb load placed on the joint now under consideration must, therefore, be distributed equally to the four rivets on each side of the joint. But why only four rivets? Is there not a total of eight?

To clarify this question, let us draw a free body of each half of the joint (Fig. 4-14). From this figure, it is evident that free body A can be

Figure 4-14

balanced only by placing a load of 30,000 lb on each strap plate. Likewise, free-body B must have the same forces on its two strap plates in order to be perfectly balanced. But each free body is now similarly loaded. Consequently, only those rivets on one side of the joint need be involved in any investigation of stresses, since they restrain the entire load.

Upon application of the 60,000-lb load, the main plate in each free body described above would tend to slip out from between the two strap plates. Of course, the rivets restrain the plates from moving, but the tendency to slip is still there. Figure 4-15 shows the position of the various parts of free body A if the rivets should fail. Note that failure would occur on two sections of each rivet simultaneously. These rivets are, therefore, in

Figure 4-15

double shear. Since the load passes through the center of gravity of the rivet group, the shearing unit stress developed on the cross sections of these rivets is

$$s_s = \frac{P}{A_s} = \frac{P}{n \times \pi d^2/4} = \frac{60,000}{2 \times 4 \times 0.60} = 12,000 \text{ psi} \qquad (4.8)$$

Bearing unit stress. As previously described, a failure in bearing implies a compression or wrinkling failure in either the main plate or butt straps of a joint. A rivet producing a bearing unit stress is assumed to bear upon one half of the rivet hole. It is further assumed that the rivet imposes on that half of the rivet hole with which it theoretically

Figure 4-16

comes in contact a uniformly distributed compression stress s_b. By a method analogous to that used in finding the resultant pressure on thin cylinders, we can obtain the resultant force of this bearing by projecting the induced compressive stresses onto the vertical diametrical plane $ABCD$ (Fig. 4-16). This force is equal to

$$P = A_{ABCD} \times s_b = A_b s_b = s_b t d \tag{4.9}$$

If several rivets are effective in resisting the bearing stress, as is the case in our present problem, their combined projected areas must be included in the above formula in the following manner:

$$P = \Sigma \, A_b s_b = s_b \Sigma \, t d \quad \text{or} \quad s_b = \frac{P}{\Sigma \, t d} \tag{4.10}$$

Figure 4-17 indicates the areas that are subjected to bearing unit stress under the action of force P. Since the strap plates as well as the main plate are involved, the proper evaluation of t in the above formula is essential.

Figure 4-17

When the load is applied, the restraining forces in the main plate and butt straps are simultaneously induced. Since all rivets take an equal amount of load and are of the same diameter throughout the length of the grip, the question as to whether the maximum bearing stress is located in the butt straps or in the main plate depends upon a comparison of their thicknesses. If the thickness of the main plate should exceed the combined thickness of the two butt straps, the maximum bearing unit stress would be located in the butt straps. If the thickness of the main plate is the same as the combined thickness of the two butt straps, the bearing unit stress would be the same in each one. Such is the case in our present problem. It is well to investigate the thickness of the various plates before a bearing stress investigation is made even though in practice the thickness of butt straps generally exceeds one half of the main-plate thickness.

The bearing unit stress between the rivets and the main plate of our present problem is, therefore,

$$s_b = \frac{P}{\Sigma \, t d} = \frac{60,000}{4 \times \frac{7}{8} \times \frac{3}{4}} = 22,800 \text{ psi}$$

Tensile unit stress on net section. To investigate the tensile unit stress on the net section of any row of rivets, a free-body analysis is important, since ultimate failure may occur in either the main or strap plates, as was indicated for the bearing unit stress in the previous article. Figures 4-18(a) and (b) show how these failures may take place in the joint used for illustration. To verify the possibility of such failures, let us study the flow of load through the riveted joint.

Figure 4-18

The flow chart in Fig. 4-19 is based on two facts:

(1) The strap plates *transfer* load from one main plate to another.

Figure 4-19

(2) This transferal takes place on the assumption that each rivet cross section transfers its proportional share of the total load.

Because eight equal rivet cross sections resist the full load, each transfers one eighth of the load. Thus at row 1, where each of the two rivets has two such cross sections, one on top and one on the bottom, loads of $P/4$ pass into the top and bottom butt strap. The total load transferred at row 1 is then equal to $P/2$, leaving the remaining load of $P/2$ in the main plate between rows 1 and 2. The same transference of load prevails at row 2, leaving no load in the main plate and placing the entire load on the butt straps. No tension exists in the margins of the main plate and butt straps.

Since P is an axial load, the tensile unit stress acting on any net section may be computed by the familiar $P = A_t s_t$ formula. Those conditions that will produce the desired maximum unit stress, which in turn govern the design, depend upon a combination of high load and small area. Therefore it is best to begin the stress investigation at those rows of rivets acted upon by the entire load. From Fig. 4-19, these are shown to be at (a) row 1 in the main plate and at (b) row 2 in the butt straps.

The tensile unit stress acting on row 1 of the main plate is

$$ s_{t_{1-1}} = \frac{P}{A_t} = \frac{P}{(w - n \times d')t} = \frac{60{,}000}{(6 - 2 \times 1)\frac{3}{4}} = 20{,}000 \text{ psi} \quad (4.11) $$

where w = width of plate or repeating section, n = number of rivets, d' = diameter of rivet plus $\frac{1}{8}$ in. [A.I.S.C. specification (§ 4-10)], t = thickness of plate on which the load is impressed.

Considering row 2 as mentioned above, note that while each butt strap carries only a load of $P/2$ lb and has a thickness of $\frac{3}{8}$ in., the intensity of stress is the same as that in the main plate at row 1, since both their load and thickness are one-half the main-plate values. The computation for tensile unit stress acting in the butt straps on row 2 is

$$ s_{t_{2-2}} = \frac{P}{A_t} = \frac{P}{2(w - nd')t} = \frac{30{,}000}{(6 - 2 \times 1)\frac{3}{8}} = 20{,}000 \text{ psi} $$

Had the butt straps been thinner, the maximum tensile stress in the joint would have occurred in the butt straps on the row-2 section.

Efficiency of joint. The efficiency of a riveted joint is equal to the ratio of its allowable strength to the allowable tensile strength of the solid plate of the same width and thickness. Therefore, it is necessary to obtain those allowable loads that may be applied to the joint based upon the allowable shearing, bearing, and tensile unit stresses. Dividing the least of these loads by the allowable tensile strength of the main plate with no rivet holes will give the efficiency of load transfer.

The allowable loads and efficiency for the joint under investigation are computed as follows:

Allowable shear load:

$$ P_s = A_s s_s = 8 \times 0.60 \times 15{,}000 = 72{,}000 \text{ lb} $$

Allowable bearing load:

$$P_b = A_b s_b = 4 \times \tfrac{7}{8} \times \tfrac{3}{4} \times 40{,}000 = 105{,}000 \text{ lb}$$

Allowable tensile load:

$$P_t = A_t s_t = (6 - 2 \times 1)\tfrac{3}{4} \times 20{,}000 = 60{,}000 \text{ lb}$$

Allowable tensile load of solid main plate:

$$P = A_t s_t = 6 \times \tfrac{3}{4} \times 20{,}000 = 90{,}000 \text{ lb}$$

Efficiency of joint:

$$\frac{60{,}000}{90{,}000} = 66.7 \text{ per cent}$$

Illustrative Problem 5. Determine the maximum load that can be applied to the riveted structural joint shown in Fig. 4-20. All holes are punched. Use the A.I.S.C. code.

Figure 4-20

SOLUTION. The loads that can be sustained by the shear and bearing resistance of the rivets are as follows:

$$\text{Shear} = 12 \times 0.785 \times 15{,}000 = 141{,}300 \text{ lb}$$
$$\text{Bearing} = 12 \times 1 \times \tfrac{3}{8} \times 32{,}000 = 144{,}000 \text{ lb}$$

There still remains the determination of the allowable tensile load that can be applied to the various net cross sections passing through the rivet holes.

Once again, the flow of load diagram through the joint is drawn (Fig. 4-20b). Equating the load applied to each cross section to the resistance offered, we obtain

Tension 1-1 $= (18 - 1\frac{1}{8}) \times \frac{3}{8} \times 20,000 = P; \quad P = 126,700$ lb

Tension 2-2 $= (18 - 2\frac{1}{4}) \times \frac{3}{8} \times 20,000 = \frac{11}{12}P; \; P = 128,800$ lb

Tension 3-3 $= (18 - 3\frac{3}{8}) \times \frac{3}{8} \times 20,000 = \frac{9}{12}P; \; P = 146,200$ lb

The maximum load that the joint can resist is therefore **126,700 lb.**

$$\text{Efficiency of Joint} = \frac{126,700}{18 \times \frac{3}{8} \times 20,000} \times 100 = 93.8 \text{ per cent}$$

Illustrative Problem 6. Determine the number of hand-driven rivets required for the joint shown in Fig. 4-21. Rivets are $\frac{3}{4}$ in. diameter for

Figure 4-21

member A, and 1 in. diameter for member B. Use the A.R.E.A. code. Rivet holes are punched.

SOLUTION. Member A — Rivets are in double shear:

$$\text{Shear requirement } n = \frac{25,000}{0.44 \times 2 \times 11,000} = 2.58$$

$$\text{Bearing requirement } n = \frac{25,000}{\frac{3}{4} \times \frac{3}{8} \times 20,000} = 4.45$$

Use 5 rivets.

Member B — Rivets are in single shear:

$$\text{Shear requirement } n = \frac{25,000}{0.785 \times 11,000} = 2.90$$

$$\text{Bearing requirement } n = \frac{25,000}{1 \times \frac{3}{8} \times 20,000} = 3.33$$

Use 4 rivets.

Tensile investigation:

$$\text{Cross sectional area} = 2.11 - 1.125 \times \tfrac{3}{8} = 1.69 \text{ sq in.}$$

$$\text{Allowable load} = 1.69 \times 18,000 = 30,400 \text{ lb}$$

Exceeds load applied.

Generally, in a truss design using standard shapes and rivet spacings, the tensile area available exceeds that required.

Use either the A.I.S.C. or A.R.E.A. allowable unit stresses for steel as directed in the solution to these problems.

A.I.S.C. $s_s = 15,000$ psi; $s_t = 20,000$ psi; $s_b = 32,000$ (single), 40,000 (double), psi.

A.R.E.A. Power-driven rivets: $s_s = 13,500$ psi; $s_t = 18,000$ psi; $s_b = 27,000$ psi.

PROBLEMS

4-9. A single-riveted lap joint is made from two steel plates, $2\frac{1}{2}$ in. wide by $\frac{1}{2}$ in. thick, fastened together with a $\frac{3}{4}$-in. rivet. Rivet holes punched. Compute the tensile unit stress on the net section through the rivet hole, the shearing unit stress in the rivet, and the bearing unit stress on the side of the rivet due to a tensile load of 6000 lb. (A.I.S.C.) *Answer:* $s_s = 13,630$ psi, $s_b = 16,000$ psi, $s_t = 7380$ psi.

4-10. If a single-riveted lap joint is made of $\frac{1}{2}$-in. steel plate and $\frac{3}{4}$-in. diameter rivets, find that pitch that will make the shearing strength of the rivets equal to the tensile strength of the plate. Rivet holes punched. (A.R.E.A.)

4-11. If the vertical joints of the surge tank of Problem 4-5 must have an efficiency of 85 per cent, compute the thickness of the bottom vertical plate (A.I.-S.C.). *Answer:* 0.077 in.

4-12. Determine the strength and efficiency of a double-riveted lap joint if the pitch on both rows is 4 in., rivet diameter is 1 in., and the plate thickness is $\frac{1}{2}$ in. Rivet holes punched. (A.I.S.C.)

4-13. A 3 by $\frac{3}{8}$-in. flat, carrying a tensile load of 10,000 lb, is riveted to a $\frac{3}{8}$-in. gusset plate. If $\frac{3}{4}$-in. rivets are used, find the number of rivets required to transmit the load. Rivet holes punched and reamed. (A.R.E.A.)

4-14. Determine the number of rivets necessary for each member framing into joint E of the truss shown in Fig. 4-22. Rivets are $\frac{5}{8}$ in. Rivet holes punched. (A.I.S.C.) *Answer:* (a) 6, (b) 4, (c) 3, (d) 5, (e) 4.

4-15. Two $\frac{3}{8}$-in. structural plates are joined by $\frac{3}{4}$-in. rivets to form a lap joint (Fig. 4-23). The rivets are placed in three rows, the pitch of the center row being $2\frac{1}{2}$ in. and the pitch of the outer rows, 5 in. If the tension in the cross section of the plates is 4000 lb per in. of width, find the following unit stresses in the joint: (a) shear and bearing in the rivets and (b) tension in the net section of the plate at the

Figure 4-22

outer row of rivets and at the center row of rivets. Rivet holes punched. (A.I.S.C.)
Answer: (a) $s_s = 11,360$ psi, $s_b = 17,800$ psi; (b) $12,910$ psi, $12,280$ psi.

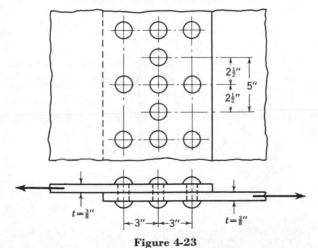

Figure 4-23

4-16. Two $\frac{1}{2}$-in. plates, each 14 in. wide, are united by five 1-in. diameter rivets in a single row parallel to the joint to form a lap joint. If the joint transmits a pull of

47,120 lb, find the maximum shearing tensile and bearing unit stresses in the joint. What is the efficiency of the joint? Rivet holes punched and reamed. (A.R.E.A.)

4-13. *The investigation and design of riveted boiler joints*

The investigation of riveted boiler joints for critical stresses proceeds in the same manner as did the investigation of the riveted structural joints. However, the stresses are determined on the assumption that the rivet, after being driven, takes the size of the rivet hole. All holes are drilled.

The design or study of the load-carrying capacity of a boiler joint proceeds on the assumption, previously given in § 4-7b, that each rivet transfers its maximum allowable load in bearing or shear. This assumption presents the major difference between the calculation of the load-carrying capacity of so-called structural and boiler joints. Fortunately, the difference is mainly one of concept rather than of numerical values. This will be shown after the following illustrative problem.

Illustrative Problem 7. A boiler 84 in. in diameter is being designed with a longitudinal triple-riveted butt joint with unequal strap plates (see Fig. 4-24). The pitch on the first row of rivets is 6 in. and on the

Figure 4-24. Repeating section (c) includes: 5 whole rivets, 9 shear areas, 5 bearing areas in main plate, 9 bearing areas in straps on each side of joint.

other two rows it is 3 in. The thickness of the main and strap plates is $\frac{5}{8}$ and $\frac{3}{8}$ in. respectively. If the rivet diameter is $\frac{7}{8}$ in., what maximum internal pressure can be applied to the boiler, using the allowable unit stresses found in the A.S.M.E. Boiler Code? Area of rivet hole $\frac{15}{16}$ in. in diameter equals 0.69 sq in.

SOLUTION. The first step in the determination of the load-carrying capacity of any riveted boiler joint is to calculate the shearing and bearing resistances of individual rivets and the tensile strength of the plates on the cross sections passing through the rivet lines. For our problem these will be

Single shear
$$P_s = 0.69 \times 8800 = 6070 \text{ lb}$$

Double shear
$$P_s = 2 \times 0.69 \times 8800 = 12{,}140 \text{ lb}$$

Bearing-strap plate
$$P_b = \tfrac{3}{8} \times \tfrac{15}{16} \times 19{,}000 = 6700 \text{ lb}$$

Bearing-main plate
$$P_b = \tfrac{5}{8} \times \tfrac{15}{16} \times 19{,}000 = 11{,}150 \text{ lb}$$

Tensile strength line 1-1 of main plate
$$P_t = (6 - \tfrac{15}{16})\tfrac{5}{8} \times 11{,}000 = 34{,}800 \text{ lb}$$

Tensile strength line 2-2 or line 3-3 of main plate
$$P_t = (6 - 2 \times \tfrac{15}{16})\tfrac{5}{8} \times 11{,}000 = 28{,}400 \text{ lb}$$

Tensile strength line 3-3 of butt straps
$$P_t = (6 - 2 \times \tfrac{15}{16}) \times 2 \times \tfrac{3}{8} \times 11{,}000 = 34{,}000 \text{ lb}$$

Tensile strength main plate no rivet holes
$$P_t = 6 \times \tfrac{5}{8} \times 11{,}000 = 41{,}300 \text{ lb}$$

Having computed these component strengths, we must now determine (on the basis of the possible methods of failure) what combination of shear, bearing, and tensile resistance will give the maximum capacity of the joint. Essential to this determination is the fact that the repeating section contains 5 rivets, with 9 shear areas, 5 bearing areas in the main plate, and 9 bearing areas in the butt straps. A study of the strengths of various combinations is now presented.

(1) *By shearing all rivets.* Because 3 whole and 4 half-rivets are included on one side of the joint within the confines of the section, and because 1 whole rivet is in single shear while all the others are in double shear, there are 9 rivet cross sections capable of taking shear. The allowable shear load is, therefore

$$P = 9 \times 6070 = 54{,}630 \text{ lb}$$

(2) *By bearing in the main plate.* 5 rivets are active in bearing. Their total resistance is equal to

$$P = 5 \times 11{,}150 = 55{,}750 \text{ lb}$$

(3) *By bearing in the butt straps:*

$$P = 9 \times 6700 = 60{,}300 \text{ lb}$$

(4) *By shear on line 1-1 and bearing in the main plate on lines 2-2 and 3-3:*

$$P = 6070 + 4 \times 11{,}150 = 50{,}670 \text{ lb}$$

(5) *In tension on line 1-1:*

$$P = 34{,}800 \text{ lb}$$

(6) *In tension on line 2-2 of the main plate.* It is obvious that before the main plate can fail along line 2-2, the rivet on line 1-1 must also fail. The minimum allowable resistance for this condition will therefore be

$$P = 6070 + 28{,}400 = 34{,}470 \text{ lb}$$

(7) *In tension on line 3-3 of the main plate.* In this situation, the rivets of lines 1-1 and 2-2 must fail in either shear or bearing. The minimum load is

$$P = 6070 + 11{,}150 \times 2 + 28{,}400 = 56{,}770 \text{ lb}$$

(8) *In tension on line 3-3 of the butt straps*

$$P = 34{,}000 \text{ lb}$$

The maximum load that the joint can safely resist is, therefore, 34,000 lb, i.e., the least of the loads computed for conditions (1) through (8). Because failure is in the butt straps, the joint is not considered of good design.

The corresponding safe internal pressure that may be used safely in the tank is determined as follows:

$$6 \times 84 \times P = 34{,}000 \times 2$$

$$P = \frac{68{,}000}{504} = 135 \text{ psi}$$

The efficiency of the joint based on allowable stresses is

$$\frac{34{,}000 \times 100}{41{,}300} = 82.2 \text{ per cent}$$

Note that were the efficiency to be based on the corresponding ultimate stresses, its value would be exactly the same.

PROBLEMS*

4-17. Determine the maximum allowable load that may be applied to the joint shown in Fig. 4-25. Rivets are $\frac{3}{4}$ in. Compute its efficiency. *Answer:* $P_t =$ 15,200 lb. Efficiency = 82 per cent.

---

*Use the selected stresses of the A.S.M.E. Boiler Code in the solutions to these problems.
Allowable stresses for steel: $s_s = 8800$ psi; $s_t = 11{,}000$ psi; $s_b = 19{,}000$ psi.
Ultimate stresses for steel: $(s_s)_u = 44{,}000$ psi; $(s_t)_u = 55{,}000$ psi; $(s_b)_u = 95{,}000$ psi.

Figure 4-25

4-18. A boiler shell is 5 ft in diameter and $\frac{5}{8}$ in. thick. The efficiency of its longitudinal joint is 80 per cent. If the allowable tensile unit stress is 11,000 psi, what is the maximum allowable steam pressure? With this pressure, what is the total pressure on the head of the boiler? *Answer:* 183.3 psi, 519,000 lb.

4-19. A spherical gas tank 50 ft in diameter holds gas at a maximum pressure of 35 psi. If it is to have double-riveted butt joints with an efficiency of 85 per cent, what must the thickness of the plates be?

4-20. A boiler 100 in. in diameter, having plates $\frac{3}{4}$ in. thick, is subjected to an internal pressure of 160 psi. The longitudinal joint is a double-riveted butt joint with two cover plates each $\frac{5}{16}$ in. thick. The diameter of the rivets is $\frac{7}{8}$ in., the pitch is 3 in., and the distance between rows is 3 in. Find the maximum bearing, shearing, and tensile unit stresses in the joint. *Hint:* Use $2P = plD$ to obtain load on repeating section. *Answer:* $s_s = 8700$ psi, $s_b = 20,500$ psi, $s_t = 18,700$ psi.

4-21. Two $\frac{3}{8}$-in. boiler plates are united by a triple-riveted lap joint of $\frac{3}{4}$-in. rivets. The pitch is $4\frac{1}{2}$ in. in the outer rows and $2\frac{1}{4}$ in. in the center rows. What is the strength in pounds per linear inch of joint?

4-22. A boiler 4 ft in diameter is made of $\frac{1}{4}$-in. steel plate. The longitudinal joints are fastened with a single row of $\frac{3}{4}$-in. rivets placed with a pitch of $2\frac{1}{2}$ in. What maximum pressure should be permitted? What is the efficiency of this joint? *Answer:* 64 psi, 56.1 per cent.

4-23. A boiler of $\frac{5}{16}$ in. steel plate is designed with a double-riveted longitudinal lap joint with $\frac{5}{8}$ in. rivets spaced $2\frac{1}{2}$ in. center to center in each row. What is the efficiency of the joint?

4-24. A longitudinal joint of a tank, 50 in. in diameter, is a triple-riveted lap joint for which the pitch of the rivets is 3 in. in each row. The rivet holes are 1 in. in diameter, and the steel plates for the tank are $\frac{1}{2}$ in. thick. Find the efficiency of the joint. Also determine the maximum safe internal pressure for the tank. *Answers:* 66.7 per cent, 146.8 psi.

4-25. Two $\frac{3}{4}$-in. steel plates are united to form a butt joint with three rows of 1-in. diameter rivets on each side. The pitch of the two outer rows is 10 in. and the pitch of the four inner rows is 5 in. The $\frac{1}{2}$ in. butt straps are of equal width. Find the efficiency of the joint. *Answer:* **89.5 per cent.**

4-14. Maximum design efficiency

As has been indicated, every riveted joint owes its strength to its resistance in shear, bearing and tension. The maximum load that may be applied to the joint is dependent on the least of these resistances, or any of their combinations. Should one of them have a low value, the additional strength offered by the other resistances would be wasted. It is therefore advisable to have each of the resistances in shear, bearing or tension equal each other. In so doing, the joint will have been most efficiently designed.

WELDED JOINTS

4-15. General discussion

The origin of welding dates back to the decade following 1880. Owing to several drawbacks, welding was not in common use until World War I, when extensive research eliminated many of the difficulties hindering its growth. Since that time, the phenomenal rise of welding as a means of joining structural and machine members has caused a decrease in the use of rivets and bolts and has also precipitated the decline in the use of metal castings in preference to fabricated members (Fig. 4-26).

Figure 4-26. Field welding: connecting beam and column. (Courtesy of Lincoln Electric Co.)

Welding, as ordinarily considered for structural use, may be defined as a method of joining metals by fusion without the application of pressure. To accomplish the fusion process, heat is generally supplied by either an electric arc or by an oxyacetylene torch. The metal at the joint, together with additional metal supplied in the form of filler metal, is melted, forming a small pool or crater. Upon cooling, the weld and base metal form a continuous and almost homogeneous joint.

The design of welded joints constitutes only one of the several very important problems arising in the application of welding to structural and machine parts. The procedure that must be followed, the proper amperage and voltage of the welding machine, the rate of cooling, and the development of internal stresses are some of the other important factors that must be considered.

These added considerations were, in the past, primarily the concern of the welder. With the inception of better methods and standardizations, much of this responsibility has now been shifted from the welder to the welding code. Seriously flawed work has been substantially eliminated by requiring each welder to pass rigid qualification tests and to submit his work to the careful scrutiny of a trained inspector. To further test the safety of welded joints, X-rays and gamma rays are frequently used to locate internal flaws.

4-16. Types of welded joints — definitions

There are various types of welded joints in common use. They are made by the use of (1) fillet welds, (2) butt welds, (3) plug or slot welds, (4) resistance welds, and (5) tack welds. A brief description of each follows.

Fillet welds. If a weld is placed in a corner made by two adjoining structural members, it is called a *fillet-weld*. Several examples of fillet welds are shown in Fig. 4-27.

Size. Fillet welds are generally specified with equal legs. The length of these legs is, therefore, conveniently used to represent the *size of the fillet weld*.

Throat. The minimum thickness of a weld measured in its cross section along a straight line passing through its *root* is called the *throat* of the weld (Fig. 4-28a). The effective throat thickness of an equal-leg 45° fillet weld shall be considered as 0.707 times the nominal size of the weld.

Butt-welds. When the edges of two structural or machine members are butted together and welded, the weld used is a *butt-weld*. Butt welds are used more frequently for joining machine parts than for joining structural members. The frequent need for beveling the edges of a butt joint makes it more expensive. Figure 4-29 shows several butt-welded joints.

(a)

(b)

Figure 4-27

Throat. The effective throat thickness of a complete-penetration butt weld is considered to be the thickness of the thinner part joined. If a butt weld were to be made with an incomplete penetration, its strength would have to be reduced in accordance with the welding code used.

Plug and slot welds. Upon occasion, structural members are joined using plug welds (Fig. 4-30a). These joints are made by filling with weld metal, holes punched in one of the overlapping members of the joint. Plug welds are used in joints where fillet welds are either insufficient to connect the members of the joint properly or the position of butt and fillet welds is impractical. Slot welds (Fig. 4-30b) are also used to overcome difficulties involved in providing sufficient strength in welded joints.

Resistance welds. Resistance welds, of which spot welds (Fig. 4-30c) are a type, are made by a simultaneous application of intense pressure and the passage of high current through two metal pieces at the point where they are to be joined. The intense heat created by the current causes the metal in both pieces to melt and merge with each other. Upon

Figure 4-28. (a) Welding terms; (b–h) acceptable and defective fillet-weld profiles.

Figure 4-29

Plug welds
(a)

Slot welds
(b)

Spot welds
(c)

Figure 4-30

cooling, the two metal pieces are securely joined. They are frequently used in the assembly of small electrical and mechanical equipment.

Tack welds. Tack welds are used, as their name implies, for holding metal parts in position while the major welding operation is in progress.

4-17. Welding specifications and allowable unit stresses

In response to numerous requests from municipal and other authorities, the American Welding Society published in 1928 the first edition of its Code for Arc and Gas Welding in Building Construction*. It has since been revised, upon occasion, in cooperation with the major engineering societies interested in welding. This specification governs the broad uses of welding in the fabrication of buildings.

The more detailed requirements governing design and fabrication procedures involved in building construction are contained in the Specification for the Design, Fabrication, and Erection of Structural Steel for

---

* The name of the 1928 code was *Code for Fusion Welding and Gas Cutting in Building Construction*.

Buildings by Arc and Gas Welding, prepared by the American Institute of Steel Construction. Both codes are at present in complete harmony and are used in conjunction with one another.

The allowable welding unit stresses adopted by both codes for welds made by the ordinary coated electrodes or gas welding rods for structural-steel fabrication are as follows:

Shear on section through throat of fillet weld, or on faying surface area of filled plug or slot weld:

$$s_s = 13,600 \text{ psi}$$

Tension on section through throat of butt weld:

s_t = same as corresponding allowable stress for base metal
  = 20,000 psi

Compression (crushing) on section through throat of butt weld:

s_c = same as corresponding allowable stress for base metal
  = 20,000 psi

Shear in section through throat of butt weld:

s_s = same as corresponding allowable stress for base metal
  = 13,000 psi

4-18. *Design of welded joints — fillet-welded joints*

The design of any fillet-welded joint requires the determination of three values: (1) the size of the weld, (2) the length of weld, and (3) the proper distribution of the weld.

The size of a fillet weld to be used depends upon the thickness of the parts to be joined, the strength desired, and the economy of making the joint. It is usual to limit the maximum size of a fillet weld applied to a square edge of a plate or section to $\frac{1}{16}$ in. less than the nominal thickness of the edge. Where fillet welds are applied at rounded edges of flanges or at toes of angles, the size of weld is generally limited to three fourths of the thickness joined. A minimum size of weld generally bears a relationship with the maximum thickness of the member welded. This is generally specified in accordance with the welding code being used. The American Institute of Steel Construction Specification, for instance, presently requires a minimum of a $\frac{3}{16}$-in. fillet weld to be used with thicknesses up to and including $\frac{1}{2}$ in. Fillet welds with at least $\frac{1}{2}$-in. legs must be used with all thicknesses up to and including 6 in.

Economy also dictates to a great extent the size of the fillet weld to be used. Owing to (1) the larger proportion of metal per inch of throat required for increasingly larger welds, (2) the increased labor cost in making welds of two or more passes, (3) the necessity of making connections in small space, and (4) the limitations of welding technique, the costs of welds might appear to vary directly with their size. In contradiction to this premise, however, the use of larger welds allows the use of larger welding rods, which in turn provide a greater rate of weld-metal output in pounds per hour. The practical evaluation of these factors has established the $\frac{5}{16}$-in. weld as the most common size for structural welding. This size of weld is the largest weld that can be conveniently made with one pass of the welding rod. Larger fillet welds generally require two or more passes. Since the cost of fillet welds increases approximately in proportion to the square of their size, the use of fillet welds larger than $\frac{5}{16}$ in. should be based on structural reasons that warrant their higher cost.

The critical stress in a fillet weld shall be considered as the average shearing unit stress that occurs on its throat section. Although tests made through the elastic range show that the stress at the ends of a weld, pulled lengthwise, is higher than that near its mid-point, consequent yielding at points of high stress under higher loads produces fair uniformity. To determine the general formula for shear stress on the throat section of a fillet weld, therefore, let us use (Fig. 4-31), assuming the stress to be uniformly distributed.

$$P = R_1 + R_2 \text{ (internal resistive forces)}$$

Figure 4-31

Considering the effective area of a fillet weld as the product of its effective length and effective throat thickness, the resisting force offered by one of the fillet welds is

$$R_1 = R_2 = 0.707a \times l \times s_s \qquad (4.12)$$

Equating the horizontal forces on the joint, we obtain

$$P = 2 \times 0.707a \times l \times s_s$$

or if $2l = L$, the total length

$$P = 0.707a \times L \times s_s \qquad (4.13)$$

Should L be made equal to 1 in. and $s_s = 13,600$ lb per sq in., the value of P in the above formula would be

$$P = 0.707a \times 1 \text{ in.} \times 13,600 \text{ psi} = 9600a \qquad (4.14)$$

If, then, a were made equal to 1 in., the value of allowable load P would be equal to 9600 lb. In other words, a 1-in. weld 1 in. long would resist 9600 lb of force. A $\frac{1}{2}$-in. weld could carry only half as much, or 4800 lb. To obtain the strength of any weld 1 in. long merely requires the multiplication of the size of the weld by 9600. Table 5 tabulates the strengths of various welds.

TABLE 5
STRENGTH OF FILLET WELD PER INCH OF LENGTH

Size of Weld	Strength Per In.	Size of Weld	Strength Per In.
$\frac{1}{8}$ in.	1200 lb	$\frac{1}{2}$ in.	4800 lb
$\frac{3}{16}$ in.	1800 lb	$\frac{9}{16}$ in.	5400 lb
$\frac{1}{4}$ in.	2400 lb	$\frac{5}{8}$ in.	6000 lb
$\frac{5}{16}$ in.	3000 lb	$\frac{3}{4}$ in.	7200 lb
$\frac{3}{8}$ in.	3600 lb	$\frac{7}{8}$ in.	8400 lb
$\frac{7}{16}$ in.	4200 lb	1 in.	9600 lb

Illustrative Problem 8. If, in Fig. 4-31, load P were equal to 60,000 lb, what length of $\frac{5}{16}$-in. weld would be required on each side of the plate to resist the load? Use the A.I.S.C. allowable welding stresses.

SOLUTION. Solving for L in equation 4.13, we get

$$L = \frac{P}{0.707a \times s_s}$$

$$= \frac{60,000}{0.707 \times \frac{5}{16} \times 13,600} = \frac{60,000}{9600 \times \frac{5}{16}} = 20 \text{ in.}$$

and

$$l = 10 \text{ in.}, \text{ effective length required on each side}$$

Or, by establishing the fact that every $\frac{1}{8}$ in. of leg in a fillet weld 1 in. long produces 1200 lb of resistance, and that a $\frac{5}{16}$-in. weld would, therefore, carry 3000 lb per in., we may by simple division divide the 3000 into the 60,000 lb and obtain a total length of weld required of 20 in.

Illustrative Problem 9. The long leg of a single 5 by $3\frac{1}{2}$ by $\frac{3}{8}$-in. angle is to be welded to a gusset plate with $\frac{5}{16}$-in. side-fillet welds (Fig. 4-32). Determine the amount of weld needed at each side of the angle to develop the full capacity of the angle economically. Allowable unit stress in angle is 20,000 psi. Consult Table 18 for characteristics of angle.

Figure 4-32

Solution. The load to be resisted is equal to the area of the angle times the allowable unit stress.

$$P = as = 3.05 \times 20{,}000 = 61{,}000 \text{ lb}$$

The total length of weld required to restrain this force is ($\frac{5}{16}$-in. fillet-weld capacity = 3000 lb per in. of weld).

$$L = \frac{61{,}000}{3000} = 20.3 \text{ in.}$$

The proper distribution of this length of weld to each side is our next problem. Since the center of gravity of the angle is not on the center line of the attached leg, the amount of weld on each side must be proportioned in such a way as to make the *resultant* resistive force of both welds act colinear with the applied force of 61,000 lb. To perform this distribution, use is made of the theorem which states that the algebraic sum of the moments of component forces about a point is equal to the moment of their resultant. If, then, the moment center is selected on the action line of the resultant (namely, the centroidal axis of the angle) its moment is zero, and the algebraic sum of the moments of the two weld forces must also be equal to zero. Stated differently, the moments of these two weld forces taken about the centroidal axis of the angle must balance and be equal to each other.

We may therefore write

$$x \times 3000 \times 3.39 = (20.3 - x) \times 3000 \times 1.61$$

The allowable strength of the weld might have been omitted, as the cancellation indicates.

$$3.39x + 1.61x = 32.7$$

$$x = \frac{32.7}{5.0} = 6.5 \text{ in., effective length at top of angle}$$

$$20.3 - x = 13.8 \text{ in., effective length at bottom angle}$$

The effective length of a fillet weld is considered as the over-all length of the full-size fillet.

4-19. End-fillet welds

From studies made by the American Bureau of Welding*, fillet welds placed at the ends of structural members transverse to the direction of loading average 35 per cent greater strength than side fillet welds of equal dimension. Test results on side fillet welds, however, show less variation in load resistance.

When end-fillet welds are used together with side-fillet welds, a statically indeterminate condition is imposed upon the joint. Not all designers are agreed that an equal load should be delegated to every inch of weld in such a joint.

In the opinion of the formulators of the code already discussed, however, sufficient similarity does exist, particularly after localized yielding, to warrant the assumption of equal distribution of stress to both side and end-fillet welds. The effective throat section acted upon by the critical shear stress is again assumed to form the basis of the design.

Figure 4-33

* H. M. Priest, "Strength of Structural Welds," *Engineering News Record*, Sept. 17, 1941.

Illustrative Problem 10. If in Fig. 4-33 $\frac{5}{16}$ in. side- and end-fillet welds are to be used to fasten the 4-in. wide tension member to the gusset plate, what distribution of welds will be necessary? $P = 60,000$ lb.

SOLUTION. The total length of weld necessary, inasmuch as a $\frac{5}{16}$-in. fillet weld 1 in. long can restrain a load of 3000 lb, is

$$L = \frac{60,000}{3000} = 20 \text{ in.}$$

The end-fillet weld is then equal to 4 in., and the remainder is distributed equally between the two sides, 8 in. each.

Illustrative Problem 11. Referring to Illustrative Problem 9, what distribution of welds would be necessary if an end-fillet weld were also used (Fig. 4-34)?

Figure 4-34

SOLUTION. Here, the resistive forces are augmented by the resistance in the end-fillet weld. If the end-fillet weld is divided into its portions on either side of the centroidal axis and included in the moments of the resistive forces, this problem is not unlike that of its predecessor.

The total length of $\frac{5}{16}$-in. weld required is again

$$L = \frac{61,000}{3000} = 20.3 \text{ in.}$$

Of this amount, only 15.3 in. must be distributed to the two sides as 5 in. of weld is placed at the end of the angle. The method of distribution, as previously shown, is slightly different, however, since that portion of the end-fillet weld above the gravity axis has a different resistive moment than that below. The proper distribution may then be made by taking the algebraic sum of the resisting moments about the centroidal axis, eliminating the allowable strengths which were previously shown to be unnecessary.

$$x \times 3.39 + 3.39 \times 1.69 = 1.61 \times 0.80 + (15.3 - x)1.61$$
$$3.39x + 1.61x = 24.6 + 1.29 - 5.73$$
$$x = \frac{20.16}{5} = 4.03 \text{ in., effective length, top weld}$$
$$15.3 - x = 11.3 \text{ in., effective length, bottom weld}$$

4-20. Design of butt joints

All butt joints placed perpendicular to the applied load are designed on the basis of the tensile or compressive stress induced on the effective throat section.

Illustrative Problem 12. Two 4 by $\frac{1}{2}$-in. structural-steel plates are to be butt welded at their ends. How much tensile load is the joint capable of carrying?

SOLUTION. The effective weld area under load is equal to 2 sq in. As previously noted, the allowable tensile unit stress applied to the throat of a butt weld is equal to the allowable tensile unit stress of the base metal, which for structural steel, is 20,000 psi. Thus,

$$P = 2 \times 20,000 = 40,000 \text{ lb}$$

The 100 per cent transmission of load allowed by the welding code is entirely justifiable, since welded joints made with ordinary care and nspection are invariably stronger than the base metal.

4-21. Design of plug and slot welds

The effective area of fillet-welded plug or slot welds is determined only on the basis of their resistance to shear. If these welds are of the unfilled type, their effective length shall be considered as the length of the center line of the weld passing through the center of the plane occupying the full effective throat. If the plug and slot welds are filled, their effective shearing area is considered as the nominal cross-sectional area of the hole or slot in the plane of the faying surface. Slot welds are not used as frequently as plug welds. In order to restrict the load that can be applied to a slot weld, its maximum length may not exceed ten times the thickness of the base metal and its width cannot be greater than 3 times the thickness of the weld metal or less than thickness of the part plus $\frac{5}{16}$ in., rounded to the next odd sixteenth. The diameter of plug welds must also not exceed 3 times the thickness of the weld metal.

Illustrative Problem 13. If the two plates shown in Fig. 4-35 are to be joined together by means of four filled plug welds, 1 in. in diameter, how much load can the joint carry?

Figure 4-35

SOLUTION. Allowing a shearing unit stress of 13,600 psi on the cross section of each of the plug welds, the value of P will be

$$P = 4 \times 0.7854 \times 13,600 = 42,700 \text{ lb}$$

Illustrative Problem 14. A steel plate 5 in. wide and $\frac{5}{8}$ in. thick is welded to an I-beam by means of a partly filled $1\frac{1}{4}$ by 6-in. slot weld. Determine its allowable resistance to load if $\frac{1}{2}$-in. welds are to be used.

SOLUTION. The length of the weld along the center line of the throat plane consists of

$$
\begin{array}{ll}
2 \text{ long sides at } 5\frac{7}{8} \text{ in.} = & 11\frac{3}{4} \\
1 \text{ short side at } 1 \text{ in.} = & \underline{1} \\
& 12\frac{3}{4}
\end{array}
$$

Ascribing 4800 lb per in. of length to the weld, allows a resistance of

$$P = 12\frac{3}{4} \times 4800 = 61,200 \text{ lb}$$

PROBLEMS

Use American Welding Society allowable stresses in the following problems where necessary

4-26. If the spherical gas tank in Problem 4-19 is composed of two hemispheres butt-welded together, what internal pressure may be applied if the thickness of the plate is $\frac{3}{4}$ in? *Answer:* 100 psi.

4-27. A 5 by $\frac{1}{2}$-in. steel plate is to be welded to a gusset plate with $\frac{5}{16}$-in. side-fillet welds. What length welds are required to develop the maximum tensile unit stress of 18,000 psi in the plate?

4-28. An 8-in., 11.5-lb channel placed horizontally is to have its back welded to the flange of a vertical H beam (Fig. 4-36). If the flange of the H beam is 8 in. wide, will $\frac{5}{16}$-in. side-fillet welds be sufficient to hold the compressive load of 60,000 lb placed on the channel? What most economical procedure should be followed if the side welds are insufficient? *Answer:* No. Use 8 in. on each side with 4 in. on end.

| Figure 4-36 | Figure 4-37 |

4-29. A 6-in., 8.2-lb channel is butt-welded to the back of an 8-in., 11.5-lb channel. What is the maximum permissible tension that may be applied to the 6-in. channel? What reaction load is the butt weld capable of taking in shear? Assume an average 0.2-in. throat thickness for the weld (Fig. 4-37).

4-30. A 4 by 3 by $\frac{3}{8}$ in. angle is to have its 4-in. leg welded to a gusset plate with $\frac{1}{4}$-in. welds. What length of weld and where must it be placed to restrain a tensile load of 50,000 lb? *Answer:* 6.65 in. at toe, 14.15 in. at heel.

4-31. If in Problem 4-30, the weld were to be placed along the end of the 4-in. leg as well as on its sides, what most economical distribution could be made? *Answers:* 4.66 in. at toe, 4 in. on end, 12.14 in. at heel.

Chapter Five

TORSION

5-1. Introduction

If a member is subjected to the action of a pair of equal and oppositely directed couples lying in parallel planes, that portion of the member between the couples is said to be in torsion. Since couples always produce rotation, the portion of the member between the oppositely directed couples will be subjected to a twisting action. One of the objects of this chapter will be to determine the relationship between twisting couples and the resulting stresses and strains, particularly in circular shafts, since these are most frequently used to transmit torsion.

5-2. Development of torsion

When two readily observable equal couples act in opposite directions on planes perpendicular to the axis of a shaft (Fig. 5-1a), the determination of

$$T = Pp$$
Resisting torque $= Pp = T_R = Qq$
(a)

$$T = T_R$$
(b)

Figure 5-1

110

the magnitude of the twisting moment is simply the moment, or *torque*, of one of the couples.

If only one of the couples (the applied torque) is visible and equilibrium is still maintained, it follows that the shaft must be restrained by an equal couple developed by burying one end in a mass of concrete (Fig. 5-1b). The magnitude of the torque on the shafts of both Figs. 5-1(a) and (b) will, of course, be equal to the same Pp value.

The effectiveness of a couple in producing torsion in a shaft is maximum when the couple acts in a plane perpendicular to the axis of the shaft. If the couple is rotated out of this plane, only that component of the couple that is in the plane perpendicular to the shaft produces torsion (Fig. 5-2). The other component produces only bending because it lies in

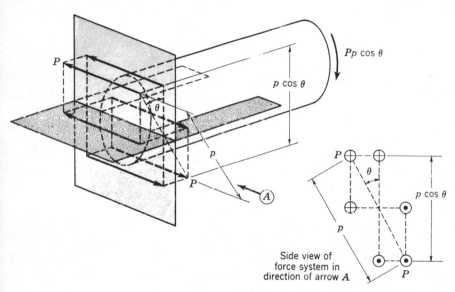

Figure 5-2

the horizontal plane containing the axis of the shaft. A couple lying in any plane containing the axis of the shaft can produce no twisting or rotation of the shaft. For example, if a boy should hang from a doorknob, the door would not swing.

Resolution of a force into a force and a couple.　　Often, the presence of a couple acting on a shaft is obscured. This is especially true when a single force is applied to the end of a lever arm fastened to a shaft. Since no reaction is visible, the presence of a couple is not always detected. Take, for example, the case presented in Fig. 5-3. Only one force P is applied, and yet we know that the obvious purpose of the wrench is to twist the shaft.

This problem can be clarified by recalling the method used in mechanics to resolve a force into a force and a couple. To illustrate its use, let us add at point A in Fig. 5-3, two opposing forces equal and parallel to force P. Certainly their addition to the shaft causes no change in equilibrium, since they themselves are balanced. They alter neither the original conditions of the problem nor its final outcome. They do, however, simplify the problem by separating into convenient fractions the action of twisting and bending produced by force P.

Figure 5-3

Consider the forces P and P'. Since they are equal, parallel, and of opposite direction, they constitute a *couple*. Moreover, they are in a plane perpendicular to the axis of the shaft and *can produce only torsion*.

Force P'' acts as a *single force* and as such *can produce only bending*. The detailed study of its effects will be made in Chapter 6. This action of force P'' does not, however, influence the twisting action of the couple PP'. The complete study of problems of this type involves investigation of the combined effects of both the couple and the single force.

It is recommended that the above resolution of forces be made whenever a force acts off the center line of a shaft causing it to rotate about its longitudinal axis. The resolution should be made on the axis line passing through the center of gravity of the resisting section so that the two forces constituting the couple lie in a plane perpendicular to the shaft.

Shafts operating at constant speed. The study of mechanics reveals that any unbalanced system of forces or couples acting on a body produces acceleration. A shaft operating at constant speed is, therefore, theoretically acting under the same balanced conditions that prevail under static torque. Because of the maintenance of equilibrium, it is permissible to use the principles of torsion herein developed to determine the operational stresses of shafts rotating at constant speeds.

PROBLEMS

5-1. A cantilevered shaft, 3 ft. long, is rotated by a lever having an effective moment arm of 30 in. If the force applied at the handle of the lever is 50 lb, what will be the torque supplied to the shaft? Is this the only effect? Explain. *Answer:* 1500 in.-lb.

5-2. A shaft is acted upon by forces A and B, as shown in Fig. 5-4. Calculate the torque. (a) What would be the torque on the shaft if forces A and C were to act in the position shown? Also, forces A and D? (b) What, if any, bending effect would each of the couples AB, AC, and AD produce? *Answer:* (a) 300 ft-lb in each case.

5-3. If force A in Fig. 5-4 were to act alone through a lever, what torque would be produced on the shaft? What dissimilarity in conditions would be produced by this single force as compared to the couples in the previous problem?

Figure 5-4. All forces shown are applied externally.

Figure 5-5

5-4. The windlass shown in Fig. 5-5 is operated at constant speed by a man applying a force of 80 lb to the crank. If the two gears are 4 and 24 in. in diameter, what maximum weight may be lifted by the cable passing over the 6-in. diameter sheave? What is the torque acting on each of the shafts?

5-5. Two pulleys, 12 in. and 24 in. in diameter, respectively, are placed on opposite ends of a horizontal shaft of 2 in. diameter. If the belt placed around the 24-in. pulley has 2000- and 500-lb tensile forces acting vertically downwards on opposite sides of the pulley, what torque is acting on the shaft? What must the

Figure 5-6

torque be on the 12-in. pulley to maintain equilibrium? What single force (other force of couple obscured) acting tangentially to the surface of the 12-in. pulley will keep the shaft in equilibrium?

5-6. In the gear train shown in Fig. 5-6, a clockwise torque of 1000 in.-lb is applied to wheel A without moving gear E. Calculate the torque in shafts B, C, and D. *Answers:* $T_B = 500$ in.-lb, $T_C = 250$ in.-lb, $T_D = 125$ in.-lb.

5-3. Development of torsion formula

Proper shaft design requires a knowledge of the relationship between the applied torque and the resulting stresses and strains. Therefore, it is important to discover first how these stresses and strains vary qualitatively on any one cross section. Let us consider the shaft shown in Fig. 5-7(a) acted upon by an applied couple T and resisting couple T_R. Perfect balance exists over the full length of the shaft because the couples T and T_R at either end are equal to each other. Moreover, each intermediate section offers a resistance capable of maintaining this balance. To deter-

Figure 5-7

mine the couples involved in this balancing operation, let us pass plane RS (Fig. 5-7a) through the shaft perpendicular to its axis at any inter- mediate point. To rebalance the right-hand segment (Fig. 5-7c) a new T_R couple must act on its exposed section. The left-hand segment (Fig. 5-7b) is balanced by a couple T also acting on the exposed section. Thus each free body segment is under the same torque condition that prevailed on the uncut shaft. Because these couples were required at a random intermediate section, they must also exist on every section.

It is a generally accepted fact that when a couple acts on any section, it twists or rotates that section about its center of resistance. In the case of a circular section, the center of resistance and the rotation point is located at its center because of symmetry. Therefore the axis of the shaft contains the rotation point of each section and remains straight even though the shaft should twist.

Suppose, now, we consider the right-hand segment to be reduced in length to an infinitesimal dl as shown in Fig. 5-7(d). As the torques T and T_R act on either side of the segment and cause a relative motion of one side with respect to the other, the following deductions can be made:

(1) If a point on the exposed faces of the segment moves, it will travel in a circular path.

(2) The farther the point is from the center of rotation, the greater will be the distance travelled.

(3) The relative motion of initially opposite points increases proportionally with the distance from the center.

(4) The direction of this relative motion or strain at any point is tangent to the circle passing through that point.

(5) The strain, because of the parallel movement of the one end section relative to the other, is definitely of the shear type.

It was previously indicated that unit strain was the result of unit stress, and that the two were proportional to each other below the proportional limit. Based on these two facts, it must also be true that the shearing unit stress below the proportional limit varies directly with the distance from the center and acts in the direction of the strain, tangent to the circle passing through the point where the shearing unit stress is developed. Expressed mathematically,

$$\frac{s_s}{r} = \frac{(s_s)_\rho}{\rho} \qquad (5.1)$$

where r = radius of shaft and ρ = any radial distance shorter than the radius r.

Turning now to the free body shown in Fig. 5-8, let us consider the resistance offered by the shearing stresses developed on the exposed section.

At any distance ρ, let us draw a narrow circular band of very small width — so small that the shearing resistance acting thereon is a constant $(s_s)_\rho$. If, then, the circular

Figure 5-8

element whose area equals dA were divided into n parts, the shearing force on each part would be

$$\frac{dA}{n}(s_s)_\rho$$

The moment of this small resisting force will then be

$$\frac{dA}{n}(s_s)_\rho\rho$$

But there are n parts included in dA. The total resisting moment of the force developed on dA is, therefore,

$$dT_R = \frac{dA}{n}(s_s)_\rho\rho n = dA(s_s)_\rho\rho$$

Substituting for the value of $(s_s)_\rho$ its equal $\dfrac{s_s}{r}\rho$ we obtain

$$dT_R = \frac{s_s}{r}\rho^2\, dA$$

The circular element chosen is only one of the many that can be included on the cross section. *If the resisting moment of every circular element could be added together, their sum would be equal to T_R*, i.e., *the resisting moment required to hold the free body in equilibrium*, and also to T, the applied torque. Thus, by integration,

$$T = T_R = \int_0^r \frac{s_s}{r}\,\rho^2\, dA$$

But since s_s/r is included in the resisting torque of every circular element, it may be placed on the outside of the integral sign.

$$T = \frac{s_s}{r}\int_0^r \rho^2\, dA \tag{5.2}$$

However, $\displaystyle\int_0^r \rho^2\, dA$ is the general term for polar moment of inertia expressed as J. Therefore, we may write

$$T = \frac{s_s}{r} J \tag{5.3}$$

where s_s = maximum shearing stress occurring on the outside fibers, in psi, r = radius of shaft, in inches, J = polar moment of inertia of cross section, in in.^{4}, T = applied torque, in in.-lb. This is known as the *torsion formula*. It is applicable to the design of all circular shafts.

5-4. Torsion formula adapted for hollow circular shafts

In the development of the torsion formula above, the resisting moments of all the circular elements on the cross section were added to secure the relationship:

$$T = T_R = \frac{s_s}{r} \int_0^r \rho^2 \, dA$$

If the cylindrical shaft were hollow, the number of circular elements that could be included in the cross section would be decreased by the number excluded by the hole. The polar moment of inertia of the net section would, therefore, include only those $\rho^2 \, dA$ values for the actual circular elements that could be drawn within its boundaries. This summation can be performed by subtracting the $\rho^2 \, dA$ values omitted by inserting the hole from the $\rho^2 \, dA$ values included in the gross cross section. The above relationship may, therefore, be modified for hollow cylinders as follows:

$$T = T_R = \frac{s_s}{r} \left(\int_0^r \rho^2 \, dA - \int_0^{r_i} \rho^2 \, dA \right)$$

It follows that
$$T = T_R = \frac{s_s}{r} (J_o - J_i) \qquad (5.4)$$

where J_o = the polar moment of inertia for the cross section included within the outside circle, $\pi D_o^4/32$, and J_i = the polar moment of inertia for the cross section included within the hole, or inside circle, $\pi D_i^4/32$.

5-5. Assumptions and limitations of the torsion formula

The assumptions and limitations included in the development of the torsion formula are as follows:

(1) The imposed shearing unit stress varies directly with the distance from the center of the shaft. Photoelastic experiments have substantiated this assumption.

(2) A diameter before twisting remains a diameter after twisting. This assumption implies that the unit strain varies directly with the distance from the center of the shaft. In conjunction with the first assumption, it further implies that the material must follow a straight stress-strain curve and that the shearing proportional limit of the material must not be exceeded.

(3) A plane cross section before twisting remains plane after twisting. This is true only of circular cross sections.

(4) The torsion formula is applicable only to circular or hollow circular sections if the hole therein is concentric. (Inasmuch as the stress on a

rectangular or square section does not vary uniformly from the center to the outside fibers, Eq. 5.1 does not apply to their design.)

Illustrative Problem 1.   What percentage of the strength of a solid-steel circular shaft 5 in. in diameter is lost by boring a 2.5-in. axial hole in it? Maximum allowable unit stress is 12,000 psi. Compare the weight of the shaft before and after boring.

SOLUTION.   The maximum allowable torque that can be applied to the solid shaft is

$$T = \frac{s_s J}{r} = \frac{12,000 \times \pi \times 5^4}{2.5 \times 32} = 295,000 \text{ in.-lb}$$

The hollow shaft can be subjected to a torque equal to

$$T_H = \frac{s_s}{r}(J_o - J_i) = \frac{12,000}{2.5} \times \frac{\pi}{32}(5^4 - 2.5^4) = 276,000 \text{ in.-lb}$$

Percentage of reduction in strength equals

$$\frac{T - T_H}{T} \times 100 = \frac{295,000 - 276,000}{295,000} \times 100 = 6.45 \text{ per cent}$$

Since the length remained the same after boring, the percentage of reduction in weight is proportional to the reduction in area.

Percentage of reduction in weight equals

$$\frac{A_o - (A_o - A_i)}{A_o} \times 100 = \frac{\frac{\pi 5^2}{4} - \left(\frac{\pi 5^2}{4} - \frac{\pi 2.5^2}{4}\right)}{\frac{\pi 5^2}{4}} \times 100$$

$$= \frac{5^2 - 5^2 + 2.5^2}{5^2} \times 100 ,$$

$$= \frac{6.25}{25} \times 100 = 25 \text{ per cent}$$

The reason for sometimes using hollow shafts is apparent when consideration is given to the amount of unit stress taken by the fibers of a solid shaft close to its axis. These fibers can take only a very small part of the maximum allowable stress taken by the outermost fiber, since the shearing stress is proportional to the distance from the center of the shaft, and the maximum stress is a fixed tabular value that cannot be exceeded. Capable of taking more stress than that which is placed upon them, these inside fibers often do not sustain a sufficient amount of load to justify their inclusion in the total weight to be carried.

Illustrative Problem 2.   Compute the diameter of a hollow shaft with a drilled axial hole one-half the outside diameter that will withstand the torque applied to the solid shaft in Illustrative Problem 1. Use same maximum allowable unit stress, 12,000 psi.

SOLUTION. Torque = 295,000 in.-lb. Substituting in the torsion formula, we obtain

$$T = \frac{s_s(J_o - J_i)}{r}$$

$$295,000 = \frac{12,000 \times \frac{\pi}{32}\left[d_o{}^4 - \left(\frac{d_o}{2}\right)^4\right]}{\frac{d_o}{2}}$$

$$295,000 = \frac{12,000\pi}{16 d_o}\left(d_o{}^4 - \frac{d_o{}^4}{16}\right)$$

$$\frac{295,000 \times 256}{12,000 \times \pi \times 15} = d_o{}^3$$

$$d_o{}^3 = 133.50, \quad d_o = 5.10 \text{ in.}, \quad d_i = 2.55 \text{ in.}$$

PROBLEMS

5-7. What diameter of shaft is required to withstand a torque of 1200 in.-lb if the maximum allowable shearing unit stress is 12,000 psi? *Answer:* 0.80 in.

5-8. If a hollow shaft measuring 2 in. in outside diameter and $1\frac{1}{2}$ in. in inside diameter is to resist a torque of 6000 in.-lb, what maximum shearing unit stress will be developed? What will the shearing stress be on the innermost fibers? *Answer:* 5580 psi, 4180 psi.

5-9. An extra-strong pipe having an outer diameter of 2.375 in. and an inside diameter of 1.939 in. is being screwed into a coupling by a plumber using a 24-in. pipe wrench. If the effective moment arm is 20 in. and the force applied is 100 lb, what is the maximum shearing unit stress developed in the pipe?

5-10. Two meshed gears of 8- and 12-in. pitch diameters rotate at a constant speed (Fig. 5-9). If the 12-in. gear is driven and develops a torque of 4000 in.-lb, what maximum shearing unit stress will be found in the $1\frac{1}{4}$ in. shaft driven by the 8-in. gear? *Answer:* 6930 psi.

Figure 5-9

5-11. A solid steel shaft, 2 in. in diameter, is to be fitted and welded to the end of a hollow steel shaft having an inside diameter of 2 in. If the maximum allowable shear stress in steel is 15,000 psi, what will the minimum outside diameter have to be to transmit the maximum permissible torque? *Answer:* 2.38 in.

5-6. Shaft couplings

It often becomes necessary to join two shafts in order to transmit torque over a long distance. A common joint used for this purpose is a *bolted coupling*. In this connection, the torque from one shaft is passed through the bolts of the coupling, by their resistance to shear, to the other shaft.

If the coupling shown in Fig. 5-10(a) is separated at its joint by means of a cutting plane and Fig. 5-10(b) taken as a free body, the exposed surfaces

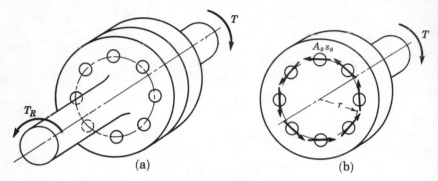

Figure 5-10

of the bolts must offer sufficient shearing resistance through their moment arm r to hold T in equilibrium. If s_s is considered as the developed shearing unit stress spread uniformly over each rivet cross section A_s, and since $T = T_R$, we may equate the moments as follows:

$$T = T_R = n \times A_s s_s \times r \qquad (5.5)$$

Illustrative Problem 3. Two shafts 5 in. in diameter are to be joined by a bolted coupling. If the maximum allowable shearing unit stress in the shafts is 10,000 psi, the diameter of the bolt circle is 10 in., and the allowable shearing unit stress in the bolt is 9000 psi, find the number of $\frac{7}{8}$-in. bolts necessary for the connection.

SOLUTION. The torque to be transferred by the coupling is found from the torsion formula as applied to the 5-in. shafts.

$$T = \frac{s_s J}{r} = \frac{10,000 \times \pi 5^4}{2.5 \times 32} = 245,000 \text{ in.-lb.}$$

To successfully transmit this torque, the resisting moment of the bolts must be equal to it.

Hence, the resisting force on one bolt equals

$$9000 \times \frac{\pi}{4}\left(\frac{7}{8}\right)^2 = 5400 \text{ lb}$$

and the resisting moment of the force on one bolt equals

$$5400 \times 5 = 27,000 \text{ in.-lb}$$

If, then, the resisting moment of one bolt is 27,000 in.-lb, and there are a total of 245,000 in.-lb to resist, the number of bolts required will be equal to

$$n = \frac{245,000}{27,000} = 9.08, \text{ or } 10 \text{ bolts}$$

This problem could, of course, be solved by direct substitution in Eq. 5.5 as follows:

$$n = \frac{T}{A_s s_s r} = \frac{245,000}{0.60 \times 9000 \times 5} = 9.08, \text{ or } 10 \text{ bolts}$$

It is suggested, however, that the first procedure, which depends on logic, be used rather than the second, which depends upon memorization of the formula.

PROBLEMS

5-12. Two 4-in. diameter shafts are to be connected by means of a coupling. What torque may safely be transmitted through this coupling if eight $\frac{7}{8}$-in. bolts having an allowable shearing unit stress of 10,000 psi are placed on a 10-in. bolt circle? *Answer:* 240,000 in.-lb.

5-13. How many $\frac{3}{4}$-in. bolts will be required in a coupling used to join two 3-in. shafts if the bolt circle is 8 in. and the torque is 125,000 in.-lb. Maximum allowable shearing unit stress in bolts is 10,000 psi.

5-14. To prevent damage to the engine and propeller of a tugboat, a short auxiliary shaft is placed between the main shaft and the propeller shaft to act as a *safety valve*. If the main and propeller shafts are each 6 in. in diameter and the auxiliary is 5 in., how many 1-in. bolts are required in each coupling if the bolt circle is 12 in. in diameter and the maximum torque to be restrained is computed on the basis of a proportional limit stress of 24,000 psi being attained in the auxiliary shaft? Maximum allowable shearing unit stress in bolts is 10,000 psi. *Answer:* Use 13 bolts.

5-15. Two 4-in. diameter solid steel shafts are to be joined by means of flanged couplings and four $\frac{1}{2}$-in. diameter steel bolts set on a bolt circle d in. in diameter. Determine the diameter of the bolt circle in order that the bolts and the steel shafts be equally strong in resisting torsion. Maximum allowable $s_s = 8000$ psi. *Answer:* 32 in.

5-16. A coupling flange (Fig. 5-11) is made by joining a hollow steel shaft, $3\frac{3}{4}$ in. O.D. by $2\frac{1}{2}$ in. I.D., to the center of a steel disk, 10 in. in diameter and $\frac{3}{4}$ in. thick, with a circumferential fillet weld. What is the theoretical size of the 45° fillet weld that would be required to develop the maximum torque? Maximum allowable shear stress in shaft and bolts = 15,000 psi. Maximum allowable bearing stress of bolts against plate = 30,000 psi. Consider center of 45° shear plane in weld to be located 2 in. from center of shaft. *Answer:* 0.52 in.

Figure 5-11

5-7. The relationship between horsepower, rpm, and torque

One of the most useful relationships in mechanical and electrical design is the relationship between the horsepower, speed, and torque as applied to a shaft. With this relationship the horsepower delivered by a shaft can be computed, if we know the speed and torque supplied to the shaft. Or, the torque capable of being delivered by a shaft can be determined by using the speed and horsepower of the motor or engine employed. To obtain greater facility in the use of the relationship, let us first develop it step by step.

Figure 5-12

Figure 5-12 shows a shaft acted upon by a weight W placed at the end of a rope wrapped around the shaft several times.

Suppose the shaft is rotated so that weight W is lifted a distance of $2\pi r$; then, the work done in lifting weight W a distance of $2\pi r$ (one revolution of the shaft, where $r = $ in.) is

$$W \times 2\pi r \text{ in.-lb (force} \times \text{distance)}$$

The work done in lifting weight W through q revolutions of the shaft equals

$$W \times 2\pi r \times q \text{ in.-lb}$$

If weight W is to be lifted through q revolutions in t minutes, the rate of work performed equals

$$\frac{W \times 2\pi r \times q}{t} \text{ in.-lb per min}$$

But $q/t = n$, angular speed per min and $Wr = T$, the torque supplied to the shaft; therefore, the rate of work performed in the shaft = $2\pi Tn$ in.-lb per min.

To convert in.-lb per min to ft-lb per min requires dividing by 12, and since 33,000 ft-lb per min equal one horsepower, we may write

$$\mathrm{Hp} = \frac{2\pi Tn}{12 \times 33,000} \tag{5.6}$$

It should be recalled that to use this formula properly, T must be in inch pounds and n in revolutions per minute.

Illustrative Problem 4. A pulley 6 ft in diameter is mounted on a 2-in. shaft operating at 150 rpm. Placed around the pulley is a belt whose opposite tensions are 1500 and 1100 lb (Fig. 5-13). (a) Find the horsepower being transmitted. (b) What is the maximum shearing unit stress in the shaft?

Figure 5-13

SOLUTION. To find the horsepower being transmitted requires knowledge of both the speed and the torque. The torque, determined from the belt tensions and the radius of the pulley, is

$$T = (1500 - 1100) \times 36 = 14,400 \text{ in.-lb}$$

The horsepower being transmitted is, therefore,

$$\mathrm{Hp} = \frac{2\pi Tn}{12 \times 33,000} = \frac{2\pi \times 14,400 \times 150}{12 \times 33,000} = 34.36$$

The maximum shearing unit stress in the shaft is

$$s_s = \frac{Tr}{J} = \frac{14,400 \times 1}{(\pi \times 2^4)/32} = 9170 \text{ psi}$$

PROBLEMS

5-17. Determine the work produced by a 4-in. diameter shaft per revolution while transmitting 300 hp at 180 rpm. Calculate also the torque and the maximum shear stress acting on the shaft. *Answer:* 8750 ft-lb, 8350 psi.

5-18. A $1\frac{1}{2}$-in. shaft is operating at a speed of 350 rpm under a maximum shearing unit stress of 12,000 psi. Determine the horsepower being delivered by the shaft.

5-19. Determine the speed of a motor, undergoing a dynamometer test, which is delivering 25 hp under a resistance of 5000 in.-lb. If the shaft is 2 in. diameter, what is its maximum shear stress? *Answer:* 315 rpm, 3180 psi.

5-20. A $1\frac{1}{2}$-in. diameter shaft operated by a motor whose shaft horsepower equals 20 rotates at a speed of 400 rpm. What is the maximum shear stress acting on the shaft?

5-21. The wrapping and processing mechanisms of a textile machine are synchronized by a 40-ft steel shaft, $1\frac{1}{4}$ in. in diameter. If the torque necessary to operate the wrapping mechanism is 1000 in.-lb, what horsepower must be delivered to the shaft at the processing point to maintain a shaft speed of 800 rpm. What is the maximum shear stress developed in the shaft? *Answer:* 12.7 hp., 2620 psi.

5-22. What diameter of shaft will be necessary to transmit a shaft horsepower of 20 under a speed of 1200 rpm? The maximum allowable shearing unit stress is 10,000 psi. *Answer:* 1.75 in.

5-23. Find the outside diameter of a hollow shaft required to transmit a horsepower of 1000 while operating at a speed of 120 rpm, if its inner diameter is 4 in. and the maximum allowable shearing unit stress is 8000 psi.

5-8. The angle of twist produced by torque

In some instances, the controlling feature of the design of a shaft is based upon its resistance to twisting rather than its strength. Lathes, milling machines, and other precision tools usually have shafts which, if designed solely on the basis of strength, would twist too much for the high accuracy required. They are usually stiffened by increasing the diameter according to the formula about to be derived.

Figure 5-14

Derivation. Consider the strip element AB on the shaft of Fig.5-14 and the rectangular element $KLMN$, a portion of element AB. Upon application of torque T, the shaft twists so that radius OA rotates to a new position OA' and the rectangular element $KLMN$ moves to $K'L'M'N'$. In producing this movement, element $KLMN$ is distorted by the shearing unit stress. From § 2-12 unit strain is

$$\epsilon_s = \tan \phi$$

But

$$\tan \phi = \frac{s}{l}$$

Hence

$$\epsilon_s = \frac{s}{l} \quad \text{or} \quad \frac{r\theta}{l}$$

where θ is expressed in radians.

It is common practice when determining relationships between a deformation and a force to apply Hooke's law for the particular type of stress under consideration.

$$G = \frac{s_s}{\epsilon_s}$$

Since

$$s_s = \frac{Tr}{J} \quad \text{and} \quad \epsilon_s = \frac{r\theta}{l}$$

$$G = \frac{Tr/J}{r\theta/l} = \frac{Tl}{J\theta} \tag{5.7a}$$

or

$$\theta = \frac{Tl}{GJ} \tag{5.7b}$$

where θ = angle of twist in radians, T = torque, expressed in in.-lb, l = length of shaft in in., G = shearing modulus of elasticity in psi, J = polar moment of inertia in in.⁴

Illustrative Problem 5. Compute the diameter of a solid steel shaft necessary to carry a torque of 400,000 in.-lb if the twist is not to exceed 1° in 5 ft, the maximum allowable shearing unit stress is to be held at 12,000 psi, and G = 12,000,000 psi.

SOLUTION. The diameter required to meet the twist specification is as follows:

$$\theta = \frac{Tl}{GJ}$$

$$\frac{1°}{57.3} = \frac{400,000 \times 5 \times 12 \times 32}{12,000,000 \times \pi d^4}$$

$$d^4 = \frac{400,000 \times 5 \times 12 \times 32}{12,000,000 \times \pi} \times 57.3 = 1170$$

$$d = 5.85 \text{ in.}$$

The diameter required to hold the maximum shearing unit stress at 12,000 psi is

$$s_s = \frac{Tr}{J} = \frac{T(d/2)}{(\pi d^4)/32} = \frac{16T}{\pi d^3}$$

Hence, $$d^3 = \frac{16T}{s_s \pi} = \frac{16 \times 400,000}{12,000 \times \pi} = 170$$

$$d = 5.53 \text{ in.}$$

It is, therefore, necessary to use a diameter of at least 5.85 in. to meet the more stringent condition of twisting.

Illustrative Problem 6.   A hollow steel cylindrical shaft 10 in. in diameter and 6 in. in outside diameter is stressed to 8000 psi. (a) What horsepower is being delivered when the shaft is turning at 1000 rpm? (b) What is the twist in degrees for 100 ft of this shaft? $G = 12 \times 10^6$ psi.

SOLUTION. (a) Since the torque is necessary to determine the horsepower, let us use the torsion formula for its determination.

$$T = \frac{s_s(J_o - J_i)}{r} = \frac{8000 \times (\pi/32)(10^4 - 6^4)}{5} = 1,368,000 \text{ in.-lb}$$

Inserting the torque in the horsepower formula, we obtain

$$\text{Hp} = \frac{2\pi \times 1,368,000 \times 1000}{12 \times 33,000} = 21,700$$

(b) The twist of the shaft is

$$\theta = \frac{Tl}{GJ} = \frac{1,368,000 \times 1200}{12,000,000 \times (\pi/32)(10^4 - 6^4)}$$

$$= 0.16 \text{ radians} = 0.16 \times 57.3 = 9.2°$$

PROBLEMS

5-24. If a 1-in. diameter steel drill rod 6000 ft long is used in drilling an oil well, is it possible that the rod may twist a complete revolution without exceeding its maximum allowable shearing unit stress of 20,000 psi? Show figures. *Answer:* Yes. 38.2 revolutions.

5-25. Determine the limiting length of a $\frac{1}{2}$-in. diameter Duralumin (2017-T3) shaft that will not exceed a twist of 10° when subjected to a torque of 500 in.-lb.

5-26. A 1-in. diameter steel shaft is twisted 1° in a length of 3 ft. Determine the torque required. *Answer:* 571 in.-lb.

5-27. Determine the angle of twist of the shaft in Problem 5-21. *Answer:* 9.57°.

5-28. Four gears are arranged as shown in Fig. 5-15. If the torque supplied at the 24-in. gear A is 2000 in.-lb, through what angle could gear A be rotated if gear D were maintained stationary? Both shafts are made of steel. *Answer:* 9.18°.

Figure 5-15

5-29. A solid circular shaft of steel is used to transmit 200 hp at 600 rpm. (a) What diameter of shaft is required if the allowable maximum shearing stress is 20,000 psi? (b) If a hollow shaft is used that has an inside diameter equal to the diameter of the solid shaft determined in part (a), what must be the outside diameter of this shaft if the angular twist of the two shafts is to be equal?

5-30. A hollow steel shaft 10 ft long, with 6 in. O.D. and 3 in. I.D., is driven by a diesel engine with 200 brake hp when the shaft is operating at 300 rpm. Calculate the shaft's angle of twist. *Answer: 0.185°.*

5-31. Pulleys A, B, and C are joined by solid steel shafting and are 30 in. and 18 in. apart, respectively. The torque applied at the driving pulley, A, is 3540 ft-lb; the torque delivered at pulley B is 2150 ft-lb; the torque delivered at pulley C is 1390 ft-lb. (a) If maximum allowable s_s is 8000 psi for the steel shaft, determine the required shaft diameters for each section. (b) If the shaft has a 3-in. diameter over its entire length, find the angle of twist in degrees between A and C. NOTE: The shaft rests in bearings just beyond A and C. Disregard any beam action due to transverse loads. *Answers:* (a) $d_1 = 3.0$ in., $d_2 = 2.2$ in., (b) 0.952°.

5-32. A shaft of length l, and fixed at one end, is acted upon by a torque T at a point $\frac{2}{3}l$ from the fixed end. If the opposite end is now fixed and T released, what are the end restraining moments in terms of T?

5-33. A shaft l ft long and fixed at each end has applied at a point a feet from one end a torque T. Determine the end restraining moments in terms of T, the segmental distances a and b, and length l. *Answer: Ta/l, Tb/l.*

5-34. A 6-ft hollow aluminum shaft with 3 in. O.D., 2 in. I.D., has 2 in. of its length slipped over a 2-in. diameter solid steel shaft 8 ft 2 in. long. Both are then fixed at their outer ends. If a torque of 10,000 in.-lb is applied to the aluminum shaft at its overlapped end, and then fastened rigidly in its distorted condition to the unstressed steel shaft, what will the maximum shear stress in the aluminum and steel shafts be when the applied torque is released? Consider the lengths of the aluminum and steel in the compound shaft to be 6 and 8 ft respectively. *Answers:* 837 psi, 2270 psi.

5-35. A compound shaft *AD* fixed at each end consists of three segments. Segment *AB*, 2 in. in diameter and 2 ft long is made of aluminum; *BC*, 3 in. in diameter and 3 ft long, is made of bronze; *CD*, 2 in. in diameter and 4 ft long is made of steel. If similarly directed torques are applied at *B* and *C* equal to 5,000 and 10,000 in.-lb respectively, determine the restraining torques at the supports. *Answers:* $T_L = 5890$ in.-lb, $T_R = 9110$ in.-lb.

5-9. Mechanical properties in torsion

Torque-twist curves (Fig. 5-16), similar in shape and character to the stress-strain curves discussed in Chapter 3, are drawn from data obtained from torsion tests. The data from such a test consist of corresponding values of torque and relative twist taken over a 6- to 10-in. test length.

Figure 5-16

Those points on a torque-twist curve representing the yield stress, proportional limit and elastic limit are located similarly and are identical in definition to those obtained from a stress-strain curve obtained from an axial test. Their actual numerical values, however, must be computed from their corresponding torques using the torsion formula.

In order for the ultimate stress to be obtained with validity from the torsion formula, the variation of shear stress across the cross section must be linear throughout the entire torque-twist test. This is generally not the case. Only in the torsion tests of thin-walled hollow tubes and of isotropic, homogeneous materials with straight torque-twist curves is this a possibility. The stress obtained from the torsion formula using the maximum torque is a fictitious stress called the modulus of rupture (see § 5-13).

The value of modulus of elasticity is computed from Eq. 5.7a:

$$G = \frac{Tl}{\theta J}$$

by substituting T/θ, the slope of the torque-twist curve below the proportional limit, l the test length, and J, its polar moment of inertia.

5-10. Longitudinal shear stresses produced in shafts by torsion

Figure 5-17(a) shows a very thin disk cut from a shaft subjected to torsion and placed in equilibrium as a free body (thickness exaggerated). If, from the surface of this disk, there is cut a free body consisting of a square element one unit deep (Fig. 5-17b), the previously mentioned shearing

(a)   (b)

Figure 5-17

unit stresses s_s, acting in the two exposed circular planes, can be shown acting on areas $ABCD$ and $EFGH$. Since these areas and the stresses acting upon them are equal, the forces so produced consitute a couple. But an element acted upon by only one couple cannot be in equilibrium: Another couple is required to balance the free body.

This necessary balancing couple must be in the same plane as the applied couple. Since the unit stresses on planes $ABCD$ and $EFGH$ have been already determined as shear, the only other possible planes on which the forces of the balancing couple can act are $BCGF$ and $ADHE$. The stresses on these planes must also be equal and consist of shear, since only the resultant shear forces provide the necessary couple. Let us temporarily designate the shearing unit stresses on planes $BCGF$ and $ADHE$ as s'_s. From the geometry of the element, all four of the side areas are equal. We may, therefore, write the moment of equation of the shear forces acting on the element about line AD as

$$s_s{'} \times \text{area } EFGH \times a = s'_s \times \text{area } BCGF \times a$$

But since area $EFGH$ = area $BCGF$ and $a = a$, then

$$s_s = s'_s \tag{5.8}$$

It may, therefore, be stated that as a shaft is twisted, there are two simultaneously produced equal-shearing stresses at every point on the shaft, one parallel to the axis, the other perpendicular to both the axis and the radius passing through the point.

In fact, this proposition may be extended to include any body subjected to shearing stress. Shear is not necessarily produced by torsion: It may be obtained by direct forces as shown in Chapter 2. Thus, it may be further stated that if a plane passing through a point in a body has a shearing unit stress acting upon it, there must be simultaneously induced a shearing unit stress of like magnitude on a plane perpendicular to it. These shearing stresses act in a direction perpendicular to the line of intersection of the planes in which they operate.

5-11. *The maximum diagonal stresses produced by torsion*

In conjunction with the development of the two aforementioned equal-shearing unit stresses, maximum normal stresses equal in magnitude to the shear stresses are developed on the two planes making 45° to the shear planes. On one 45° plane, the normal stress is tensile in nature, whereas on the other 45° plane, the stress is compressive.

PROOF. If a plane is passed through points, F, G, A, and D of Fig. 5-17 and the right-hand portion used as a free body (Fig. 5-18), stresses must

Figure 5-18

occur on the exposed plane to recreate the conditions of equilibrium. Since the two known shearing forces are equal and perpendicular, their resultant is perpendicular to, and passes through, the center of the diagonal plane. To balance this resultant requires an equal and opposite force acting on the action line of the resultant. Because this equilibrant acts at the center of the diagonal plane and is perpendicular to it, the stresses placed upon it are normal to the plane and are of a tensile nature.

The magnitude of this tensile unit stress can be determined by writing an equation balancing the forces along a line perpendicular to the diagonal plane.

$$\Sigma F_x = s_t \times FADG = s_s \times FBCG \times \cos 45° + s_s \times ABCD \times \sin 45°$$
$$s_t \times FADG = s_s(FBCG \times \cos 45° + ABCD \sin 45°)$$

But area $FADG$ = area $FBCG \cos 45°$ + area $ABCD \sin 45°$

Hence, $s_t = s_s$ (5.9)

In a similar manner, it can be shown by passing a plane through points B, C, H, and E (Fig. 5-19) and using the upper portion as a free

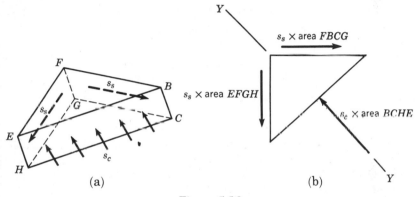

Figure 5-19

body, that the induced stress is a compressive stress equal to the shearing unit stress.

$$\Sigma F_y = s_c \times BCHE = s_s \times EFGH \cos 45° + s_s \times FBCG \sin 45°$$
$$s_c \times BCHE = s_s(EFGH \cos 45° + FBCG \sin 45°)$$

But $BCHE = EFGH \cos 45° + FBCG \sin 45°$

Hence, $s_c = s_s$ (5.10)

Therefore, it becomes evident that the two equal and mutually perpendicular shear stresses develop simultaneously with two other stresses, s_t and s_c, acting at an angle of 45° to the shear planes with equal intensity.

The normal stresses s_t and s_c as found on the *diagonal planes* of their respective free bodies were sufficient in themselves to balance the resultant of the two perpendicular shear forces. The s_t and s_c stresses required no shear component to assist them in making this equilibrium condition possible. As indicated before (§ 2-6), a normal stress that is unaccompanied by shear is a maximum normal stress. This condition is also true as regards the. s_t and s_c stresses just found. Since they have no accompanying shear, they are, therefore, maximum normal stresses. If an angle other than 45° had been selected, the normal stress acting on the exposed plane would have been less than the maximum value and would have acted together with a component shear stress. A detailed study of these conditions will be made in Chapter 12.

Thus, as a shaft is twisted, the critical stresses developed are as follows:

(1) The maximum shearing unit stress s_s equal to Tr/J acting at the surface of the shaft on planes perpendicular to the axis.

(2) The maximum shearing unit stress s_s acting at the surface of the shaft on planes passing through the longitudinal axis.

(3) The maximum tensile unit stress $(s_t)_{max.}$ acting at the surface of the shaft at an angle of 45° to the maximum shear stresses.

(4) The maximum compressive unit stress $(s_c)_{max.}$ acting at the surface of the shaft at an angle of 90° to the maximum tensile unit stress.

These four stresses are equal to one another and are produced simultaneously.

5-12. *The importance of the critical stresses developed in shafts*

It will be recalled from our previous discussion of the strengths of various materials that their resistances in tension, compression, and shear may vary considerably. Some materials may be weakest in shear, some in tension, and still others in compression. Failure will occur in torsional members on those planes for which the strength is least. Since all the maximum stresses develop equally and simultaneously, that stress first to arrive at its ceiling value will produce rupture.

Figure 5-20

The character of the failure of a shaft subjected to torque action may be forecast if the three strengths are known. For instance, a steel shaft will fail on a plane perpendicular to its longitudinal axis (Fig. 5-20a), because

(1) Steel is weaker in shear than in tension or compression.

(2) A maximum shearing stress is developed on this plane.

(3) The gripping action at the shaft ends increases the resistance to a longitudinal shear failure.

In contrast, cast-iron shafts being weak in tension will fail along a helical plane inclined approximately 45° to the axis of the shaft (Fig. 5-20b and c). A piece of blackboard chalk will also rupture in the same characteristic manner.

In the light of the previous remarks, the design of a shaft must be governed by the weakest strength of the material to be used.

Illustrative Problem 7.   A shaft is to be made from a new material having the following ultimate strengths: $s_t = 20,000$ psi, $s_c = 30,000$ psi; and $s_s = 30,000$ psi. If a safety factor of 4 is to be used, what diameter is required to resist a torque of 1000 ft-lb?

SOLUTION. A glance at the three ultimate strengths reveals the ultimate tensile unit stress to be the lowest. The design must, therefore, be made on the basis of a working unit stress of

$$(s_t)_w = \frac{20,000}{4} = 5000 \text{ psi}$$

At the very moment that the torque has developed this maximum tensile unit stress of 5000 psi, the maximum shearing unit stress on the plane perpendicular to the axis is also 5000 psi. Since the relationship of diameter, torque, and maximum shearing unit stress is contained in the torsion equation, the use of the maximum shearing unit stress of 5000 psi as a limiting stress in the formula will provide the necessary diameter to also limit the tensile stress to 5000 psi. These working stresses are assumed to be below the proportional limit, so that the torsion formula will be applicable.

Hence, $s_s = \dfrac{Tr}{J}$ and $T = 1000$ ft-lb, or 12,000 in.-lb

$$5000 = \frac{1000 \times 12(d/2)}{\pi d^4/32} = \frac{12,000 \times 16}{\pi d^3}$$

$$d^3 = \frac{12,000 \times 16}{\pi \times 5000} = 12.20, \qquad d = 2.30 \text{ in.}$$

PROBLEMS

5-36. A high-carbon steel (0.7 per cent carbon) shaft is to be designed to take a torque of 40,000 in.-lb with a safety factor of 5. (a) Determine its diameter and the maximum shear, tensile, and compressive unit stresses. (b) Indicate by a sketch of the shaft the direction in which stresses will act. (c) If the torque were to be increased to cause rupture, how would the shaft fail? (d) Indicate the anticipated plane of failure on the sketch of (b). Refer to Table 2 for stresses. *Answer:* (a) 2.34 in.

5-37. A ceramic insulator will have imposed upon it a torque of 300 in.-lb. If the ultimate strengths in shear, tension, and compression are, respectively, 5000, 4000, and 50,000 psi, what must its diameter be? How would it fail? Use a safety factor of 5.

5-38. A cast-iron cylindrical supporting rod 1 in. in diameter is to be used occasionally to resist a twisting action. What amount of torque in inch-pounds can it safely withstand if a factor of safety of 5 is to be used? Ultimate unit stresses in shear, tension, and compression are, respectively, 30,000, 20,000, and 60,000 psi. *Answer:* 785 in.-lb.

5-39. A delicate mechanical apparatus requires a Duralumin (2017-T3) shaft $\frac{1}{4}$ in. in diameter. Determine the allowable torque in inch-pounds that may be applied to the shaft using a factor of safety of 5. Consult Table 2. How will it fail?

5-13. Modulus of rupture in torsion

Should the value of the maximum torque required to rupture a shaft be placed in the torsion formula and a solution made for the corresponding shearing unit stress, the stress

$$s_r = \frac{T_{\text{max.}} \, r}{J} \tag{5.11}$$

thus obtained would be known as the shearing *modulus of rupture*. It is generally a fictitious stress, since the stress at the ultimate stress is ordinarily above the proportional limit. This fact, it will be recalled, invalidates the use of the torsion equation, because one of the assumptions made in its derivation requires a constant stress-strain ratio. In order that the shearing modulus of rupture be equal to the ultimate shearing unit stress, the stress-strain curve would have to be a straight line to the point of rupture. Few materials have this characteristic.

Although the shearing modulus of rupture may equal the ultimate shearing unit stress, it generally exceeds it. The truth of this statement may be verified by the following reasoning.

If the shearing stress produced on the outermost fiber is equal to a stress below the proportional limit, the variation of shear stress over the cross section will be a constant. This variation in shear stress will continue to be constant, and the torsion equation will remain valid as long as the stress on the outermost fiber does not exceed the proportional limit. However, if the stress exceeds the proportional limit, the variation is no longer constant. Those outer elementary areas stressed beyond the proportional limit seek to deform at a correspondingly greater rate — that is, comparable to that indicated by the portion of shear stress-strain diagram above the proportional limit. This is impossible, since the outer

areas are integrally connected to the inner areas that conform to the more slowly
developing strain obtained below the proportional limit. Therefore, if the outer
areas are prevented from deforming as
much as they desire, the stress imposed
thereupon must remain at a lower value.

As the torque continues to increase,
the stress variation over the cross section
decreases until at the maximum torque
the stress s_u* on all the fibers is essentially the same (Fig. 5-21). The torque
under this condition is approximately
equal to

Figure 5-21

$$T_{max.} = \int_0^r s_u \times dA \times \rho = s_u \int_0^r 2\pi\rho \times d\rho \times \rho$$

$$= s_u \times \frac{2\pi r^3}{3} \times \frac{2r}{2r} = \frac{4}{3} \times \frac{s_u J}{r} \qquad (5.12)$$

But
$$T_{max.} = \frac{s_r J}{r} \qquad (5.13)$$

therefore,
$$s_r = \frac{4}{3} s_u \qquad (5.14)$$

When the torsion equation is used in finding the shear modulus of
rupture, the resisting torque is the result of an assumed straight-line
variation of stress from the center of the shaft. In order that the assumed
stress might provide the same resisting torque as the actual stress, the
inner areas must assume a proportionately greater part of the twisting
restraint. Thus the maximum stress computed by the torsion equation
(that is, the modulus of rupture), is the product of an assumption known
to be invalidated and is greater than, the actual maximum stress.

Although moduli of rupture are fictitious values of stress, they can
be and are used advantageously to determine maximum torques that
may be applied to shafts.

Illustrative Problem 8. Between the crankshaft and propeller shaft
on a small freighter there is to be placed an auxiliary shaft that will purposely fail when the torque attains a value of 200,000 in.-lb. If the modulus
of rupture of the steel used in the shaft is 40,000 psi, how large must its
diameter be?

SOLUTION.

$$s_r = \frac{T_{max.} \, r}{J}$$

---

* Stress s_u is usually found by testing a hollow cylinder to failure in torsion.

$$40{,}000 = \frac{200{,}000(d/2)}{(\pi d^4)/32}$$

$$d^3 = 25.4 \qquad d = 2.94 \text{ in.}$$

PROBLEMS

5-40. A $\frac{1}{2}$-in. steel shaft attains a maximum torque of 700 in.-lb before failing. Determine its modulus of rupture. *Answer:* 28,500 psi.

5-41. Would a hollow torsion specimen give a modulus of rupture closer to the actual ultimate shearing unit stress than a solid torsion specimen? Give reason for your answer.

5-14. Non-circular thin-walled tubes subjected to torsion. — shear flow

In certain structures, notably those of the aircraft industry, stability is obtained through the torsional resistance of their membrane covering. These coverings will often take the shape of non-circular thin-walled tubes or shells. Some of these tubes may even have walls of varying thickness. The study of the shear stresses which are developed call for a special approach not heretofore considered.

Shearing stresses. A tube of uniform cross section but of unequal wall thickness, shown in Fig. 5-22, is subjected to torque T. Assuming the contour of the cross section to be retained as the torque is applied, resisting shearing stresses which are directed tangent to the periphery of the shell will be developed on the cross section. The moment of the resulting shear forces taken about any point O in the plane of the section will be equal to the applied couple T.

Figure 5-22

Consider now the variation of the shear stresses as they act on the exposed cross section of the shell. On an elementary free body I of equal width and length, shear stress $(s_s)_1$ acts on its edge to produce a force equal to $(s_s)_1 t_1 \, ds$, where t_1 is the thickness of I. As indicated in § 5-10, such a force is restrained by an equal force on the opposite edge and an opposing couple of similar forces on the perpendicular edges. A similar arrangement of forces must act on the adjacent element II.

It now becomes apparent that the two shear forces on the common faces must be equal and that

$$(s_s)_1 \times t_1 = (s_s)_2 \times t_2 = s_s \times t = q \qquad (5.15)$$

It follows also that the product of the stress and thickness at all points is equal. This continuity of equality about the entire shell is analogous to the uniformity of flow of water in a continuous pipe of varying diameter. Thus the term *shear flow* (q) was originated to convey the equality of the product of stress and thickness at all points. Its use has been extended to include shear on thin sections regardless of how produced.

The moment of the shear force on any cross-sectional element taken about point O is equal to $s_s \times t \times ds \times \rho$. The total resistance torque is thus equal to

$$T_R = \int s_s \times t \times ds \times \rho = q \int \rho \, ds$$

But $\rho \, ds/2$ is equal to the area of the shaded elementary triangle in Fig. 5-22. The total area of the cross section within the median line of the shell is therefore

$$\int \frac{\rho \, ds}{2}, \quad \text{making} \quad \int \rho \, ds = 2A \quad \text{and}$$

$$T_R = 2qA = T \qquad (5.16)$$

from which
$$q = \frac{T}{2A} \quad \text{and} \quad s_s = \frac{T}{2At} \qquad (5.17)$$

Angle of twist. The angle of twist of the shell may be determined by the use of the conservation of energy principle discussed in § 3-8. We shall assume all the stresses to be below the proportional limit and that the torque T produces an angle of twist equal to θ. Thus, expressing the equality of external and internal energy, we have

$$\frac{1}{2}T\theta = \frac{s_s^2}{2G} \times \text{volume of shell}$$

$$= \int_0^s \frac{s_s^2}{2G} \times tL \, ds$$

where s is the length of the median line of the shell cross section.

Substituting the equivalent value of s_s from Eq. 5-17, we obtain

$$\frac{1}{2} T\theta = \int_0^s \frac{T^2}{4A^2t^2} \times \frac{tL\, ds}{2G}$$

from which

$$\theta = \frac{TL}{4A^2G} \int_0^s \frac{ds}{t} \tag{5.18}$$

or

$$\theta = \frac{Lq}{2AG} \int_0^s \frac{ds}{t} \tag{5.19}$$

In using the equations developed above it is well to remember that while shearing stresses vary in a shell of unequal thickness, the shearing strains will also vary. That implies that the elementary volumes such as I and II, located about the cross section will distort unequally, causing a warping of the section. This warping must be permitted without distorting the contour of the cross section to insure the validity of the derived equations. Sharp corners, abrupt changes in section, holes, and so forth will, of course, have a modifying effect on the stresses and twists computed.

Illustrative Problem 9. Determine the shearing stresses acting on the cross section of Fig. 5-23(a) due to a torque of 40,000 in.-lb. Calculate the twist of the tube if $L = 10$ ft. $G = 4 \times 10^6$ psi.

Figure 5-23

Solution. The shear flow

$$q = \frac{T}{2A} = \frac{40,000}{2 \times 78.54} = 254.4 \text{ lb per in.}$$

therefore

$$(s_s)_{AB} = \frac{254.4}{0.400} = 636 \text{ psi}$$

$$(s_s)_{BC} = \frac{254.4}{0.600} = 424 \text{ psi}$$

$$(s_s)_{CD} = \frac{254.4}{0.200} = 1272 \text{ psi}$$

$$(s_s)_{DA} = 424 \text{ psi}$$

The computation of the angle of twist is dependent upon our evaluation of $\int ds/t$. In view of the constant thicknesses we may use the finite summation $\Sigma \, \Delta s/t$ in its stead. This term is depicted graphically in Fig. 5-23(b). The angle of twist is therefore

$$\theta = \frac{10 \times 12 \times 254.4}{2 \times 78.54 \times 4 \times 10^6} \times 85.2 = 0.00414 \text{ radians}$$

PROBLEMS

5-42. Show that the equation for shear flow (Eq. 5.17) is identical to the torsion formula $s_s = Tr/J$ when applied to cylindrical thin-walled cylinders.

5-43. Compare the shear stresses in the hollow sections shown in Fig. 5-24 if the torque applied is equal to 8000 in.-lb. Wall thickness for each section equals $\frac{1}{4}$ in.

Figure 5-24

5-44. A tube with a hollow square cross section, measuring 10 in. between the center lines of walls, is subjected to a torque of 10,000 in.-lb. If the wall thicknesses for the four sides are successively $\frac{1}{4}$, $\frac{3}{8}$, $\frac{1}{2}$, and $\frac{3}{4}$ in., what are the shear stresses in the walls? What will the angle of twist be equal to if L is 10 ft and $G = 4 \times 10^6$ psi? *Answers:* $q = 50$ lb per in, .00075 radian.

5-45. In the wood spar section shown in Fig. 5-25 the maximum shear stress is 200 psi. Determine the maximum torque the section can carry. What will its angle of twist be if $L = 12$ ft and $G = 2 \times 10^6$ psi?

Figure 5-25   **Figure 5-26**

5-46. Find the shear distribution and the angle of twist for the section shown in Fig. 5-26 if $L = 12$ ft, $G = 4 \times 10^6$ psi, and $T = 5000$ in.-lb? *Answer:* 0.0126 radian.

5-15. *Torsion of non-circular cross sections*

The torsion formula (Eq. 5-3) is used only to determine the torsional resistance of a straight shaft of circular cross section with or without a concentric circular core. This restricted usage was created by the assumption that the stresses acting on concentric circular elements varied directly with their distance from the center of rotation. The more unlike a cross section is to a circular section, the greater is the discrepancy between the actual and theoretical stress distribution assumed for the torsion formula. As one approaches a rectangular section, the similarity of stress distributions is considerably changed. This is also true of the strain.

Rubber models show clearly the nonuniform variation of surface strain in non-circular sections subjected to torsional forces. It will be observed that in Fig. 5-27(b) and (c) that the elements on the surface of the elliptical

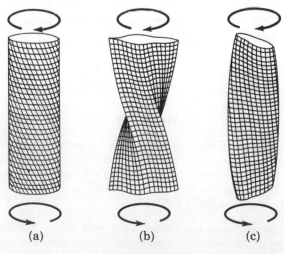

Figure 5-27

and rectangular cross-sectioned rods are not equally distorted, and cause the section to warp. On the contrary, Fig. 5-27(a), a rod of circular cross section, shows equal element distortion, and a perfectly plane cross-sectional periphery. Obviously, the unequal element distortions indicate nonuniformly varying shear strains and corresponding nonuniformly varying shear stresses. The torsion formula derived for shafts having circular sections cannot, therefore, be used for those having non-circular sections.

It is of interest to note that on both the elliptical and rectangular cross sections, the maximum stress is not located at the fiber farthest removed from the center, but at the ends of the shortest axis of symmetry. Even more surprising is the fact that the corners of the rectangular cross section show no shear stress at all.

Membrane analogy. Invaluable in the determination of the torsional characteristics of non-circular cross sections is the membrane analogy. This important experimental device introduced by Prandtl in 1903, is based upon theory which reveals definite relationships between the torsional characteristics of a cross section and physical measurements of an inflated membrane or soap bubble placed over an opening of the same or geometrically similar section.

Assuming that the membrane can carry no shear and that its deflections are small (Fig. 5-28), the following relationships exist between the inflated membrane and the member subjected to torsion:

(1) The shear stress at any point A (Fig. 5-28) of the cross section is proportional to the slope at the corresponding point A' of the membrane ($s_s = k\alpha$).

(2) The torsional resistance of a member is proportional to twice the volume under the membrane ($T_R = k \times 2V$). Note that the proportionality constant k is the same in relationships 1 and 2.

(3) The direction of the shear stress at any point A of the given cross section is tangent to the contour passing through that point on the membrane.

(4) The shear flows acting on those thin-walled tubes of varying cross section located between contours are equal.

The determination of the proportionality constant k (indicated in 1 and 2 above) for any one membrane is made by introducing the known theoretical relationship of shear stress to torque as obtained by the torsion formula for circular cross section. The ability to relate these stresses and torque to the corresponding slopes and volume of a membrane inflated over a circular hole enables the calculation of k required in the solution of shear stresses and torques for non-circular sections. It is imperative for this analysis to have the inflation pressures under each membrane exactly the same.

α_A = slope of soap bubble at A measured in vertical plane containing r_1

2 × volume ~ T_c

(a)

I

(b)

ρ α_B

(a)

II

(b)

1. For given T_c and circular cross section, obtain $(s_s)_{max.}$ from torsion formula.
2. Obtain surface slopes and volume under circular membrane I(a).
3. Then $(s_s)_A = (s_s)_{max.} \times r_1/r = k\alpha_A$. Compute k.
4. Obtain volume under rectangular membrane.
5. Compute corresponding torque T_R on rectangular section II(a): $T_R = T_c(2V_R/2V_c)$.
6. Obtain slope at B (IIa). Stress at B is $(s_s)_B = k\alpha_B$ or $(s_s)_B = (s_s)_A \times \alpha_B/\alpha_A$.

SOAP FILM
APPARATUS

Figure 5-28. Membrane analogy procedure for finding shear stresses and torques of noncircular cross sections.

It is more common, however, to avoid the determination of k by using a circular membrane adjoining the non-circular membrane and inflating each *simultaneously* with the same pressure. In so doing, the circular membrane acts as a calibrating agent and provides the simple relationships

$$\frac{T_c}{T_n} = \frac{V_c}{V_n} \quad \text{and} \quad \frac{\alpha_c}{\alpha_n} = \frac{(s_s)_c}{(s_s)_n}$$

where the subscripts c and n refer to the circular and non-circular cross sections. Suppose then, that by careful micrometer measurements it is determined that the volume under a non-circular membrane is half that under a circular one. Assuming the circular shaft to be 2 in. in diameter and subjected to 10,000 in.-lb, its maximum stress is 6370 psi as obtained by the torsion formula. This stress would be proportional to the slope of the membrane at the edge of the circular hole. At a point on the non-circular membrane where the slope is exactly the same, the corresponding shear stress would be identical if the torque on that section were 5000 in.-lb. Correspondingly, under the action of the same torque, points having twice the slope would have twice the shear stress. Thus by comparing the volume

Circular section   Elliptical section   Rectangular section

$$(s_s)_{max} = \frac{5.09T}{d^3} \quad (5.17) \qquad (s_s)_1 = \frac{5.09T}{ab^2} \text{ (max.)} \quad (5.19) \qquad (s_s)_1 = C_1\frac{T}{ab^2} \text{ (max.)} \quad (5.22)$$

$$\theta = \frac{10.18TL}{Gd^4} \quad (5.18) \qquad (s_s)_2 = \frac{5.09T}{a^2b} \quad (5.20) \qquad \theta = C_2\frac{TL}{Gab^3} \quad (5.23)$$

$$\theta = \frac{16TL}{\pi abG}\left(\frac{1}{a^2}+\frac{1}{b^2}\right) \quad (5.21)$$

a/b	c_1	c_2	a/b	c_1	c_2
1.0	4.81	7.09	3.0	3.74	3.80
1.5	4.33	5.10	4.0	3.55	3.56
2.0	4.07	4.37	6.0	3.34	3.34
2.5	3.88	4.02	10.0	3.20	3.20
			α	3.00	3.00

Figure 5-29. Comparative shear stress distributions on circular, elliptical, and rectangular cross sections subjected to torsion.

and slopes of the circular membrane to the volume and slopes of the membrane of a non-circular section, the shearing stresses can be obtained for any torque applied to the non-circular section.

Although such a quantitative comparison is invaluable, the membrane analogy may also be used qualitatively by making mental comparisons of circular and non-circular membranes. In so doing, values of maximum and minimum shear stress and comparative torques may be approximated.

The theoretical solution of non-circular torsional problems is beyond the scope of this book. For the few solutions possible, a knowledge of the Theory of Elasticity is required. In Fig. 5-29 are presented theoretical formulas derived for elliptical and rectangular cross sections.

PROBLEMS

5-47. Compare the torsional resistance and twist of the following steel cross sections, using a maximum shear stress of 10,000 psi and $l = 10$ ft.

(1) A solid circular section 2 in. in diameter.

(2) A hollow circular section 2 in. O.D. and $1\frac{1}{2}$ in. I.D.

(3) A square section 2 in. on a side.

(4) A rectangular section 2 in. wide by 4 in. long.

(5) An elliptical section 2 in. minor diameter by 4 in. major diameter.

5-48. Compare the torsional rigidities of the following sections shown in Fig. 5-30 by applying the membrane analogy qualitatively. The total length of $\frac{1}{4}$ in. thickness in each figure is equal to 10 in.

Figure 5-30

5-49. A T and circular membrane on a membrane analogy device showed volumes of 0.8 and 2.0 in.^{3}, and maximum slopes of 45° and 30°, respectively. If the circular section is 2 in. in diameter and its maximum shear stress allowed is 15,000 psi, what are the maximum shear stress and corresponding torque developed on the T section? *Answers:* 9440 in.-lb., 22,500 psi.

Chapter Six

SHEAR- AND BENDING-MOMENT DIAGRAMS

6-1. *The different types of beams*

A beam, generally speaking, is any bar or structural member that may be 'subjected to bending by transverse forces. This broad definition includes a great many irregularly shaped members acted upon by forces located in many planes. Therefore, it becomes necessary to confine this preliminary study to beams that are initially straight and of uniform symmetrical cross section and that have all applied loads acting in the plane of symmetry (Fig. 6-1). Beams need not be horizontal; they may be vertical or on a slant. They may have either one, two, or several reactions. To simplify further discussion, let us classify beams by the type and

Figure 6-1

number of their reactions in the following manner:

Simple. Any beam whose ends rest on supports which do not restrain its deflection when it is subjected to load.

Continuous. Any beam resting on three or more supports (Fig. 6-2b).

Cantilever. Any beam supported at one end only (Fig. 6-2c).

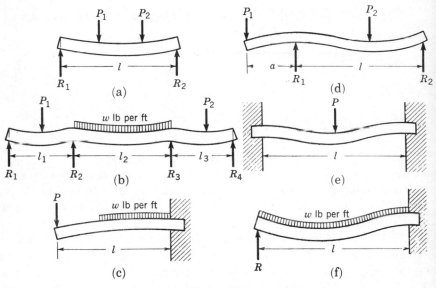

Figure 6-2

Overhanging. Any beam with one or two supports not located at the ends of the beam (Fig. 6-2d).

Restrained. Any beam that has located at either one or more reaction points restraining forces which prevent its free deflection. These restraining forces may be supplied, for instance, by building one or both ends of a beam into a concrete wall (Figs. 6-2e and f). A continuous beam consists of a series of restrained beams.

6-2. Distributed and concentrated loads

Whenever a load can be considered located over a short distance of a beam relative to its entire length, it may be considered as a concentrated load. Such a load is shown on a loading diagram as a single force — for instance, P in Fig. 6-2(c). Loads applied to the beam by other beams framing into it at right angles or by a loaded differential pulley mounted on a beam are representative of concentrated loads.

Frequently, loads are spread uniformly over the length of a beam, as in the case of a load of sand or wheat. These uniform loads are considered to bear on a beam with equal intensity on every unit length of contact. Only in the investigation of other external forces, such as reactions, can a uniform load ever be bunched together at its center of gravity and assumed to act as a concentrated load. (See Chapter 1.)

Distributed loads may also be *uniformly varying and nonuniform*. In a uniformly varying load, the load increases or decreases at a definite rate along the length of a beam, such as water pressure acting on a vertical beam. Where the load is nonuniform, no regularity exists in its distribution; for example, unequal piles of coal scattered about the floor of a storage bin.

6-3. The internal resistance of a beam

When a beam does not collapse under an applied load, it is because of the development of its internal resistance stresses. If for any reason these resisting stresses were subsequently prevented from acting, collapse would be inevitable. If the beam broke because of an excessive amount of applied load, it would necessarily be inferred that on the cross section where failure took place the maximum resisting stresses had been exceeded. It is the intent of the discussion that follows to establish where on the beam the most critically stressed section occurs and how, by the application of subsequent theory, the size of the beam can be made large enough to reduce the induced stresses to a safe value. Free bodies, as discussed in Chapter 1, will be used extensively. A review may be very profitable at this point.

To commence our search for the most critically stressed section or sections, let us center our attention on the beam shown in Fig. 6-3. Its

Figure 6-3

own weight will be considered negligible in comparison to the magnitude of the applied concentrated loads and, therefore, will not appear in the computations.

By passing a vertical section through the beam at a point 1 ft from R_1, the resisting stresses on that section are instantly reduced to zero and the beam collapses. To restore the original state of equilibrium to the two portions of the beam, the internal forces, which previously acted on the cut surfaces, must be replaced. These resisting forces are obtained by applying the three laws of equilibrium.

6-4. The vertical shear, C-T couple, and bending moment

Utilizing the smaller and more simple portion of the beam first, let us restore to the exposed section those forces that are required to balance the 6.4-kip reaction. Since the 6.4-kip reaction would tend to push the free body vertically upward, another 6.4-kip force (V_L) must act vertically downward on the exposed section to keep it in vertical balance (Fig. 6-4a).

Figure 6-4

Immediately upon the application of this force, however, it is evident that the body is still not in equilibrium but is being acted upon by a couple. Another couple, the so-called $C\text{-}T$ couple, is therefore required, and must, of course, be placed on the exposed section. Its action must be such as not to interfere with the 6.4-kip force already obtained, and should act opposite to the prevailing couple. These requirements necessitate the action of the forces of the couple perpendicular to the plane, with the C force acting in compression on the top of the beam and the T force acting in tension at the bottom. It is well to recall at this point that in all simple beams bent in a downward direction, the bottom fibers stretch and the upper fibers contract. These phenomena are effects produced by the internal C and T forces just mentioned and can be observed by bending any flexible material.

The magnitude of the $C\text{-}T$ couple acting on the exposed section is, as previously stated, equal to the moment of the 6.4-kip forces, or $6.4 \times 1 = 6.4$ ft-kips. It is customary to take moments of these forces about a point on the action line of the restraining vertical force V_L.

Considering, now, the other longer portion of the beam (Fig. 6-4b), it is evident that a similar operation of balancing is required. Equating the vertical forces, including the assumed V_R force, we obtain

$$\Sigma V = 6 + 4 - 3.6 - V_R = 0$$

$$V_R = 6.4 \text{ kips acting upward}$$

This force is exactly equal to the vertical force on the exposed section of the shorter portion of the beam but acts in the opposite direction. Considered together, these oppositely directed parallel forces, V_L and V_R, being of like magnitude and acting on opposite sides of the sectioning plane, produce an *internal-resisting shear action* on that plane. Although this shearing action has been revealed by the use of free bodies, it occurs in like magnitude on the corresponding section in the actual uncut beam, since the same equilibrium conditions must be maintained in both. It may further be concluded that shearing forces are developed on every vertical cross section of the actual beam where the forces on either side of the section are out of balance. The amount of this unbalance is equal to the algebraic sum of the vertical forces on either the left or right side of the section, and is called the *internal-resisting shear force*, or, more simply, the *shear on the section*.

Although the above equation indicates that a 6.4-kip internal-resisting shear force was required to balance the vertical forces to the right of the section, equilibrium cannot be assured unless the moments also equal zero. Assuming a clockwise resisting moment M_R on the exposed section, the moment equation taken about a point on the action line of the internal shear force is

$$\Sigma M = 6 \times 1 + 4 \times 5 - 3.6 \times 9 + M_R = 0$$

$$M_R = 6.4 \text{ ft-kips}$$

It is interesting to note that this internal-resisting moment is exactly equal to the internal-resisting moment acting on the exposed section of the left-hand portion of the beam. Also, since this couple of 6.4 ft-kips must be directed clockwise, the upper force C of the couple must act into the section (compression), and the lower force T must act out of the section (tension). The stresses on the top and bottom of the beam on either side of the section are, therefore, of like character and are continuous across the section. Although free bodies obtained by cutting the beam were used in analyzing the stress condition on the exposed surfaces, the uncut beam has the identical stress condition on the corresponding section, since both the free bodies and the beam are in equilibrium under the action of the same forces.

The magnitude of the internal-resisting moment (or the C-T couple) on any section is, as has been indicated in the previous moment equations, *equal to the algebraic sum of the moments of the forces to either the right or left side of the section*. This algebraic sum of moments produces the applied bending moment to the section and is differentiated from the C-T couple which, although equal to it in magnitude, acts oppositely to it. The *C-T* couple is, in other words, the equilibrant of the applied bending moment. The term *bending moment* is more frequently used than either *C-T* couple or internal-resisting moment.

6-5. Shear- and bending-moment variations

Since the design of a beam depends on a knowledge of the variation of shear and bending moment along its length, it shall be necessary to continue our study of internal shears and *C-T* couples at successive one foot intervals along the beam.

At the second foot mark is located the 6-kip load. Because it is impossible to divide a concentrated load by the passage of a sectioning plane and because the magnitude of the resisting shear force varies in accordance to which side of the concentrated load we choose to locate our section, we must use two sections, each an infinitesimal distance to left and right of the 6-kip load. The two free bodies required are shown in Fig. 6-5. The right-hand portion of the beam is omitted in each case.

To left of load.

$$\Sigma V = 6.4 - V_{2-} = 0$$
$$V_{2-} = +6.4 \text{ kips}$$
$$\Sigma M = 6.4 \times 2 - M_{2-} = 0$$
$$M_{2-} = +12.8 \text{ ft-kips}$$

To right of load.

$$\Sigma V = 6.4 - 6 - V_{2+} = 0$$
$$V_{2+} = +0.4 \text{ kips}$$
$$\Sigma M = 6.4 \times 2 - 6 \times 0.0 - M_{2+} = 0$$
$$M_{2+} = +12.8 \text{ ft-kips}$$

Figure 6-5. Shear- and bending-moment determinations of sections immediately to left and right of 6-kip concentrated load.

The magnitude of the bending moment on these two sections will, for all practical purposes, be the same since the sections are separated by an infinitesimal distance producing no appreciable change in moment arms. The equations and calculation of the bending moment, or *C-T* couple, at these two sections are given in Fig. 6-5.

The remainder of the shear- and bending-moment equations together with their corresponding free bodies are shown in Figs. 6-6 to 6-8.

Figure 6-6

Section 3:

$$\Sigma\, V = 6.4 - 6 - V_3 = 0$$
$$V_3 = 0.4 \text{ kips}$$
$$\Sigma\, M = 6.4 \times 3 - 6 \times 1 - M_3 = 0$$
$$M_3 = 13.2 \text{ ft-kips}$$

Section 4:

$$\Sigma\, V = 6.4 - 6 - V_4 = 0$$
$$V_4 = 0.4 \text{ kips}$$
$$\Sigma\, M = 6.4 \times 4 - 6 \times 2 - M_4 = 0$$
$$M_4 = 13.6 \text{ ft-kips}$$

Section 5:

$$\Sigma\, V = 6.4 - 6 - V_5 = 0$$
$$V_5 = 0.4 \text{ kips}$$
$$\Sigma\, M = 6.4 \times 6 - 6 \times 3 - M_5 = 0$$
$$M_5 = 14.0 \text{ ft-kips}$$

Located 6 ft from R_1 is a concentrated load of 4 kips. Using the procedure explained for the 6-kip concentrated load, the necessary free bodies (Fig. 6-7) and equations are as follows:

Section 6−:

$$\Sigma\, V = 6.4 - 6 - V_{6-} = 0$$
$$V_{6-} = 0.4 \text{ kips}$$
$$\Sigma\, M = 6.4 \times 6 - 6 \times 4 - M_{6-} = 0$$
$$M_{6-} = 14.4 \text{ ft-kips}$$

Section 6+:

$$\Sigma\, V = 6.4 - 6 - 4 + V_{6+} = 0$$
$$V_{6+} = -3.6 \text{ kips}$$
$$\Sigma\, M = 6.4 \times 6 - 6 \times 4 - 4 \times 0.0 - M_{6+} = 0$$
$$M_{6+} = 14.4 \text{ ft-kips}$$

Figure 6-7

Figure 6-8

In the above shear equation, attention should be called to the change in direction of the resisting shear force.

For convenience, the shear- and bending-moment evaluations for the remainder of the sections (Fig. 6-8) will be obtained using the right-hand portion of the beam as a free body. This procedure will eliminate the necessity of using a greater number of loads in the determination of shear and bending moment. An explanation of the conventional use of plus and minus signs will be given in the following section.

Section 7:
$$\Sigma V = V_7 - 3.6 = 0$$
$$V_7 = 3.6 \text{ kips}$$
$$\Sigma M = 3.6 \times 3 - M_7 = 0$$
$$M_7 = 10.8 \text{ ft-kips}$$

Section 8:

$$\Sigma V = V_8 - 3.6 = 0$$
$$V_8 = 3.6 \text{ kips}$$
$$\Sigma M = 3.6 \times 2 - M_8 = 0$$
$$M_8 = 7.2 \text{ ft-kips}$$

Section 9:

$$\Sigma V = V_9 - 3.6 = 0$$
$$V_9 = 3.6 \text{ kips}$$
$$\Sigma M = 3.6 \times 1 - M_9 = 0$$
$$M_9 = 3.6 \text{ ft-kips}$$

Since no intervening loads are present between forces V_9 and R_2, the shear on all sections between these two forces must also be equal to 3.6 kips. As one passes beyond R_2, the shear must return to zero, since the beam was previously placed in equilibrium by requiring the algebraic sum of all vertical forces to equal zero.

The bending moment between section 9 and R_2 decreases to zero as R_2 is approached, since the moment arm of the reaction becomes increasingly smaller.

6-6. Signs for shear and bending moment

In order that a common understanding be developed concerning the direction of shear and bending moment, a conventional method of determining their proper signs must be consistently followed. That system most generally used is given below.

Shear. This criterion applies solely to the left-hand portion of the beam. Thus, as is indicated in Fig. 6-9(a), if the algebraic sum of the verti-

Positive shear   Negative shear
(a)   (b)

Figure 6-9

cal forces to the left of the section acts upward and the internal-resisting shear acts downward, the shear is positive. Conversely, the shear will be negative when the reverse is true as shown in Fig. 6-9(b).

Moment. The bending moment at any section is positive if the algebraic sum of the moments to the left of the section is directed clockwise. An algebraic sum of moments to the left of the section is negative if it is directed counterclockwise (Fig. 6-10a).

Moment criteria to left of section   Positive bending   Negative bending
(a)   (b)

Figure 6-10

An even more general statement producing the same results is that a bending moment is positive if it produces compression on the upper fibers. Conversely, if tension occurs on the upper fibers the bending moment is negative. This is illustrated in Fig. 6-10b.

PROBLEMS

6-1a, b, c, d. Determine the magnitude of the internal shear force and the bending moment (*C-T* couple) acting on sections *A-A* and *B-B* of the beams shown in Fig. 6-11. Draw a free body for each section studied and show the resisting force and couple acting in their proper directions.

Figure 6-11

6-2. Determine the magnitude of the internal-resisting forces and couple acting on section *A-A* of Fig. 6-12. *Hint.* Resolve the 10-kip force into components. *Answer:* Shear, 3.53 kips; moment, 28.24 ft-kips; compression, 20.24 kips.

6-3. Determine the magnitude of the internal shear force and the bending moment acting on sections *A-A*, *B-B*, and *C-C* of the beam shown in Fig. 6-13. *Answers:* $V_A = +7.0$ kips, $M_A = +4.0$ ft-kips, $V_B = -3.0$ kips, $M_B = 9.0$ ft-kips, $V_C = -1.5$ kips, $M_C = +1.5$ ft-kips.

Figure 6-12

Figure 6-13

SHEAR- AND BENDING-MOMENT DIAGRAMS

6-7. Shear diagram

A shear diagram is a graphical representation of the variation of the internal-resisting shear along the full length of the beam. Every properly conducted design of a beam should include the construction of its shear diagram. It reveals at a glance the complete story of the shear and, in particular, those sections that are critically stressed.

Referring to the problem used in the discussion of the internal-resisting forces in a beam, let us tabulate the values of internal shear force with their proper sign, as instructed in § 6-6.

$$\begin{array}{ll}
V_0 = 0.0 \text{ kips} & V_6 = +0.4 \text{ kips} \\
V_{0+} = +6.4 \text{ kips} & V_{6+} = -3.6 \text{ kips} \\
V_1 = +6.4 \text{ kips} & V_7 = -3.6 \text{ kips} \\
V_{2-} = +6.4 \text{ kips} & V_8 = -3.6 \text{ kips} \\
V_{2+} = +0.4 \text{ kips} & V_9 = -3.6 \text{ kips} \\
V_3 = +0.4 \text{ kips} & V_{10-} = -3.6 \text{ kips} \\
V_4 = +0.4 \text{ kips} & V_{10} = 0.0 \text{ kips} \\
V_5 = +0.4 \text{ kips} &
\end{array}$$

By plotting these values on an axis equal to the length of the beam, the shear diagram is obtained (Fig. 6-14). The most critically stressed portion of the beam with reference to shear is shown to be included between R_1 and the 6-kip concentrated force.

Figure 6-14. Shear diagram.

Although the risers in the above diagram are shown slightly inclined for the sake of clarity, their horizontal projections represent minute distances between adjacent sections. In all subsequent shear diagrams, therefore, risers will be shown vertical, which indicates more accurately their proper position.

A simplification.   Now that the groundwork of shear determination has been laid, an even more convenient method of analyzing the shear forces in a beam can be considered. This simple method conceives of the shear diagram as being an *accumulative algebraic sum* of the vertical forces to the left of a section as one proceeds from the left to the right end of the beam. Starting from zero shear force at the horizontal axis, the shear diagram passes through upward and downward jogs, eventually to end once more on the horizontal axis. Each upward jog is equivalent to an upward-acting force, and each downward jog is equivalent to a downward-acting force. The magnitude of the load is represented by the length of the jog.

Thus, if we could consider the beam covered by a piece of paper and slowly exposed by moving the paper from left to right, the algebraic sum of the loads exposed would be equal to the ordinate to the shear diagram at the section located by the left edge of the paper.

6-8. Bending-moment diagram

A bending-moment diagram is a graphical representation of the variation of the bending moment or internal-resisting moment along the full length of the beam. The bending moment diagram for the beam just discussed in §§ 6-3

Figure 6-15. Bending-moment diagram.

to 6-7 is obtained by plotting the values computed in § 6-5 on a horizontal axis equal to the length of the beam (Fig. 6-15). These values with their proper sign are retabulated below for convenience.

$$M_0 = \quad 0.0 \text{ ft-kips} \qquad M_6 = +14.4 \text{ ft-kips}$$
$$M_1 = \quad +6.4 \text{ ft-kips} \qquad M_7 = +10.8 \text{ ft-kips}$$
$$M_2 = +12.8 \text{ ft-kips} \qquad M_8 = \quad +7.2 \text{ ft-kips}$$
$$M_3 = +13.2 \text{ ft-kips} \qquad M_9 = \quad +3.6 \text{ ft-kips}$$
$$M_4 = +13.6 \text{ ft-kips} \qquad M_{10} = \quad 0.0 \text{ ft-kips}$$
$$M_5 = +14.0 \text{ ft-kips}$$

Since by inspection, the beam under consideration must bend concave upward, the sign of all the calculated bending moments may have been easily ascertained as being positive. The most critical bending moment to be resisted by the beam is indicated by the maximum ordinate as occurring under the 4-kip load.

6-9. Definitions — shear and bending moment

Inasmuch as the determination of shear and bending moment in beams is imperative to the design of beams, it is important that their definitions, given below, be committed to memory.

The shearing force occurring on any section perpendicular to the longitudinal axis of a straight beam is equal to the algebraic sum of the vertical forces or components to either the left or to the right of that section.

The bending moment occurring on any section perpendicular to the longitudinal axis of a straight beam is equal to the algebraic sum of the moments of the forces to either the left or to the right of that section.

Illustrative Problem 1.   Draw the shear and moment diagram of the beam shown in Fig. 6-16.

Figure 6-16

SOLUTION. The uniform load included on this beam will offer no difficulty in the determination of shear and bending moment if it is allowed to remain in its distributed position. Any attempt at concentrating a uniform load for the determination of shear and bending moment will generally result in confusion for the beginner. As indicated previously, only in the computation of *unknown external forces* — that is, reactions in this case, is it advisable to concentrate distributed loads.

Reactions. The reactions R_1 and R_2 are obtained by taking moments successively at points A and B. Too much emphasis cannot be placed upon their correct calculation, since an error is usually detected upon the completion of the moment diagram, and only after a considerable amount of work has been performed. The computation of reactions R_1 and R_2 follow.

$$
\begin{array}{ll}
\Sigma M_A & \Sigma M_B \\
6 \times 3 = -18 & 6 \times 13 = +78 \\
12 \times 3 = +36 & 12 \times 7 = +84 \\
3 \times 8 = +24 & 3 \times 2 = + 6 \\
\hline
+42 - 10R_2 = 0 & +168 - 10R_1 = 0 \\
R_2 = 4.2 \text{ kips} & R_1 = 16.8 \text{ kips}
\end{array}
$$

Check:

$$\Sigma R = \Sigma P$$
$$4.2 + 16.8 = 6.0 + 12.0 + 3.0$$
$$21.0 = 21.0$$

Computation of shear forces.   Although drawing free bodies to the left or right of every foot section (see § 6-7) results in an absolutely sure method of gaining data for the shear diagram, it is a lengthy procedure. For the sake of simplicity, let us think of the shear curve as being an accumulative algebraic sum of the vertical forces to the left of a section as we proceed from the left to the right of the beam. In tabular form, these algebraic sums are (in kips):

$$
\begin{aligned}
V_0 &= 0 \\
V_{0+} &= -6 \\
V_1 &= -6 \\
V_2 &= -6 \\
V_{3-} &= -6 \\
V_{3+} &= -6 + 16.8 = +10.8 \\
V_4 &= -6 + 16.8 - 2 \times 1 = +8.8 \\
V_5 &= -6 + 16.8 - 2 \times 2 = +6.8 \\
V_6 &= 6 + 16.8 - 2 \times 3 = +4.8 \\
V_7 &= -6 + 16.8 - 2 \times 4 = +2.8 \\
V_8 &= -6 + 16.8 - 2 \times 5 = +0.8 \\
V_9 &= -6 + 16.8 - 2 \times 6 = -1.2 \\
V_{10} &= -6 + 16.8 - 2 \times 6 = -1.2 \\
V_{11-} &= -6 + 16.8 - 2 \times 6 = -1.2 \\
V_{11+} &= -6 + 16.8 - 2 \times 7 - 3 = -4.2 \\
V_{12} &= -6 + 16.8 - 2 \times 7 - 3 = -4.2 \\
V_{13-} &= -6 + 16.8 - 2 \times 7 - 3 = -4.2 \\
V_{13+} &= -6 + 16.8 - 2 \times 7 - 3 + 4.2 = 0
\end{aligned}
$$

Note. $V = 0$: (1) at R_1 and R_2. (2) at 5.4 ft to right of R_1, or section 8.4.

As demonstrated above, the calculation of shear, where uniform load is encountered, proceeds with no difficulty if that load is left in its distributed form. The shear diagram is shown in Fig. 6-16(b).

Computation of bending moments. The valuation of the bending moments, or the required C-T resistance couples, will be obtained by writing the algebraic sums of the moments of the forces to the left or right of the sections. A mental picture of the pertinent free body should be kept in mind while analyzing these equations. The proper sign of the bending moment should be checked in accordance with the criteria given in § 6-6.

Taken to the left of section:

$$M_0 = 0 \text{ ft-kips}$$
$$M_1 = -6 \times 1 = -6 \text{ ft-kips}$$
$$M_2 = -6 \times 2 = -12 \text{ ft-kips}$$
$$M_3 = -6 \times 3 = -18 \text{ ft-kips}$$
$$M_4 = -6 \times 4 + 16.8 \times 1 - 2 \times 1 \times \tfrac{1}{2} = -8.2$$
$$M_5 = -6 \times 5 + 16.8 \times 2 - 2 \times 2 \times 1 = -0.4$$
$$M_6 = -6 \times 6 + 16.8 \times 3 - 2 \times 3 \times 1\tfrac{1}{2} = +5.4$$
$$M_7 = -6 \times 7 + 16.8 \times 4 - 2 \times 4 \times 2 = +9.2$$
$$M_8 = -6 \times 8 + 16.8 \times 5 - 2 \times 5 \times 2\tfrac{1}{2} = +11$$
$$M_9 = -6 \times 9 + 16.8 \times 6 - 2 \times 6 \times 3 = +10.8$$

Taken to the right of section:

$$M_{10} = +4.2 \times 3 - 3 \times 1 = +9.6 \text{ ft-kips}$$
$$M_{11} = +4.2 \times 2 = +8.4 \text{ ft-kips}$$
$$M_{12} = +4.2 \times 1 = +4.2 \text{ ft-kips}$$
$$M_{13} = 0 \text{ ft-kips}$$

As revealed by the moment diagram, the maximum bending moment or the maximum C-T couple of -18 ft-kips is located on that section immediately above R_1. There is, to be sure, a maximum positive moment acting on the beam whose approximate magnitude is equal to 11 ft-kips. But because most beams have uniform cross sections that are symmetrical to the neutral axis and are made of materials equally strong in tension and compression, the maximum intensity of stress is developed by the maximum numerical value of bending moment. It is for such beams that the -18 ft-kips bending moment would prove critical.

Beams of nonuniform or irregular cross section or of materials weak in either tension or compression do not necessarily have their designs controlled by the maximum bending moment, but by that moment that will produce the least favorable stress condition. A reversal of sign in the bending moment that produces an exchange in position of the compression and tension forces in the C-T couple may inadvertently place a force where the beam is least capable of carrying it. It is well, therefore, to

know all the maximum moments (positive and negative), and the laws
governing the variation of bending moments over the length of the beam.
By writing these laws algebraically, the determination of moments anywhere on the beam may be simplified.

6-10. *Algebraic expressions of shear and moment*

The algebraic expressions for the variations of shear and bending
moment are portrayed graphically by the shear and moment curves
already plotted in Fig. 6-16(b) and (c). In this connection, it should be recalled that the straight lines and continuous curves comprising the shear-
and bending-moment diagram obey definite yet altogether different algebraic laws. Referring again to the beam of Fig. 6-16 and using the same
procedure as before for obtaining shear and bending moments, we shall
separate and express algebraically each portion of its shear and moment
diagram. The equations, referred to the left-hand end of the beam, are
as follows:

FOR SHEAR

From section   0 to   3 . . . . $V_x = -6.0$ kips

From section   3 to   9 . . . . $V_x = 10.8 - 2(x - 3)$
$$= -2x + 16.8$$

From section   9 to 11 . . . . $V_x = -1.2$

From section 11 to 13 . . . . $V_x = -4.2$

FOR MOMENT

From section 0 to 3, $M_x = -6x$

From section 3 to 9, $M_x = -6x + 16.8(x - 3) - \dfrac{2(x - 3)(x - 3)}{2}$

$$= -x_2 + 16.8x - 59.4$$

From section 9 to 11, $M_x = -6x + 16.8(x - 3) - 2 \times 6 \times (x - 9 + 3)$
$$= -1.2x + 21.6$$

From section 11 to 13, $M_x = -6x + 16.8(x - 3) - 2 \times 6 \times (x - 6) - 3(x - 11)$
$$= -4.2x + 54.6$$

As may already have been surmised, these equations are general-
izations of the expressions for shear and moment obtained previously for
the shear- and bending-moment diagrams. To procure a shear or bending
moment at a particular section, we need only insert the corresponding
length into the proper equation, and solve.

It is important to note that for that portion of the beam between
sections 3 and 9, the moment equation is of the second degree (that is, it
contains an x^2 term) and when plotted, produces a parabolic curve. All
the other moment and shear equations are represented by straight lines.

6-11. Locating a maximum bending moment

When the maximum moment ordinate occurs at a sharp point on the moment curve, the determination of its location is made by observation (see moment curve of Fig. 6-15). However, if a maximum bending moment occurs on the top of a smooth parabolic curve, as in the case of the maximum positive moment of Fig. 6-16, the exact determination can be made by taking the derivative of the moment equation applicable to this section, equating the derivative to zero and solving thus:

The equation

$$M_x = -x^2 + 16.8x - 59.4$$

when differentiated yields

$$\frac{dM_x}{dx} = -2x + 16.8$$

Placing this equation equal to zero and solving gives $x = 8.4$ feet.

An alternate method for obtaining the location of maximum moment can be made from the differentiated equation. Note that

$$\frac{dM}{dx} = -2x + 16.8 = V_x \quad \text{(the shear equation at the point of maximum moment)}$$

To set the differentiated equation equal to zero and solve is tantamount to obtaining the value of x when V_x is equal to zero. Thus the result of this illustration may be generalized as follows:

A maximum bending moment is obtained whenever the shear diagram cuts the horizontal axis.

Note that this statement does not allude only to *the* maximum-bending moment. Since there may be several maximum-bending moments for one beam depending on the magnitude and location of its loads and reactions, *the* maximum-bending moment is the greatest of the several possible maximum moments.

The location of the maximum positive moment on the beam shown in Fig. 6-16 is 5.4 ft to the right of reaction R_1. The exact value of the bending moment is obtained by inserting the value of 8.4 ft (the value of x is determined from the left-hand end of the beam) into the bending moment equation applicable to that portion of the beam and solving for M_x.

$$M_x = -x^2 + 16.8x - 59.4 = -8.4^2 + 16.8 \times 8.4 - 59.4$$
$$= -70.6 + 141.2 - 59.4 = 11.2 \text{ ft-kips}$$

6-12. The point of inflection

At the very beginning of our study in stresses and strains, it was stated that there could be no stress without an accompanying deformation.

When, in the loading of a uniform cross-sectioned beam, internal-resisting C-T couples are produced, each section must deform in proportion to the magnitude of resisting moment acting upon it[*]. The combined effect of all the sectional deformations is found in the deflection curve of the beam. Those sections that resist the greatest amount of moment suffer the greatest deformation. Those sections that have no bending moment applied to them (that is, where

Figure 6-17

the moment equals zero) are subject to no bending deformation and are consequently straight. When such a point lies between zones of positive and negative moment, it is known as a *point of inflection*. It might also be termed as that point on a beam where the curvature reverses itself (Fig. 6-17).

To locate the point of inflection in a beam requires the solution of the proper moment equation set equal to zero. For the beam of Fig. 6-16, this solution is as follows:

$$M_x = -x^2 + 16.8x - 59.4 = 0$$

from which

$$x = 5.08 \text{ ft} \quad \text{or} \quad 11.72 \text{ ft}$$

Obviously, the correct answer is 5.08 ft, since it falls within the limits of the curve on the moment diagram. The 11.72-ft answer refers to that intersection with the horizontal axis that would occur if the curve were extended. It has no meaning for the present problem.

The selection of the proper equation for the determination of a point of inflection is generally based upon the approximate drawing of a moment diagram. Usually, that curve which crosses the horizontal axis is not difficult to find. If, by chance, a selection is made that results in an imaginary answer, the most probable adjoining equation should be chosen. This equation will generally provide the desired result.

PROBLEMS

6-1a, b, c, d. Determine the magnitude of the maximum vertical shear and bending moment for the beams shown in Fig. 6-18. Locate these values on the shear- and bending-moment diagram. Disregard the weight of the beam.

Answer: (a) $\dfrac{P}{2}, \dfrac{Pl}{4}$; (b) $\dfrac{wl}{2}, \dfrac{wl^2}{8}$; (c) $-P, -Pl$; (d) $-wl, -\dfrac{wl^2}{2}$.

---

[*]Deformations due to shearing stresses have been omitted from this discussion. For all beams, other than those that are short and stubby, the deflection due to the shearing stresses is so small as to be inconsequential.

6-5a, b, c, d. The following shear diagrams, Fig. 6-19, have been drawn for beams whose loading diagrams have been lost. Draw the picture of the beam with loads in their correct locations.

Figure 6-18

Figure 6-20

Figure 6-19

Couples applied at ends of beam

6-6. Draw the shear- and bending-moment diagram for the beam shown in Fig. 6-20. *Hint.* The same rules for determining shear and bending moment at any section remain valid regardless of the type of loading.

6-7a, b, c, d, e, f, g, h. Draw the shear- and bending-moment diagrams for the beams in Fig. 6-21(a) to (h), indicating thereon all controlling ordinates. Determine the maximum shear and bending moment. Disregard the weight of the beam. *Answers:* (a) Maximum shear, +30 kips, maximum moment, +200 ft kips; (c) +7.0 kips, +32.5 ft-kips; (e) +12.56 kips, +65.7 ft-kips; (g) +12.62 kips, +59.4 ft-kips.

6-8a, b, c, d, e, f, g, h. Draw the shear- and bending-moment diagrams for the beams in Fig. 6-22(a) to (h), indicating thereon all controlling ordinates. Determine the shear- and bending-moment equations for portions of the beams marked "Eq." Calculate the position and the magnitude of maximum shear and bending

Figure 6-21

Figure 6-22

moment. Locate the points of inflection. Disregard weight of beam. *Answer:* (a) Max. shear, 7.75 kips; max. moment, 27.50 ft-kips; (b) 10 kips, −50 ft-kips; (c) −11.5 kips, −60 ft-kips; (d) −16.8 kips, −65 ft-kips; (e) −20 kips, −150 ft-kips; (f) −6 kips, −30 ft-kips; (g) −8.83 kips, −30 ft-kips; (h) 10.7 kips, 17 ft-kips.

6-9. After drawing the shear- and bending-moment diagrams for the two cantilever beams shown in Fig. 6-23, discuss the differences imposed upon these diagrams by placing the couple on the beam in the two different ways.

6-10. A typical column supporting an overhead electrification system has loads applied to it as shown in Fig. 6-24. Draw the shear- and bending-moment diagrams giving all controlling ordinates. Assume the foundation to be capable of resisting forces P_1 and P_2, with a moment about the base of 10,000 ft-lb. *Answer:* Maximum shear, 2160 lb, maximum moment, 21,650 ft-lb.

Figure 6-23   Figure 6-24

6-11. Draw the shear- and bending-moment diagram for the beam shown in Fig. 6-25. Determine the algebraic equation of the shear- and bending-moment curve. Determine the exact location and magnitude of the maximum bending moment. Disregard the weight of the beam.

Figure 6-25

THE SHEAR-AREA METHOD OF CONSTRUCTING BENDING-MOMENT DIAGRAMS

6-13. *The theory of the shear-area method*

In § 6-11 it was shown that the derivative of the moment equation with respect to x was equal to the shear, or mathematically stated

$$\frac{dM_x}{dx} = V_x$$

This expression may be changed to read as follows:

$$dM_x = V_x\,dx \tag{6.1}$$

Stated simply, this equation says that the difference between the bending moments acting on two vertical sections of a beam separated by an infinitesimally small distance, dx, is equal to the product $V_x\,dx$. But $V_x\,dx$ is equal to the area of the shear diagram included between the extremes of this same distance dx (Fig. 6-26). Thus we may conclude that the difference

Figure 6-26

between these or any other two bending moments separated by a distance dx is equal to the area of the shear diagram between them (shown cross-hatched).

This axiomatic statement may be expanded into a more useful form if we establish from it the difference in moments M_1 and M_2 between any two points on the beam. For this determination we must add all of the $V_x\,dx$ areas between these two points. Thus by integration we obtain

$$\int_{M_1}^{M_2} dM_x = \int_{x_1}^{x_2} V_x\,dx \tag{6.2}$$

which in turn equals $M_1 - M_2$, the sum of the $V_x\,dx$ areas between x_1 and x_2, or simply stated, the area of the shear diagram between those two points.   Because in this summation process some shear areas may be positive and some negative, the shear areas are added algebraically. It is also well to bear in mind that bending moments must carry their correct sign.

As shown in Fig. 6-26, the difference in bending moment between sections A and B of the previous beam is equal to the intervening shear diagram.

$$M_B - M_A = \frac{10.8 \times 5.4}{2} = 29.2 \text{ ft-kips}$$

Added to the negative moment of -18 ft-kips at section A, the maximum moment at section B becomes $29.2 - 18 = 11.2$ ft-kips.

Before going into further detail, let us place in definition form the shear-area method of constructing bending-moment diagrams. It is as follows: *The difference in bending moment between any two sections A and B on a straight beam loaded with concentrated* or uniform loads is equal to the algebraic sum of the shear area between those two sections.*

6-14. The application of the shear-area method

Let us now proceed to unfold this method in more detail. For our illustration, let us return to the beam of Fig. 6-16, which we have already analyzed by the longer free-body method.

Figure 6-27. All values on shear curve are in kips; all values on moment curve are in ft-kips.

* Does not include couples acting at a point (see § 6-15).

Starting from the left-hand end, we note that the shear area for each 1-ft interval of the overhang is equal to $-6 \times 1 = -6$ ft-kips (Fig. 6-27). Since the moment at the very end is zero, the addition of -6 ft-kips of shear area gives a moment at section 1 of -6 ft-kips. Adding the two subsequent -6-ft-kip shear areas successively produces the moments at the second and third foot section of -12 and -18 ft-kips, respectively. Observe that the moment diagram is a straight line because of the addition of *equal* magnitudes of shear area.

Continuing on toward the right-end of the beam, positive-shear area is encountered. If this positive area is added algebraically to the -18 ft-kips acting at R_1, this moment will sharply decrease in negative magnitude, and if enough positive-shear area is available, will itself ultimately become positive. Adding successively, therefore, the shear areas per foot of beam beyond R_1 to the moment of -18 ft-kips gives bending moments at the succeeding foot points on the beam, as illustrated below.

-18.0 ft-kips, moment at R_1
$\underline{+9.8}$ ft-kips, shear area between 3 and 4
-8.2 ft-kips, moment at section 4
$\underline{+7.8}$ ft-kips, shear area between 4 and 5
-0.4 ft-kips, moment at section 5
$\underline{+5.8}$ ft-kips, shear area between 5 and 6
$+5.4$ ft-kips, moment at section 6
$\underline{+3.8}$ ft-kips, shear area between 6 and 7
$+9.2$ ft-kips, moment at section 7
$\underline{+1.8}$ ft-kips, shear area between 7 and 8
$+11.0$ ft-kips, moment at section 8
$\underline{+0.2}$ ft-kips, shear area between 8 and 8.4
$+11.2$ ft-kips, moment at 8.4, maximum positive moment

In keeping with the previously proven parabolic equation for this portion of the moment curve, the positive-shear areas, because of their decreasing magnitude, cause the moment curve to rise sharply and then to *taper off*, becoming horizontal at the point of zero shear, or maximum bending moment.

From the zero-shear point located at 8.4 ft to the right of the left end to the right end of the beam, only negative-shear area is encountered. If as the definition states, "the difference in bending moment between any two sections is the algebraic sum of the shear area between these sections," the ensuing moment diagram should become less positive and tend toward the zero-moment line.

Adding the subsequent increments of negative-shear area to the maximum positive moment of 11.2 ft-kips at section 8.4 gives the following bending moments.

+11.2 ft-kips, moment at section 8.4
—0.4 ft-kips, shear area between 8.4 and 9
+10.8 ft-kips, moment at section 9
—1.2 ft-kips, shear area between 9 and 10
+9.6 ft-kips, moment at section 10
—1.2 ft-kips, shear area between 10 and 11
+8.4 ft-kips, moment at section 11
—4.2 ft-kips, shear area between 11 and 12
+4.2 ft-kips, moment at section 12
—4.2 ft-kips, shear area between 12 and 13
0.0 ft-kips, moment at section 13

NOTE: These computations are based on the fact that the moment at the left end of the beam equals zero. Should the moment there not equal zero, the moments here computed would change by its magnitude, algebraically added.

Immediately after the maximum moment point, the moment curve slowly starts on its downward path. Since the shear area starts from zero, we know that a point of tangency must exist at the point of maximum bending moment. The curve is still parabolic until section 9 is reached. Thereafter, because of the equal shear increments between sections 9 and 11, and 11 and 13, the curve moves downward along two successive *straight* lines of different slope.

As skill is acquired in the forming of these bending-moment diagrams, entire portions of positive and negative shear areas may be added instead

Figure 6-28

of the smaller increments. Keeping in mind the relative magnitude of the shear-area increments, their sign and sequence, the proper curvature of the moment curves may be ascertained.

Illustrative Problem 2.   Draw the shear- and bending-moment diagram for the beam shown in Fig. 6-28. Determine the maximum-shear and the maximum positive and negative bending moments. Locate the inflection points.

SOLUTION. *Finding the reactions:*

ΣM_{R_2}

	4×13	52
$14 \times 1 \times$	$3 =$	42
	$3 \times \ \ 6 =$	18
	$-6 \times \ \ 2 =$	-12
	$10R_1 =$	100
	$R_1 =$	10 kips

ΣM_{R_1}

	$3 \times \ \ 4 =$	12
	$6 \times 12 =$	72
$14 \times 1 \times$	$7 =$	98
	$-4 \times \ \ 3 =$	-12
	$10R_2 =$	170
	$R_2 =$	17 kips

$$\Sigma V = 4 + 14 + 3 + 6 - 10 - 17 = 0$$
$$0 = 0$$

Therefore, equilibrium is checked.

Shear- and bending-moment diagram.   Of significant importance in the shear diagram is the fact that all the diagonal lines are of one slope. This is the result of having uniform load of equal intensity acting on the beam. Had there been several intensities of uniform load, there would have been as many different slopes.

There are five separate portions to the bending-moment diagram. Close scrutiny reveals that in traveling from the left to the right end of the beam, a new moment curve is induced whenever a concentrated load or a variation of uniform load is encountered.

The proper curvature of the moment curve is again obtained by adding (mentally if possible) the comparative sizes of successive increments of shear area, 1 ft long.

Maximum shear and bending moment.   The maximum shear is always equal to the maximum ordinate of the shear curve. In our case, it is $+10$ kips.

The maximum moment of -20 kips occurs on the beam over reaction R_2. At this point, the upper fibers are in tension and the lower fibers, in compression. At the maximum *positive* bending moment of 4 ft-kips, only $\frac{1}{5}$ the intensity of the maximum negative moment, the upper fibers are in compression, and the lower fibers are in tension.

Inflection points.   In view of the fact that the bending-moment diagram passes through the zero axis twice during its traverse from one end of the beam to the other, two inflection points must occur. Their locations are indicated on Fig. 6-29, which represents the approximate deflected position of the beam (shown magnified).

Figure 6-29   Figure 6-30

The inflection point, located between R_1 and the $3k$ force, is determined by setting the moment equation for that portion of the beam (Fig. 6-30) equal to zero and solving for x.

$$\Sigma M_x = -4x + 10(x-3) - 1(x-3)\frac{(x-3)}{2} = 0$$

$$-4x + 10x - 30 - \frac{x^2}{2} + \frac{6x}{2} - \frac{9}{2} = 0$$

$$x^2 - 18x + 69 = 0$$

$$x = \frac{+18 \pm \sqrt{18^2 - 4 \times 69}}{2}$$

$$= \frac{+18 \pm 6.93}{2} = \frac{11.07}{2} = \ = 5.53 \text{ ft (correct)}$$

$$= \frac{24.93}{2} = 12.4 \text{ ft (irrelevant)}$$

The application of the above moment equation, not extending beyond the point 7 ft from the left end, renders the 12.4-ft answer irrelevant. If the curve had extended beyond the 12.4-ft point, the answer would have been relevant and would have indicated the distance of the point of inter-

Figure 6-31

section of the moment curve with the axis line from the left-hand end of the beam.

The second inflection point is obtained by solving the moment equation for that portion of the beam (Fig. 6-31) on which it occurs — that is, between the 3-kip load and R_2.

$$M_x = -4x + 10(x-3) - 1\frac{(x-3)^2}{2} - 3(x-7) = 0$$

$$x^2 - 12x + 27 = 0$$
$$(x - 9)(x - 3) = 0$$
$$x = 9 \text{ ft}$$
$$x = 3 \text{ ft (irrelevant)}$$

Obviously, the value of x equal to 3 ft is irrelevant to our problem, since it occurs outside of the limits of the moment equation. The other answer, $x = 9$ ft, falls within the limits of the section under consideration and is, therefore, valid.

6-15. Effect of couples

If a couple acts through a crossarm or some other restraining device fastened to a beam at one point, the full effect of the couple must be felt at that point. The total moment ordinate, located at the point of action of the couple, must always include the magnitude of the couple. Often a moment ordinate may straddle the zero axis. As already indicated, the sum of the positive and negative portions must equal the magnitude of the couple.

If the forces of the couple act as previously mentioned, at one point on the beam, their presence is not detected on the shear diagram. This gives rise to the one exception to be noted in following the shear-area method of conducting bending-moment diagrams, namely, in determining the difference in bending moment between any two points A and B on a beam, the algebraic sum of the shear areas between these two points should include the concentrated moments produced by couples located between A and B.

Illustrative Problem 3.   Determine the shear- and bending-moment diagrams for the cantilever and simple beams of Figs. 6-32 and 6-33, acted upon by the couples shown.

Figure 6-32   Figure 6-33

SOLUTION. *Cantilever beam.* The only reaction required for the equilibrium of the cantilever beam shown in Fig. 6-32 is a couple of equal and opposite magnitude to the applied couple, located in the supporting wall. Since couples are acting at the ends of the beam, there is theoretically no shear developed on the beam. With no shear area present, there can be no difference in bending moment from point to point on the beam, with the result that the bending moment along the beam must be constant.

Simple beam.   The reactions of the simple beam shown in Fig. 6-33 are the only means by which this beam may attain equilibrium. It is, therefore, necessary that these reactions form a couple, since only another couple can balance the applied couple M_1. Taking moments about R_1

$$M_1 - R_2 \times l = 0, \qquad R_2 = \frac{M_1}{l}$$

Likewise, the moments taken about R_2 yield

$$M_1 - R_1 \times l = 0, \qquad R_1 = -\frac{M_1}{l}$$

Thus, R_1 must act downward and R_2 must act upward with equal intensity to balance couple M_1.

The shear diagram is entirely negative, since R_1 acts downward and forces any portion of the beam to the left of a section in a similar direction past the adjoining right-hand portion.

The bending-moment diagram illustrates the point previously made: that the concentrated moment must be included in the algebraic sum of the shear area for its proper construction.

PROBLEMS

6-12a, b, c, d. Given the shear and bending moment at section *A-A* of the beams shown in Fig. 6-34, determine the bending moment at section *B-B*, using the shear-area method. *Answer:* (a) −1000 lb, 17,750 ft-lb; (b) −6.0 kips, 18.0 ft-kips; (c) −12 kips, −69.5 ft-kips; (d) 2 kips, 6.5 ft-kips.

6-13a, b, c, d. Given the shear diagrams of the various beams in Fig. 6-35, construct their bending-moment diagrams.

6-14a, b, c, d, e, f, g, h. Construct the bending-moment diagram of the beams shown in Fig. 6-21, using the shear-area method. Record the magnitude of the various elementary areas on the shear diagram.

6-15a, b, c, d, e, f, g, h. Construct the bending-moment diagram of the beams shown in Fig. 6-22, using the shear-area method. Record the magnitude of the various elementary areas on the shear diagram.

Figure 6-34

Figure 6-35

6-16. A simply supported beam 20 ft long overhangs the left support 4 ft. It carries the following: 400 lb per ft from left end to left support, 2 kips at 4 ft to the right of the left support, and 800 lb per ft from the 2-kip load to the right support. Construct shear and moment diagrams giving all controlling ordinates. *Answers:* $V_{max.} = -6300$ lb, $M_{max.} = +24,800$ ft-lb.

6-17. A beam 36 ft long is simply supported with one support at the right end and the other support 6 ft from the left end. A uniform load of 200 lb per ft begins at the right end and extends for 12 ft. There is a concentrated load of 1000 lb 18 ft from the right 'end and second concentrated load of 1000 lb at the left end. A uniform load of 400 lb per ft begins 2 ft from the left end and extends to a point 22 ft from the right support. Sketch shear- and bending-moment diagrams giving values of controlling ordinates.

6-18. Draw the shear- and bending-moment diagrams for the beam shown in Fig. 6-36. Note the weight of the beam. *Answers:* $V_{max.} = -1320$ lb, $M_{max.} = -12,120$ ft-lb.

6-19. Draw the shear- and bending-moment diagram for the beam shown in Fig. 6-37.

Figure 6-36   Figure 6-37

6-20. Draw the shear- and bending-moment diagrams of the beam shown in Fig. 6-38 giving all controlling ordinates. *Answers:* $V_{max.} = \pm 12$ kips, $M_{max.} = +36$ ft-kips.

Figure 6-38

6-21. The transverse loads on a certain airplane wing are equivalent to those shown in Fig. 6-39. There is also a clockwise couple of 3315 in.-lb at A. Draw the shear- and bending-moment diagrams giving all controlling ordinates. *Answers:* $V_{max.} = +1053$ lb, $M_{max.} = -19,050$ in.-lb.

Figure 6-39

Chapter Seven

THE DESIGN OF BEAMS

7-1. Fundamental considerations

With the exception of those cases where the moment or shear is zero, there is present on every vertical section of a loaded horizontal beam an internal shear force, V, and an internal resisting couple, C-T, the magnitudes of which are recorded at corresponding positions on the shear- and bending-moment diagrams. As a result of these internal resistances, there are developed on the interior of the beam shear and bending unit stresses whose intensities are dependent upon the magnitude of the resisting forces, as well as on the size and shape of the cross section. Thus, if a cross-sectional area were to be made smaller while still retaining its characteristic shape, the internal stresses would be forced to increase to resist the total shear, V, and bending moment, C-T, acting on that section. In contrast, if the area were to be made larger, the stresses would decrease. It is the designer's responsibility to assign to a beam that cross-sectional area whose maximum stresses will not exceed the limit of the allowable working unit stresses. Naturally, the closer the maximum stresses approach the allowable values, the more economical the design will be.

The fact that the shear and bending unit stresses are of such a different character that they can be computed separately proves of immeasurable convenience. Because their maximum values act independently of one another, an area designed on the basis of the maximum internal bending moment C-T may thereafter be checked for dangerous shear stresses. The opposite procedure of obtaining the area required for shear and of checking it for dangerous bending stresses might also be followed, although this practice is not quite so common. Regardless of what procedure is followed, it should be remembered that no beam design is ever complete without it being satisfactorily shown that the induced shear and bending unit stresses are within their respective allowable limits.

In order properly to adjust or design the cross-sectional area of a beam, separate relationships for shear and bending moment must be derived. The relationship between the cross-sectional area and the bending moment that will be derived first is known as the *flexure formula*, so called because the act of bending is also known as *flexing*.

7-2. Derivation of the flexure formula

Let us consider the beam of rectangular cross section shown in Fig. 7-1-(a), loaded by forces P_1 and P_2. A free body of a portion of this beam is

shown in Fig. 7-1(b) on whose exposed section is acting an internal shear force V and the internal bending moment C-T. Considering, for the time being, only the C-T couple and the internal resisting stresses that it develops, we are at first made aware by the character of these forces that the upper fibers in this beam are in compression while those at the bottom are in tension. It should also be borne in mind that the C and T forces are actually resultants of a múltitude of minor forces produced by the internal

Figure 7-1

tensile and compressive stresses acting on the exposed ends of the fibers comprising the vertical section. Therefore, to evaluate, the magnitude of the resisting C-T couple requires the determination of the location of the C and T forces as dictated by the variation of the resisting flexural stresses acting on the cross section.

The variation of the resisting flexural stresses. The variation of the resisting flexural stresses acting on those cross sections of a beam perpendicular to its longitudinal axis is based on *the fundamental assumption that these cross-sectional planes remain plane after the beam is bent.* Except for beams made from a certain few materials, such as gray cast iron, low-strength concrete, and so forth, this assumption has been essentially substantiated. If, therefore, the movement of two cross-sectional planes of the beam, shown in Fig. 7-2 as initially separated by a small distance dx, were studied during the application of loads P_1 and P_2, the vertical projection of these planes, on the basis of this assumption, would move from the unloaded positions A-A and B-B to positions A'-A' and B'-B', respectively, when the beam was fully loaded.

The convergence of these two cross-sectional planes coupled with the presence of the C and T forces on the top and bottom of the beam, re-

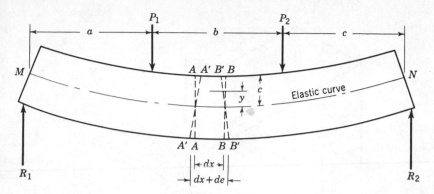

Figure 7-2

spectively, indicate that the upper fibers must have been shortened and the lower fibers lengthened in proportion to their distance from some neutral or unchanged plane of fibers. Because the length of each of the fibers between the two cross sections was dx in length before loading, the unit strain, as well as the unit stress, varied with the distance from these neutral fibers.

The location of the plane of *neutral fibers*, or neutral plane (MN, Fig. 7-2) in a beam having a rectangular cross section passes through the center of gravity axis of every section, since the C and T forces must be equal and their contributing stresses and strains symmetrical with one another. When projected into a vertical plane, this neutral plane becomes a line and is known as the *elastic curve*.

The axis about which a cross section rotates, i.e., the line of zero flexural stress, is called the *neutral axis*.

The summation of the resisting flexural stresses. If the proportional limit is not exceeded, the variation of flexural stress to the distance from the neutral axis (Fig. 7-3) may be written as

$$\frac{s_y}{y} = \frac{s}{c} \qquad (7.1)$$

Figure 7-3. Plane $A'A'$ is parallel to plane DD.

Thus, considering again the exposed section of the free body of Fig. 7-1(b) (arranged isometrically in Fig 7-4), the resisting force acting on the narrow horizontal strip dA located y distance from the neutral axis is equal to $s_y \, dA$. Its resisting moment taken about the neutral axis must therefore be $s_y \, dA \times y$.

Shear stresses
omitted for clarity

Figure 7-4

Moreover, since there are a tremendously large number of dA strips included in the depth d, each of which is located a y distance* from the neutral axis and acted upon by a unit stress s_y, the resisting moments of the forces acting on the dA areas, collectively known as the *internal C-T resisting moment* M_R, is equal to $\int s_y \, dA \, y$.

By substituting the value of s_y as obtained from Eq. 7.1,

$$M_R = \int \frac{s}{c} y \, dA \, y, \quad \text{or} \quad \int \frac{s}{c} y^2 \, dA$$

Because in Equation 7.1 the term s/c equals s_y/y (a constant) and because this ratio appears in the resisting moment of every dA area, it may be placed outside of the summation sign. Thus,

$$M_R = \frac{s}{c} \int y^2 \, dA \tag{7.2}$$

The term $\int y^2 \, dA$ will be recognized as the value of the *moment of inertia* I of the cross-sectional area taken about the centroidal axis. The value of M_R that is equal to the C-T couple must also equal, for equilibrium reasons, the value of the bending moment M at the same section. We may, therefore, write the completed equation, generally known as the *flexure formula*, as

* The value of y is not a constant but varies from 0 to c.

$$M = \frac{sI}{c} \tag{7.3}$$

in which s is the maximum flexural unit stress, commonly expressed in psi at distance c in. from the neutral axis, and I is the moment of inertia of the cross section in in.^{4} taken about the neutral axis. Should these units be employed, the value of M would be in in.-lb.

Illustrative Problem 1. At a certain section of a 4 by 10-in. timber beam, the bending moment (C-T couple) is equal to 3500 ft-lb. Determine the maximum flexure stress on the section if the 10-in. side is vertical.

SOLUTION. Rearranging Eq. 7.3 to appear as $s = Mc/I$ and substituting, we obtain

$$s = \frac{3500 \times 12 \times 5}{\frac{1}{12} \times 4 \times 10^3} = 630 \text{ psi}$$

7-3. Assumptions and limitations of flexure formula

At this point in our use of the flexure formula it is well to consider the assumptions and limitations made in its derivation. They are as follows:

(1) A transverse plane perpendicular to the longitudinal axis of the beam remains plane after the beam is bent.

(2) The modulus of elasticity in compression is the same as that in tension.

When considered together, assumptions (1) and (2) imply that:

(a) The unit stress, unit strain, and total strain are proportional to the distance from the neutral axis.

(b) The unit stress does not exceed the proportional limit of the material. These assumptions disregard the effect of any shearing strains due to the shearing resistance V, and make impossible the use of the flexure formula for curved beams. The difference in length of the fibers between any two transverse sections of a curved beam produce unit strains that are not proportional to the distance from the neutral axis.

(3) The beam must deflect normally under elastic bending stresses and not through any local collapse or twisting. This limitation implies the necessity of a beam having an ample width for its depth.

(4) The applied loads act in a plane containing the axis of symmetry of each cross section.

This closer scrutiny of the flexure formula should warn the user to view with care the extent of its field of application. To extend its usefulness beyond the scope of this limited field might easily incur disaster. On the other hand, to restrict its usefulness unnecessarily might cause excessive waste.

PROBLEMS

7-1. What is the maximum flexure stress at a section 3 ft from one end of a uniformly loaded simple beam 4 in. wide by 10 in. deep by 12 ft long? $w = 500$ lb per ft.

7-2. What maximum uniform load can a 6 by 12-in. beam withstand if its length between supports is 15 ft and the maximum allowable stress is 1200 lb per ft? *Answer: 512 lb per ft.*

7-3. A wagon axle 2-in. square is loaded as shown in Fig. 7-5. What is the maximum unit stress attained when $P_1 = P_2 = 4000$ lb?

Figure 7-5   **Figure 7-6**

7-4. A cast-iron lever (Fig. 7-6) having a $\frac{1}{2}$ by $1\frac{1}{2}$-in. cross section is used to activate a pull rod. How much pull P may be applied before the unit stress will exceed 10,000 psi? *Answer: 78.2 lb.*

7-5. A wood floor with a 15-ft span is to carry 250 lb per sq ft. If 4 by 14-in. beams are to be used, how far apart can they be placed according to the flexure formula if the flexural unit stress is not to exceed 1200 psi? *Answer: 22.3 in.*

7-6. The casting shown in Fig. 7-7 acts as a simple beam and restrains the load P. Is the most dangerously stressed section immediately below P or at section A-A? Prove your answer. *Answer:* (a) $s = 1.35P$, (b) $s = 3.75P$.

Figure 7-7   **Figure 7-8**

7-7a, b, c, d. Determine the maximum flexural stresses at sections A-A and B-B of the beams shown in Fig. 6-11. Use $I/c = 100$ in.[3]

7-8. Timber sheet piling (Fig. 7-8) are to be used to hold back water from flowing into the foundation pit of a bridge. Assuming complete rigidity at its fixed end, what depth d of water can be held back by the piling whose thickness is 3 in.? Maximum allowable unit stress $= 1800$ psi. *Answer:* 6.38 ft.

7-4. Use of flexure formula in design

To design a beam of uniform symmetrical cross section with regard to its flexural requirements, the value of M is placed equal to the maximum bending moment obtained from the moment diagram, and s is assigned the value of the maximum allowable flexure stress for the material of which the beam is made. If M in in.-lb is divided by s in psi, the value obtained is equal to the ratio I/c in in.[3] This ratio, called the *section modulus*, reflects that minimum value of resistance required to withstand the imposed bending without exceeding the allowable stress.

If the beam selected to meet this requirement is to be the most economical one, it must provide the necessary section modulus with the least amount of cross-sectional area (or weight). To assist in this selection, tables have been provided (see A.I.S.C. handbook or tables in back of book) giving the section moduli of all standard beams. The same tables provide other pertinent data such as weight, centers of gravity, moment of inertia, radii of gyration, and so forth.

Illustrative Problem 2. Determine the cross-sectional dimensions of the beam of Fig. 6-3, based on flexural requirements only, if it is to be made of southern yellow pine having a maximum allowable flexure stress of 1600 psi. The loading- and live-load bending-moment diagrams are redrawn for convenience (Fig. 7-9). Use an American Standard size beam.

Moment diagram for live load

Figure 7-9

SOLUTION. The maximum bending moment for any beam is determined by that greatest algebraic sum of moment occurring at any point on the beam which results from the action of both live and dead load. This maximum moment for our beam occurs at the 4-kip load where the moment due to live load is 14.4 ft-kips (see Figs. 6-14 and 6-15) and that due to dead load (beam assumed 15 lb per ft) is 0.18 ft-kips (say 0.2 ft-kips). It is upon their sum of 14.6 ft-kips that our flexural design is based.* Substituting in the flexure formula, we obtain

$$\frac{I}{c} = \frac{M}{s} = \frac{14.6 \times 1000 \times 12}{1600} = 109.5 \text{ or } 110$$

But

$$\frac{I}{c} = \frac{\frac{1}{12}bd^3}{d/2} = \frac{bd^2}{6}$$

Thus

$$\frac{I}{c} = \frac{bd^2}{6} = 110 \quad \text{or} \quad bd^2 = 660$$

Although any cross section whose product of b and d^2 equals 660 would meet the flexural strength requirements, there are, ordinarily, economical and structural limitations that dictate a very definite and more desirable choice.

Timber beams sold at lumber yards are cut and planed to certain standard sizes. (See A.I.S.C., *Steel Handbook*, table on Timber, American Standard sizes or Table 20 in the appendix of this book.)† In this so-called *dressing* operation, a certain amount of the original cross section as laid out on the tree trunk is lost in the form of sawdust and shavings. This loss of cross section does not reduce the cost to the purchaser, since its price is based upon its *laid out*, or nominal, cross section. For example, a common 3 by 10-in. beam is only $2\frac{5}{8}$ by $9\frac{1}{2}$ in. in cross section when dressed, but is sold on the basis of a 30 sq in. cross section. This loss of cross section reduces the value of I and c and, consequently, the strength of the beam.

In the tabulation shown below are given the cross sections of those standard timber beams whose section moduli satisfy with the least excess the minimum required value of 110.

NOMINAL SIZE	AMERICAN STANDARD DRESSED SIZE	AREA OF SECTION (in.²)	SECTION MODULUS
3 by 18 in...............	$2\frac{5}{8}$ by $17\frac{1}{2}$ in.	45.9	134
4 by 14 in...............	$3\frac{5}{8}$ by $13\frac{1}{2}$ in.	48.9	110
6 by 12 in...............	$5\frac{1}{2}$ by $11\frac{1}{2}$ in.	63.3	121
8 by 10 in...............	$7\frac{1}{2}$ by $9\frac{1}{2}$ in.	71.3	113

Although any one of these four beams would be capable of restraining the imposed load, they would not be equally acceptable on the basis of their cost or structural strength. A designer's axiom is to obtain the greatest strength for the least cost in fulfilling design requirements.

Using this thought as the background for our selection, it would appear that the 3 by 18-in. beam would be the most satisfactory. Its minimum cross-sectional area of 45.9 sq in. and its high section modulus

* The weight of a timber beam is often disregarded in design problems. To ignore the weight of beam in this problem would incur an error of only 1.25 per cent, and would not change the size requirements.

† Table from *National Lumber Manufacturers Association*.

would afford what appears to be the greatest economy with more than sufficient strength, assuming no extra charge for the 18-in. depth.* The cross section of this beam may, however, be too narrow for its height if used alone without side support. Common practice generally refrains from using a ratio of depth to width of cross section greater than 4 for beams that are unsupported laterally. *The best tentative selection would, therefore, be the 4 by 14-in. beam, which is only slightly more expensive and has a depth-width ratio of less than 4.* The magnitude of the shearing unit stress must, of course, be determined before this cross section can be finally accepted.

Figure 7-10

The problem of beam selection, as illustrated in the foregoing paragraph, indicates that the narrower and the deeper a beam can be made without failing by twisting, bearing, or some other method, the stronger it becomes. The reason for this greater strength lies in the fact that the value of the moment of inertia increases as a greater proportion of its area is located farther from the neutral axis. This also accounts for the use of *I* beams, channels, and other sections (Fig. 7-10) whose flange areas are spread as far from the neutral axis as possible to make the value of the moment of inertia $\int y^2 \, dA$ a maximum consistent with other strength requirements, such as local buckling and twisting.

PROBLEMS

Before the beam sections computed for the following problems can be considered as final, they must be checked for excessive shear stresses (article 7-13). Where weight of timber beam is to be considered, use weight found in Table 14.

7-9. A warehouse floor is to be undergirded by beams 15 ft long. If the total load is to be 250 lb per sq ft, what size of American Standard rectangular timber beams would be used, assuming a spacing of 18 in. between beams and a maximum allowable unit stress of 1500 psi? *Answer:* 4 by 14 in.

7-10. What size wood joists, spaced 16 in. center to center on an effective span of 14 ft, are required to carry a total load of 120 lb per sq ft? Allowable unit stress in wood is 1200 psi? *Answer:* 3 in. by 10 in.

---

* Generally, the use of timbers with any dimension above 12 in. calls for an additional charge per board foot (1 board foot = 1 in. thick by 12 in. wide by 12 in. long).

7-11. A simply supported timber beam 20 ft long is to carry a uniformly distributed total load of 600 lb per linear ft. Determine the section modulus required to sustain this load if the maximum allowable unit stress is 1200 psi.

7-12. A cantilever beam 9 ft long is to be made from several 2 by 10-in. nominal-size wooden planks placed vertically and bolted together. If a concentrated load of 1000 lb is to be carried at its free end, determine the number of planks necessary to sustain the load. Maximum allowable fiber stress is 1200 psi. Consider weight of beam. *Answer:* 4.

7-13. Determine that American Standard rectangular timber beam required to sustain the loading shown in Fig. 7-11. Assume $s = 1400$ psi. Consider the weight of beam. *Answer:* 6 in. by 14 in.

Figure 7-11   Figure 7-12

7-14. How deep must be the rectangular, steel lever arm included in the scale shown in Fig. 7-12 if its width is $\frac{1}{4}$ in. and its maximum allowable flexure unit stress is 18,000 psi? *Answer:* 0.98 in.

Figure 7-13

7-15. If the cast-iron offset arm shown in Fig. 7-13 is to have a critical cross section whose general dimensions are shown, what will be the exterior dimensions if $d = 2b$? Use maximum allowable fiber stress of 8,000 psi. *Answer:* 4.16 by 8.32 in.

THE USE OF THE FLEXURE FORMULA FOR BEAMS WITH OTHER THAN RECTANGULAR CROSS SECTIONS

The uniform rectangular cross section of the beam used in the derivation of the flexure formula afforded symmetry about both the vertical and horizontal axes. *Because the loads acted in the vertical plane of symmetry no longitudinal twisting could take place and the unit stress on any horizontal strip y distance from the neutral axis (see Fig. 7-4) was constant over the entire width.* Symmetry about a horizontal axis located the neutral axis at the axis of symmetry (that is, center of gravity axis) and caused the rotation about the neutral axis of all plane sections perpendicular to the longitudinal axis.

7-5. Sections having two axes of symmetry

Since I and WF cross sections also have two axes of symmetry, the flexure formula may be extended to include the design of beams having such cross sections. Equation 7.2, developed in the derivation of the flexure formula, presents

$$M_R = \frac{s}{c} \int y^2 \, dA$$

The only difference revealed in this equation when applied to a section such as an I beam is in the variation of dA. This change necessitates only a slightly more involved computation for the moment of inertia of each section considered or its selection from a handbook table. Other than for this added complication, the use of the flexure formula proceeds as with the rectangular sections.

(a)

(b)

Figure 7-14

Illustrative Problem 3. Select the most economical *I*-beam section, based upon flexural requirements, to withstand the loading imposed upon the overhanging beam shown in Fig. 7-14. The beam will be laterally supported. Use an allowable working stress of 20,000 psi. Disregard the weight of the beam.

SOLUTION. The maximum moment of 12 ft-kips, upon which the flexural portion of the design must be based, is located at left reaction R_1. Inserting this value with the allowable working stress in the flexure formula, we obtain

$$\frac{M}{s} = \frac{12 \times 1000 \times 12}{20,000} = \frac{I}{c} = 7.2 \text{ in.}^3$$

Thus, the *I* beam required to meet this loading condition most economically must weigh less than any beam having a section modulus greater than 7.2 in.³ when used in its upright position, that is, resting on its lower flange. Proceeding then to the A.I.S.C. handbook or to Table 15, we note in the column headed by *S* for the *x-x* axis that the lightest *I* beam having a section modulus of 7.2 in.³ or over is the 6 by 3⅜-in. nominal-sized *I* beam weighing 12.5 lb per linear ft.

This is the most economical beam and is recorded as

6 I 12.5

7-6. Sections having vertical axes of symmetry — loaded vertically

Beams with cross sections having a vertical axis of symmetry, such as the *T* section in Fig. 7-15, may be designed through the use of the flexure formula, since Eq. 7.2 is still applicable. The position of the neutral

Figure 7-15   Figure 7-16

axis is, however, displaced from its midway position, since symmetry no longer exists about a horizontal axis. To determine the location of the neutral axis on such sections, let us refer to Fig. 7-16. With the resisting compressive forces on the top balancing the resisting tensile forces on the bottom, we may write the equation

$$\int s_y \, dA = 0$$

Multiplying by y/y we obtain

$$\int \frac{s_y}{y} y \, dA = 0$$

Knowing that a product of two values can only equal zero when one of these values also equals zero, we may further stipulate, since s_y/y is a constant, that

$$\int y \, dA = 0$$

But $\int y \, dA$ is equal to the moment of the cross-sectional area of the beam with respect to the neutral axis. When equal to zero, it indicates that the moments of the areas above and below the neutral axis balance one another. This balance of moments also defines the neutral axis as being a centroidal axis. In other words, *the centroidal axis is coincident with the neutral axis.*

Thus, if a study of the bending stresses were to be made on a T section whose center line of stem was vertical and in the plane of the loads, the location of the centroidal axis parallel to the flange would be required. Once having located the centroidal axis, the moment of inertia of the area about this axis would have to be found for insertion in the flexure formula. It should be noted that the extreme fiber stresses for this type of cross section will not be of the same magnitude.

Illustrative Problem 4. The cast-iron T beam shown in Fig. 7-17 is subjected to two concentrated loads of 4000 and 10,000 lb at its third

Figure 7-17

points. Find the maximum tensile and compressive unit stresses acting on the beam. Disregard the weight of the beam.

SOLUTION. Inasmuch as the use of the flexure formula requires a knowledge of the moment of inertia of the section about its neutral axis, we must first proceed to obtain this value before we can obtain the required stresses.

Location of neutral axis. The moments of the areas A and B, taken about the base of the section, are

SECTION	ΔA	y	$\Delta A\, y$
A	12×5	$=$	60 in.^{3}
B	12×1	$=$	12
		$\Sigma\, \Delta A\, y$	$= \overline{72 \text{ in.}^3}$

$$\bar{y} = \frac{\Sigma\, \Delta A\, y}{\Sigma\, \Delta A} = \frac{72}{24} = 3 \text{ in.}$$

Moment of inertia about neutral axis.

SECTION

A .... $I_{c.g.} = \tfrac{1}{12} \times 2 \times 6^3 = 36$ in.^{4}
$\qquad\qquad\qquad Ay^2 = 12 \times 2^2 \qquad = 48$
B .... $I_{c.g.} = \tfrac{1}{12} \times 6 \times 2^3 = 4$
$\qquad\qquad\qquad Ay^2 = 12 \times 2^2 \qquad = \underline{48}$
$\qquad\qquad\qquad\qquad\qquad\qquad\qquad\quad 136$ in.^{4}

Maximum fiber stresses. The maximum bending moment, as determined from the bending-moment diagram, occurs under the 10-kip load and is equal to 24 ft-kips.

The maximum tensile unit stress at this section occurs at the extreme bottom fiber, located 3 in. below the neutral axis. Its value is equal to

$$s_t = \frac{Mc}{I} = \frac{24 \times 1000 \times 12 \times 3}{136} = 6360 \text{ psi}$$

The maximum compressive unit stress at this maximum moment section occurs on the extreme top fiber, located 5 in. above the neutral axis. Proceeding with its computation, we obtain

$$s_c = \frac{Mc}{I} = \frac{24 \times 1000 \times 12 \times 5}{136} = 10,600 \text{ psi}$$

Figure 7-18

This stress might also have been obtained from the fact that the flexure stress varies directly with its distance above or below the neutral axis. Knowing that a unit stress of 6360 psi exists 3 in. below the axis, we can find the stress 5 in. above by a similar triangle relationship (Fig. 7-18),

$$s_c = 6360 \times \tfrac{5}{3} = 10{,}600 \text{ psi}$$

The use of T sections in bending is particularly suited for those materials that have different tensile and compressive strengths. If a material, such as cast iron, has a lower ultimate tensile stress than an ultimate compressive stress, the intensity of the more critical tensile stress may be reduced by placing the flange of the tee on the tension side. Such sections are frequently used in machine frames.

7-7. Sections having horizontal axis of symmetry — loaded vertically

When a rolled-steel section, such as the channel of Fig. 7-19(a), has a horizontal plane of symmetry but is loaded in a plane parallel to its web, care must be taken to locate a loading plane that will prevent longitudinal twisting. Thereafter, the application of the flexure formula can proceed without difficulty.

Figure 7-19

To eliminate longitudinal twisting requires determination of the *shear center* of the cross section, the computation of which is discussed in § 7-17. It is important to note that it does not correspond to the center of gravity. Frequently, two channels are placed back to back (Fig. 7-19b) to provide the symmetry that will overcome twisting.

7-8. Sections having no axes of symmetry

If a beam has a cross section with no axes of symmetry, the flexure formula can still be used in its design, if it is loaded to prevent twisting.* Further complications arise, however, *since the bending plane will not be in the plane of loading unless it contains one of the principal axes of the section.* The neutral axis of an unsymmetrical cross section does not coincide with a principal axis unless the above stipulation is maintained.

To illustrate the point, let us consider first a beam with a rectangular cross section acted upon by a moment in the vertical plane of symmetry (Fig. 7-20a). The tensile and compressive forces *which must produce a restraining moment equal to the applied moment* balance not only about the horizontal axis of symmetry but about the vertical axis as well. Suppose now one quarter of the beam were removed (Fig. 7-20b). Certainly, the center of gravity of the cross section would rise and move to the left. To assume that bending would be about a horizontal axis through this point

---

* Load must pass through shear center (see §7-17).

Figure 7-20

would be to assume that the stresses varied as indicated in (b). The C-T resisting couple would under these circumstances then have a horizontal component for which there was no equal applied moment. Such an un-balanced situation could not exist for a body in equilibrium.

The only way a perfect balance could be attained between the applied and resisting moments would be to have the bending axis tilted (Fig. 7-20c). Under this condition, the components of the applied bending moment perpendicular and parallel to the tilted bending axis would exactly balance the corresponding components of the resisting moment.

Because of these complications, the design of a beam with an unsymmetrical cross section proceeds by first resolving the bending moment into components parallel to the two principal axes of the section (cf. § A-13, Appendix). *These moments, when considered separately, produce bending and corresponding flexural stresses about their respective principal axes.* If then, the actions of these component bending moments are combined, bending will occur about some intermediate axis and the resulting flexural stresses are obtained by adding their separate flexural stresses algebraically. That greatest value of resulting flexural stress must not exceed the maximum allowable stress for the material.

Illustrative Problem 5. A cantilever beam, made from a 6 by 6 by $\frac{1}{2}$ in. angle, 6 ft long, is loaded at its free end with a non-twisting vertical load of 500 lb. If the legs of the angle are horizontal and vertical, determine the maximum stress at point A (Fig. 7-21) resulting from the imposed load.

Figure 7-21

SOLUTION. The minor principal axis for the cross section of any standard structural steel angle is commonly known as the Z-Z axis and is tilted with respect to each of the legs. When the legs are equal in length, the tilt is 45°. From Table 19 in the back of this book, the value of radius of gyration about the Z-Z axis for the given 6 by 6 by $\frac{1}{2}$ in. angle is 1.18 in. Its corresponding moment of inertia is equal to Ar^2 or $5.75 \times 1.18^2 = 8.00$ in.^{4} To obtain the moment of inertia I_W about the major principal axis W-W, which is perpendicular to the minor principal axis Z-Z, use is made of the fact that the sum of moments of inertia on mutually perpendicular planes is a constant.* Thus

$$I_x + I_y = I_z + I_W$$

Substituting corresponding values taken directly from Table 19 yields

$$19.9 + 19.9 = \;\; 8.0 + I_W$$

from which $\qquad\qquad\qquad\qquad I_W = 31.8 \text{ in.}^4$

---

* Simplified formulas for finding I_Z and I_W of unequal leg angle sections are given in the A.I.S.C. *Steel Handbook* in the portion devoted to "Properties of Geometric Sections."

The maximum bending moment, which equals 3000 ft-lb, is then resolved into components parallel to the principal axis.

$$M_Z = M_W = 3000 \times 12 \times .707 = 25,450 \text{ ft-lb.}$$

The corresponding flexural stresses for point A are therefore

$$s_A = \frac{M_Z \times c_W}{I_Z} + \frac{M_W \times c_Z}{I_W} \tag{7.4}$$

$$s_A = \frac{25,450 \times 2.22}{8.0} + \frac{22,450 \times 3.89}{31.8}$$

$$s_A = 7070 + 3110$$

$$s_A = 10,180 \text{ psi}$$

Locating the neutral axis. The location of the neutral axis of the cross section can be obtained by finding two points at which the sum of the two flexure stresses is equal to zero. The coordinates of these points may be obtained by placing s_A in equation 7.4 equal to zero and solving in turn for values of c'_W and c'_Z that will make the flexural stresses equal to each other. Thus, for $c_Z = 3.89$ in., $c'_W = -0.977$ in. and for $c_W = 1.11$ in., $c'_Z = -4.41$ in. The neutral axis must pass through these points. As a check, it must also pass through the origin.

PROBLEMS

All beams used in the following problems are assumed to have sufficient lateral support to develop the maximum allowable flexure stress. They are also subject to review of their shearing stresses which is considered in § 7-13.

7-16a, b, c, d, e, f, g, h. Determine the most economical American Standard I beam and WF section necessary to sustain the load acting on each beam of Fig. 6-21. Use maximum allowable flexure stress = 20,000 psi.

7-17a, b, c, d, e, f, g, h. Select two channels placed back to back to support the load acting on each beam of Fig. 6-22. Use maximum allowable flexure stress = 20,000 psi. *Answer:* (a) 8 in.-13.75 lb, (b) 10 in.-20 lb, (c) 10 in.-25 lb, (d) 10 in.-30 lb, (e) 15 in.-40 lb, (f) 8 in.-13.75 lb, (g) 8 in.-13.75 lb, (h) 6 in.-13 lb.

Figure 7-22

7-18. Select the most economical American Standard I beam to sustain the load on the beam of Fig. 7-22. Use $s = 20,000$ psi. *Answer:* 12 I 35.0.

7-19. Two unequal leg angles are to be placed back to back to form a cantilever beam 8 ft long. If a uniformly distributed load of 100 lb per linear ft (includes the weight of the angles) and a concentrated load of 500 lb is located at its free end, what most economical angle section can be arranged to support this load? Use $s = 20,000$ psi. *Answer:* Two angles 6 by $3\frac{1}{2}$ by $\frac{1}{4}$ in.

7-20. A cast-iron machinery frame having a T section, shown in Fig. 7-23, is to be loaded with force P acting horizontally. What maximum value of P can be applied if the maximum allowable compressive stress is 20,000 psi and the maximum allowable tensile unit stress is 8000 psi? *Answer:* 36,300 lb.

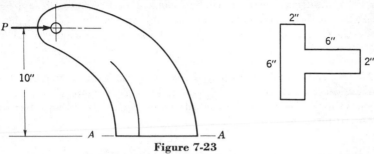

Figure 7-23

7-21. What width of flange is necessary in the T beam shown in Fig. 7-24 if the maximum tensile unit stress is to be equal to one third the maximum compressive unit stress?

Figure 7-24   Figure 7-25

7-22. What should be the total depth of the cast iron T section shown in Fig. 7-25 in order to produce simultaneously occurring tensile and compressive stresses of 8,000 and 16,000 psi at A and B respectively. *Answer:* 6 in.

7-23. An extra-strong steel pipe having an outside diameter of 4 in. and a wall thickness of 0.318 in. is to be used as a simple beam of 12 ft to support two concentrated loads of 2 kips each, located 4 and 6 ft from the left reaction. Determine the maximum flexure stress developed by the loads.

7-24. Determine the maximum value of P that can be sustained on the beam of Fig. 7-26 if the allowable tensile and compressive stresses are 8000 and 14,000 psi respectively. Disregard the weight of beam. $\bar{y} = 2.25$ in. *Answer:* 1940 lb.

Figure 7-26

7-25. Turn the beam in Problem 7-24 upside down and determine P, using the same allowable stresses.

7-26a, b, c. Determine the maximum flexural stress incurred on the following unsymmetrical sections due to a bending moment of 100,000 in.-lb. applied in a vertical plane without longitudinal twisting: (a) An 8 in. by 8 in. by $\frac{3}{4}$ in. angle, (b) An 8 in. by 6 in. by $\frac{3}{4}$ in. angle, 6 in. leg horizontal. *Answers:* (a) 10,700 psi, (b) 12,980 psi.

7-27a, b. Determine the maximum flexural stress incurred at point A on the unsymmetrical sections shown in Fig. 7-27 and Fig. 7-28 due to a bending moment 50,000 in.-lb applied in a vertical plane without longitudinal twisting. *Answers:* (a) 31,200 psi, (b) 8695 psi.

Figure 7-27

Figure 7-28

7-9. The effect of lateral buckling in beams

There is a tendency for the compression side of a long beam to buckle laterally when heavily loaded. When this tendency to buckle is prevented by lateral bracing of some sort such as is offered by a system of floor beams or tie rods, no buckling is possible and the design of the beam follows the methods previously indicated.

If, however, a long beam is laterally unbraced and is to be loaded to capacity, measures must be taken to investigate possible buckling of the compression fibers. The American Institute of Steel Construction Code handles this problem for flanged beams by decreasing the allowable stress when conditions are critical. It requires that, if the so-called ld/bt ratio of a rolled section, plate girder, or built-up section is in excess of 600, the allowable stress permitted on the compression flange cannot exceed

$$s = \frac{12,000,000}{ld/bt} \tag{7.5}$$

where l = the unsupported length of simple beam, d = the total depth of the member, b = the total width, and t = the total thickness of the compression flange, all in inches.

If the ld/bt ratio is less than 600, the allowable compressive stress of 20,000 psi suffers no reduction. On the other hand the allowable stress on the tension flange remains at 20,000 psi regardless of the length of the beam, even though with symmetrical sections the actual stress cannot at times attain to this value.

In using the above stress reduction formula for cantilever beams, the value of l is taken as twice the actual length whenever the outer end is not fully stayed against translation or rotation.

Because the value of the reduced stress in Eq. 7.5 is dependent on the dimensions of the beam and without this reduced stress, the dimensions of the beam are unobtainable, the design of a long beam having an ld/bt greater than 600 must usually be obtained by trial. If, however, the A.I.S.C. handbook is available, the graphs included therein for the selection of such simple beams makes a trial and error design unnecessary.

Illustrative Problem 6. Select the most economical WF beam 32 ft long to carry a load of 950 lb per ft in addition to its own weight. Consider the flexural condition alone.

SOLUTION. Let us arbitrarily assume the weight of the beam to be 65 lb per ft. The total load per foot would then be 1015 lb and the maximum moment $(wl^2/8)$ will equal 130.0 ft-kips.

The section modulus, assuming the allowable stress to be 20,000 psi, is equal to

$$\frac{I}{c} = \frac{130.0 \times 1000 \times 12}{20,000} = 78.0 \text{ in.}^3$$

The most economical *trial* beam (see Table 16) for this section modulus is the 12 in. $\times$ 10 in. *WF* 58 lb beam ($I/c = 78.1$ in.^{3}, $d = 12.19$ in., $b = 10.014$ in., $t = 0.641$ in.). Note that the assumed weight is slightly higher than that of the beam selected, making the computed bending moment greater than actually produced. This difference is, however, too small to necessitate changing our value. Its ld/bt ratio is $32 \times 12 \times 12.19/10.014 \times 0.641 = 729$. The allowable stress corresponding to this ratio is

$$s_a = \frac{12,000,000}{729} = 16,450 \text{ psi}$$

The required I/c is therefore $130.0 \times 1000 \times 12/16,450 = 94.8$ in.^{3}. This exceeds the available I/c of the beam selected for trial.

If we now increase the size of the beam to a 12 in. *WF* 65 lb. ($I/c = 88.0$ in.^{3}, $d = 12.12$ in., $b = 12.00$ in., $t = .606$ in.) we note that the ld/bt is reduced to 640. The corresponding allowable stress is equal to 18,720 psi, which requires a section modulus of 83.3. No other lighter beam meets the requirement of the problem. The correct beam size is therefore 12 in. *WF* 65 lb.

PROBLEMS

7-28a, b, c, d, e, f, g, h. Determine the size of the *WF* beams required to meet the bending and lateral stability conditions presented in Fig. 6-22. Include weight of beam. *Answer:* (a) 12 in. *WF* 27 lb, (c) 10 in. *WF* 39 lb, (e) 14 in. *WF* 61 lb, (g) 8 in. *WF* 24 lb.

7-29. Will greater lateral stiffness be obtained for a cantilever beam of T cross section by having the flange on top or bottom? Explain.

7-30. A cantilever beam, 10 ft long and loaded with 5 kips per ft is to be designed having a *WF* section. Select the most economical beam, considering A.I.S.C. specifications. Include weight of beam. *Answer:* 24 in. *WF* 84 lb.

7-31. It is desired to double the capacity in bending of a 24 in. *WF* 100-lb beam on a laterally unbraced span of 25 ft by welding the necessary number of 14 in. $\times$ $\frac{1}{4}$ in. cover plates, 25 ft long, to each flange, the same number to be used on top and bottom. Disregard weight of beam. (a) How many cover plates will be required? (b) How is the ld/bt ratio affected by the addition of cover plates?

7-32. A beam, 30 ft long, is loaded over its entire length with 2 kips per ft. If one reaction is at the extreme right end and the other at a point 18 ft away, what most economical *WF* beam is required to meet the A.I.S.C. specifications? Include weight of beam. *Answer:* 14 in. *WF* 61 lb.

7-10. Beams of varying section modulus

As indicated in the solutions to previous illustrative problems, the flexural portion of the design of a uniform cross-sectioned beam is governed by the maximum bending moment. On an ordinary beam, this usually occurs on only one section. All the other sections that are of equal size but are acted on by lesser values of bending moment must, consequently, be understressed. The use of material that is understressed makes necessary the carrying of weight in a beam that is not used to its maximum capacity.

This undesirable condition may be eliminated to a large extent by varying the section modulus I/c in the central portion of a beam to conform to the variation or shape of the bending-moment diagram. This would cause the maximum flexural unit stresses in this affected portion of the beam to be equal, since

$$s = \frac{M}{I/c} = \text{constant}$$

This method of reducing the weight of beams is frequently made use of in the fabrication of plate girder beams, heavy truck axles, heavy castings, and so forth (Fig. 7-29). Whether or not the cost of varying the cross section of a beam is always justifiable on the basis of the weight of material saved can be decided only on the individual merits of each case. Certainly the ordinary rolled-steel beams are of constant cross section, because the cost of rolling a beam of variable cross section would not offset the saving in material.

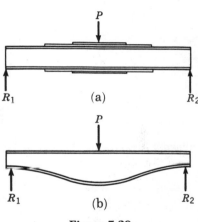

Figure 7-29

Illustrative Problem 7. A uniform load of 6000 lb per ft is to be applied to a cast WF beam 12 ft long, having a variable depth of web. The top and bottom flanges are to be made 6 in. wide by 2 in. thick and are to be held constant throughout the entire length of the beam. What total depth of section will be necessary at the center and quarter points to meet the flexural requirements if the maximum allowable stress of 10,000 psi is to be maintained at each section? Do not consider the weight of the beam.

Solution. The bending moments at the center and quarter points are 108,000 and 81,000 ft-lb, respectively. Their corresponding section moduli required are 129.6 and 97.2 in.[3]

By equating these required section moduli to an algebraically expressed section moduli of the proposed cross section in terms of d, a cubic equation can be obtained from which an exact determination of the total depth may be made.

The solution may also be made graphically. On the graph shown in Fig. 7-30 is plotted a curve of available section moduli obtained by cal-

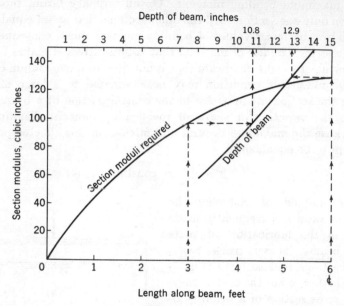

Figure 7-30

culating these values for various values of d. The values used to obtain the curve drawn were

d (in.)	I/c (in.³)
14	148.5
12	115.4
10	85.7
8	58.8

An additional curve is drawn giving the variation of M/s or section moduli required for different sections of the beam. Proceeding horizontally from this curve at the point corresponding to the section under investigation to the available section moduli curve provides the required depth of beam at the point of intersection.

For the center and quarter points, the depths required for flexure are, respectively, 12.9 and 10.8 in.

NOTE: At the ends of the beam where the bending moment is small, the depth will be controlled by the allowable shear (see § 7-12). Both conditions must be investigated thoroughly to determine the permissible depth variations throughout its length.

Illustrative Problem 8. Determine the increase in allowable bending moment obtained by welding $\frac{1}{2}$ by 6-in. cover plates on the top and bottom flanges of a 15-in. I 42.9-lb simple beam. The beam is laterally supported.

SOLUTION. The moment of inertia of the section is:

I beam... 441.8 in.[4]

Gusset plates........................ $2[\frac{1}{12} \times 6 \times (\frac{1}{2})^3 + 3 \times \overline{7.75^2}] =$ 360.2

Total moment of inertia... 802.0 in.[4]

The allowable bending moment of the section will, therefore, be

$$M = \frac{sI}{c} = \frac{20,000 \times 802}{8.0} = 2,000,000 \text{ in.-lb}$$

The allowable bending moment of the I beam (previously computed) is 1,180,000 in.-lb.

$$\therefore \text{Increase} = \frac{2,000,000 - 1,180,000}{1,180,000} \times 100 = 69.5\%$$

PROBLEMS

In the following problems, use maximum allowable flexure stress for steel = 20,000 psi.

7-33. How thick and how long must the gusset plates supplementing the top and bottom flanges of a 15-in. I 42.9-lb beam be to increase its carrying capacity of uniform load by 20 per cent? The gusset plates are to be 5.5 in. in width and welded into place. Length of beam equals 12 ft. *Answer:* 0.276 in.; 4.90 ft, placed symmetrically with center of beam.

7-34. The flag pole shown in Fig. 7-31 is acted upon by a concentrated load of 200 lb at its free end and by a uniformly distributed load of 20 lb per linear ft over its entire length. Calculate the maximum flexure stress in the flag pole.

7-35. A 16-in. *WF* 36-lb beam is 20 ft long. If two cover plates $\frac{1}{4}$ by 7 in. are placed at the top and bottom flanges, determine the maximum uniform load that can be placed on the beam. Determine the points where the outside gusset plate is no longer needed. I_{x-x} for beam is 446.3 in.[4] Consider the cover plates to be welded into place, thus requiring no deduction for rivet holes. *Answer:* 2740 lb per ft.

Figure 7-31

7-11. *Modulus of rupture in bending*

An often used, but fictitious, value of ultimate flexure stress is the *modulus of rupture*. It is calculated from the flexure equation by substituting for the value of M the maximum moment attained by the beam during an actual bending test.

To illustrate its calculation, suppose a 12-ft beam having a 4 by 12-in. cross section were to fail under a load of 20,000 lb applied at its midpoint. Its modulus of rupture would then be

$$s_r = \frac{M_u c}{I} = \frac{10,000 \times 6 \times 12 \times 6}{\frac{1}{12} \times 4 \times 12^3} = 7500 \text{ psi}$$

The reason for the fallacy. The fallacy developed in the calculation of the modulus of rupture is due to the use of the maximum bending moment. The load producing this maximum moment is almost without exception greater than that required to produce the proportional limit stress. This fact invalidates the use of the flexure equation, since one of the underlying assumptions upon which its derivation is based is that the stress distribution on any section increases linearly with the distance from the neutral axis. This provision is impossible of attainment once the proportional limit is exceeded.

The effect of using the maximum bending moment. When the stress acting upon the extreme fiber of a beam increases beyond the proportional limit, its rate of stress increase diminishes and the proportion of resisting moment that it previously carried is reduced. This lack of strength increase throws a greater burden on those fibers located closer to the neutral axis. These interior fibers find that they must produce restraining stresses at a rate faster than their ordinary rate. The effect of this increased burden placed on the interior fibers is to *warp* the linear stress distribution (Fig. 7-32) to the extent that at the ultimate load it may assume, when the deformation is great, a double rectangle shape (Fig. 7-33a).

The resisting moment corresponding to this stress condition (Fig. 7-33b) acting on a rectangular section is equal to

$$M_u = s_u \times \frac{bd}{2} \times \frac{d}{2}$$

Figure 7-32

(a)

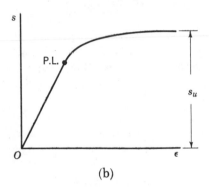

(b)

Figure 7-33

which when multiplied, top and bottom, by $1.5d/2$ becomes

$$M_u = 1.5 \frac{s_u}{c} \times \frac{bd^3}{12} = 1.5 \frac{s_u I}{c}$$

But $M_u = \frac{s_r I}{c}$. Therefore,

$$s_r = 1.5 s_u$$

It is thus apparent that the use of the flexure formula with the ultimate bending moment necessitates the use of a fictitious modulus of rupture which, for rectangular sections, is approximatley 1.5 times the more probable ultimate bending stress. It is also apparent that, as the shape of the cross section changes, the factor 1.5 will also change.

The use of the modulus of rupture. The modulus of rupture is used to determine the maximum carrying capacity of beams. It is also used to compare the strengths of similarly shaped sections. When attempts are made to compare sections of dissimilar shape, appreciable error may be involved if the sections are not symmetrical to the neutral axis. Such sections usually attain their tensile and compressive proportional stresses at different times, shifting their neutral axis and making a comparison of strengths impossible.

7-12. *The resisting moment during yield*

Plastic hinge. A beam made of a structural material having a definite yield range similar to that of low-carbon structural steel will develop, on a cross section whose fibers have all commenced yielding, a rectangular stress pattern similar to that developed at its ultimate strength (Fig. 7-33). This moment may be, and often is, considered as its *maximum useful moment* and *for a beam of rectangular cross section* is given as

$$M_p = 1.5 \, \frac{s_y I}{c} = 1.5 \, M_y$$

It is often called the *plastic moment* for it is developed while the entire section on which it acts is yielding and performing as a *plastic hinge*. For beams of other cross section, constants other than 1.5, called *shape* or *form factors*, are used to give the plastic moment. For instance, the average shape factor of WF shapes is 1.14.

The shape factor is a measure of one of the sources of reserve strength in a beam. The consideration of this reserve strength forms an important part of limit or plastic design presented in § 9-20.

PROBLEMS

7-36. A 2 by 4-in. beam 4 ft long is broken in flexure by a central load of 2000 lb acting on its 2-in: face. What is the modulus of rupture?

7-37. Flashboards are to be placed at the crest of a hydroelectric power dam. They are to be supported by nominal 3-in. diameter extra-strong pipe ($I_{x-x} = 3.894$ in.^{4}; outside diameter = 3.5 in.) placed 3 ft apart. How high should these flashboards be made if they are intended to collapse at the time the water just reaches their top? Modulus of rupture is 70,000 psi. *Answer:* 7.45 ft.

7-38. In the previous problem, what spacing of the 3-in. diameter pipe would be necessary if the flashboards were to be made 5 ft high?

7-39. A cast-iron flexure test bar is 1.2 in. in diameter and rests on supports placed 18 in. apart. If the central load at the moment of rupture is 2000 lb, determine the modulus of rupture. *Answer:* 53,000 psi.

7-13. *Shearing stresses in beams*

Rectangular beams. In addition to an internal resisting moment (C-T couple) acting on every section of a simple beam, there is generally present an internal shear force, V. In the preceding articles of this chapter, no account was taken of the effect of shear in the designs of beams. Because it may be the controlling feature, the design of a beam must be considered incomplete without a thorough investigation of its effects.

If a 4 by 6-in. beam standing on edge were to be sawed longitudinally into 6 boards 1 in. thick and 4 in. wide, and then loaded in its reassembled condition, the beam would sag and cause the individual boards to slide over each other (Fig. 7-34c and d). The evidence of sliding is made apparent from an inspection of end sections mn and op. Originally, these two sections were perfectly flat (Fig. 7-34a and b). They would have remained so had not the beam been cut. Since cutting did take place, the various portions of the beam readjusted their relative positions. Top section m_2o_2, having previously been subjected to compression, elongated when cut from the remainder of the beam. Obviously, the stresses that had restrained the section from sliding when in its original form had been released. Section n_2p_2, having been previously in tension, contracted when severed from the original beam. Again, this adjustment accompanied the release of resistance stresses present on the sliding plane before cutting took place. Since each of the boards slid by its adjacent section, the resistance offered by the original beam on these sliding planes must have been of a shearing nature.

Figure 7-34

The horizontal shearing stresses just discussed act on every horizontal plane of the original beam for each such plane is a potential sliding surface. A further study of their development and variation throughout a beam, as well as the vertical shearing stresses with which they are intimately connected, take place in the following derivation.

Derivation. Let us consider the simple rectangular beam shown in Fig. 7-35 loaded by a concentrated load P. As the full effect of this load takes place, sections 1 and 2 are acted upon by internal-resisting moments M_1 and M_2 and vertical shearing forces V_1 and V_2, respectively. Endeavoring to analyze the stress condition in the beam, let us cut a free body, a rectangular prism $(ABED\text{-}HJKL)$, out of the top portion of the beam.

On the exposed sides of this free body act longitudinal compression stresses developed by the internal moments M_1 and M_2. Since M_1 and M_2 are not the same (see moment diagram Fig. 7-35a), the maximum compressive stresses, s and s', are also different, s being larger than s'. Acting on

Figure 7-35

either side of the free body on the small elementary areas da are the general stresses s_y and s'_y situated a distance y from the neutral axis. The product of these stresses times the area on which they act, $s_y \, da$ and $s'_y \, da$, give the force acting on each elementary area. Since each of the side areas $ABJH$ and $DEKL$ of the free body contain many such elementary areas, each with its own individual force, the total or resultant forces R and R' acting on these two sides will be equal to the addition of all the individual forces. Hence,

$$R = \int_m^c s_y \, da$$

$$R' = \int_m^c s'_y \, da$$

Since R and R' are unequal, there is obviously an additional force acting on the free body to produce equilibrium. This additional force must act on the only remaining internal plane previously in contact with the original beam (plane $HJKL$). Because this plane is horizontal and the required force must also be horizontal, the stresses induced must be shear stresses.

If the average shear stress on plane $HJKL$ equals s_s, the total force $s_s b \, dx$ must be equal to the difference in the resultant forces R and R'. Thus, we may write

$$R - R' = \int_m^c s_y \, da - \int_m^c s'_y \, da = s_s b \, dx$$

But, since
$$\frac{s_y}{y} = \frac{s}{c} \quad \text{and} \quad \frac{s'_y}{y} = \frac{s'}{c}$$

we may write
$$\int_m^c \frac{s}{c} y \, da - \int_m^c \frac{s'}{c} y \, da = s_s b \, dx$$

Because the ratios s/c and s'/c are included in the force acting on every elementary area, they are constants and may be written outside of the integral signs.

$$\frac{s}{c} \int_m^c y \, da - \frac{s'}{c} \int_m^c y \, da = s_s b \, dx$$

or
$$\frac{s - s'}{c} \int_m^c y \, da = s_s b \, dx$$

Substituting $s = Mc/I$ and $s' = M'c/I$, we obtain
$$\frac{M - M'}{I} \int_m^c y \, da = s_s b \, dx$$

However, the value of $M - M'$ is equal to the change of moment over the infinitesimally small distance dx, and is represented by dM. By substituting and rearranging, the equation becomes

$$s_s = \frac{dM}{dx} \times \frac{1}{Ib} \int y \, da$$

Recalling from Chapter 6 that
$$\frac{dM}{dx} = V$$

and from the study of Mechanics that
$$\int_m^c y \, da = \bar{y} \int_m^c da = a\bar{y} \Big]_m^c$$

the moment of the area between m and c about the neutral axis, we may write the equation in its final form

$$s_s = \frac{V}{Ib} a\bar{y} \tag{7.6}$$

where s_s = horizontal shearing unit stress on any very narrow strip passing crosswise through a beam, V = the total internal-shearing force acting on the vertical plane passing through point where s_s is desired (obtained from shear diagram), I = moment of inertia of section of beam passing through point where s_s is desired, b = width of beam at point where s_s is desired, a = area of section located between the closest extreme fiber and the strip on which s_s is desired, $\bar{y}$ = distance from the neutral axis to the center of gravity of area a.

A further discussion of this formula may best be directed toward the solution of an illustrative problem.

Figure 7-36

Illustrative Problem 9. Determine the horizontal shearing unit stress at point 0, 2, 4, and 6 in. above the neutral axis on section *A-A* of the beam shown in Fig. 7-36. The beam is 6 in. wide and 12 in. deep.

SOLUTION. The total shear V acting on section *A-A* (just to the right of R_1) is equal to 5.9 kips.

The moment of inertia of the section about the neutral axis is equal to

$$I = \tfrac{1}{12}bd^3 = \tfrac{1}{12} \times 6 \times 12^3 = 864 \text{ in.}^4$$

Figure 7-37

The values of $\bar{y}$ and a for each of the four points at which the horizontal shear stress is desired are shown in Fig. 7-37 and are tabulated as follows:

ABOVE NEUTRAL AXIS

0 in. . . . . $a = 36$ sq. in.
                                                                                                $\bar{y} = 3$ in.
2 in. . . . . $a = 24$ sq. in.
                                                                                                $\bar{y} = 4$ in.
4 in. . . . . $a = 12$ sq. in.
                                                                                                $\bar{y} = 5$ in.
6 in. . . . . $a = 0$ sq. in.
                                                                                                $\bar{y} = $ meaningless

The values of the horizontal shearing unit stress at each of these four points can now be found by substituting the correct value in the shear equation just derived.

ABOVE NEUTRAL AXIS

0 in. . . . . $s_s = \dfrac{5.9 \times 1000}{864 \times 6} \times 36 \times 3$
                                                                          $= 123$ psi

2 in. . . . . $s_s = \dfrac{5.9 \times 1000}{864 \times 6} \times 24 \times 4$
                                                                          $= 109.2$ psi

4 in. . . . . $s_s = \dfrac{5.9 \times 1000}{864 \times 6} \times 12 \times 5$

$$= 68.3 \text{ psi}$$

6 in. . . . . $s_s = 0$, since $a = 0$

Plotting these values on a graph, we obtain a parabolic curve as shown by Fig. 7-38. Had the values of shearing unit stress been obtained for the corresponding points below the neutral axis, we should have found correspondingly equal magnitudes. By completing the curve, it will be noted that the maximum value of horizontal shearing unit stress occurs on the neutral plane, where $a\bar{y}$ is a maximum and the bending stresses are equal to zero.

Figure 7-38. Values are in psi.

7-14. Expression for maximum shearing stress in rectangular beams

Because of its frequent use in design, an expression for the maximum horizontal shearing stress occurring in rectangular beams may be derived from Eq. 7.6.

$$(s_s)_{\text{max.}} = \frac{V}{Ib} a\bar{y}$$

$$= \frac{V}{\frac{1}{12}bd^3 b} \times \frac{bd}{2} \times \frac{d}{4}$$

$$= \frac{3V}{2bd} = \frac{3}{2}\frac{V}{A} \qquad (7.7)$$

where A is the entire cross-sectional area of the beam.

Thus, the maximum horizontal shearing stress for Illustrative Problem 9 might have been computed thus:

$$(s_s)_{\text{max.}} = \frac{3}{2}\frac{V}{A}$$

$$= \frac{3}{2}\frac{5.9 \times 1000}{6 \times 12} = 123 \text{ psi}$$

7-15. Relationship between vertical and horizontal shearing stresses

In Chapter 5, there was developed a primary law of strength of materials concerning the relationship of the shearing stresses acting at any point on a loaded body. The law stated that "if a plane passing through a point in a body has acting upon it a shearing unit stress, there must be simultaneously induced a shearing unit stress of like magnitude on a plane perpendicular to it." Thus, in our computation of the horizontal shearing stress at any point in a beam, the value obtained applies equally well to the magnitude of the vertical shearing unit stress occurring at the same point.

Because of the similarity in magnitude of the horizontal and vertical shearing unit stresses and because the horizontal as well as the vertical shearing stress varies parabolically with a maximum value of $1.5V/A$ occurring at the neutral surface, it is apparent that the vertical shearing stress given by the equation

$$s_s = \frac{V}{A}$$

where A is the total area of the cross section, is merely an average unit stress acting on a vertical cross section.

7-16. Shear stresses in I beams

Beams made of standard structural shapes that are symmetrical to the plane of loading and whose boundaries are either perpendicular or parallel to this same plane have horizontal shear stresses which may be assumed to be uniformly distributed across the width of the beam. The derivation of the shear stress equation is based upon this assumption which permits its use in the determination of shear stress on I- and WF-beam sections.

Inasmuch as the magnitude of the induced shearing stress varies inversely with the thickness or breadth of the section, it is to be expected that the shearing unit stress in the flanges should be small. Conversely, the shearing unit stress in the web should be relatively high. Multiplying the shear stress in the flange and in the web by their respective areas, it is noted that by far the greater percentage of the shearing resistance is developed in the web. In common practice, therefore, the shearing resistance of an I beam is assumed to be taken by the web only. The approximate shearing unit stress computed on this basis will then be equal to

$$(s_s)_{\text{av.}} = \frac{V}{td} \tag{7.8}$$

where t = thickness of web and d = depth of I beam.

A comparison of the exact and approximate methods of shear-stress determination on an I-beam section will be made in the following problem.

Illustrative Problem 10. Determine the shear-stress distribution curve for the I-beam section shown in Fig. 7-39 by the exact and approximate methods. $V = 20,000$ lb.

SOLUTION. *Moment of inertia.*

$$I = \tfrac{1}{12} \times 5 \times \overline{14^3} = \quad 1142$$
$$-2 \times \tfrac{1}{12} \times 2 \times \overline{12^3} = -576$$
$$= \overline{\quad 566} \text{ in.}^4$$

Values of $a\bar{y}$. Rather than obtain the values of a and $\bar{y}$ separately, it will be easier to determine their product from its equal $\Sigma \Delta ay$. Pertinent cross-sectional areas are shown in Fig. 7-40.

The values of $a\bar{y}$ will be determined at the following positions measured from the neutral axis — 0 in. (at the neutral axis), 2 in., 4 in., 6— in. (just under the flange but in the web), and 6+ in. (just inside the flange).

At the neutral axis:

$$\Sigma \Delta ay = 5 \times 6.5 = 32.5$$
$$= 6 \times 3.0 = \underline{18.0}$$
$$a\bar{y} = \overline{50.5} \text{ in.}^4$$

Figure 7-39

At 2 in. above the neutral axis:

$$\Sigma \Delta ay = 5 \times 6.5 = 32.5$$
$$= 4 \times 4.0 = \underline{16.0}$$
$$a\bar{y} = \overline{48.5} \text{ in.}^3$$

Figure 7-40

At 4 in. above the neutral axis:

$$\Sigma \Delta ay = 5 \times 6.5 = 32.5$$
$$= 2 \times 5.0 = \underline{10.0}$$
$$a\bar{y} = \overline{42.5} \text{ in.}^3$$

At 6— in. above the neutral axis:

$$\Sigma \Delta ay = a\bar{y} = 5 \times 6.5 = 32.5 \text{ in.}^3$$

At 6+ in. above the neutral axis:

$$\Sigma \Delta ay = a\bar{y} = 5 \times 6.5 = 32.5 \text{ in.}^3$$

Values of shearing unit stress.

EXACT METHOD

At neutral axis:

$$s_s = \frac{20,000}{566 \times 1 \text{ in.}} \times 50.5 = 1785 \text{ psi}$$

At 2 in. above neutral axis:

$$s_s = \frac{20,000}{566 \times 1 \text{ in.}} \times 48.5 = 1715 \text{ psi}$$

At 4 in. above neutral axis:

$$s_s = \frac{20,000}{566 \times 1 \text{ in.}} \times 42.5 = 1500 \text{ psi}$$

At 6− in. above neutral axis:

$$s_s = \frac{20,000}{566 \times 1 \text{ in.}} \times 32.5 = 1150 \text{ psi}$$

At 6+ in. above neutral axis:

$$s_s = \frac{20,000}{566 \times 5 \text{ in.}} \times 32.5 = 230 \text{ psi}$$

APPROXIMATE METHOD

$$s_s = \frac{V}{td} = \frac{20,000}{1 \text{ in.} \times 14 \text{ in.}} = 1430 \text{ psi}$$

By plotting the values obtained, we may draw the shear-stress distribution curves shown in Fig. 7-41.

Figure 7-41

The proportion of the shear resistance taken by the flanges, assuming a straight-line variation of stress from the inside to the outside fibers, is

$$V_f = \tfrac{1}{2} \times 230 \times 1 \times 5 \times 2 = 1150 \text{ lb}$$

$$\text{Per cent shear} = \frac{1150}{20,000} \times 100 = 5.74 \text{ per cent}$$

PROBLEMS

7-40a, b, c, d. Determine the maximum horizontal shearing unit stress in each of the beams shown in Fig. 6-11. Use I beams selected on basis of allowable flexure stress of 20,000 psi.

7-41a, b, c, d, e, f, g, h. Determine the maximum horizontal shearing unit stress for the beams shown in Fig. 6-22. Use American Standard timber sections designed on basis of 1200 psi flexural stress.

7-42. A timber beam 6 in. wide, 12 in. deep, and 12 ft long is supported at its ends and carries a concentrated load of 12,000 lb at its mid-point. Compute the horizontal shearing unit stresses at 2-in. intervals from the neutral axis on the most critical shear section. *Answer:* On N.A.: 125 psi, 2 in. above: 111.2 psi, 4 in. above: 69.5 psi.

7-43. Determine the average and exact maximum shearing unit stress in a 15-ft steel beam having a cross section shown in Fig. 7-42 and loaded uniformly with 1000 lb per ft.

Figure 7-42   Figure 7-43

7-44. An airplane spar is made as shown in Fig. 7-43. What is the maximum shearing unit stress on this section if V is 2600 lb? *Answer:* 228 psi.

7-45. Two 6 by 6-in. beams are bolted together to form one beam 6 in. wide, 12 in. deep, and 10 ft long. If the bolts are placed 4 in. apart in one row and the beam is loaded with a concentrated load at the center to cause a maximum flexural stress of 1800 psi, what is the total shearing force on one bolt?

7-46. If a rectangular cross-sectioned simple beam is loaded at its center with a concentrated load and is 6 in. in width and d in. in depth, compute the critical length above which flexure governs and below which shear is the controlling factor. *Answer:* $d = 2ls_s/s$.

7-47. A beam having the cross section shown in Fig. 7-44 is 18 ft long and is freely supported at points 4 ft from either end. It carries a uniformly distributed load of 1000 lb per ft. Find the intensity of the maximum shear stress. *Answer:* 228 psi.

Figure 7-44   Figure 7-45

7-17. Shear center

A prismatic beam subjected to bending will twist about its longitudinal axis (Fig. 7-45) whenever the internally developed shear forces produce an unbalanced moment about that axis. To overcome such undesirable twisting action, the resultant of the bending forces should pass through the *shear center*. Where this is done, the twisting moment created by the internal shear forces is balanced by an equal and oppositely directed moment created by the applied forces.

7-18. Analysis of internal shear forces — I beam

In order to firmly establish the basic principles upon which the concept of a shear center rests, let us analyze the development of the internal shear forces in a horizontal I beam acted upon by vertical forces passing through the centroidal axis of its cross sections (Fig. 7-46). Note first that the maximum flexural stresses developed by such forces vary in magnitude from section to section in accordance with the variation of the moment diagram. Second, the variation of the flexure stresses acting on two arbitrarily selected cross sections located dx distance apart is proportional to the distance from the neutral axis and is indicated by the dash lines shown on Fig. 7-46(c). Consider now the four free bodies, E, F, G, and H, taken from the flanges of the I beam, each Δs in width. Because of the difference in the flexure stresses over the dx distance, the longitudinally directed normal forces in these free bodies differ by the amount dT or dC. To insure equilibrium in the longitudinal direction, these free bodies must have acting on those planes parallel to the vertical plane of symmetry an oppositely directed *shear force* equal to dT or dC. The free bodies are still not balanced, however, because the longitudinal forces are not collinear and produce couples equal to $\frac{1}{2}(dT \times \Delta s)$ or $\frac{1}{2}(dC \times \Delta s)$. To complete the balance of the

Figure 7-46

free body, lateral shear forces V_F are developed in the flanges, the moment of which equals that of the longitudinal forces. It is the development of these laterally directed shear forces that initiates the concept of a shear center.

It is to be noted that each V_F force varies directly with the Δs distance used. It will have a value of zero at the tip of the flange and a maximum value at the junction of the flange and web. The vertical shear force acting on the web varies parabolically as proved in § 7-15 (see Fig. 7-41).

In Fig. 7-46(d) are shown the location and direction of the shear forces acting on either side of the elementary portion of the I beam. Because the V_F forces on the opposite sides of each flange area act in opposing directions and are equal to each other, perfect balance is obtained in the horizontal direction. Furthermore, the moments of these V_F forces acting on either cross section about any point in their plane are in perfect balance.

To insure the continuance of this perfect balance of shear forces (which is synonymous to saying that we will have no twisting action), the force P acting on the beam must act in the vertical plane of symmetry. To do otherwise would produce a moment about the longitudinal axis which could be equalized only by the development of further shear forces.

7-19. Shear forces on a section unsymmetrical about the vertical axis

Suppose now, the left side of each flange were to be removed, changing the I cross section to that of a channel, Fig. 7-46(e). Assuming the flexural stresses to remain the same (by reducing the load P) the shearing forces would not be altered and would act in the same direction. The shear forces in the flanges, however, because of dissymmetry, would no longer be in balance and would produce a moment twisting the beam.

Figure 7-47. Rotation of force P acts through centroid instead of shear center.

7-20. *Shear center-channel section*

This twisting action can easily be overcome, however, by offsetting the load P from the center line of the web a distance e so that its moment about a point on that center line will equal the moments of the induced shear forces (Fig. 7-47). The balance of the forces involved is shown most clearly on Fig. 7-48, where the force P is resolved into a force and a couple, P_1 and PP_2. Mathematically, the rotational balance is expressed by the equation

$$Pe = 2V_F h \tag{7.9}$$

where V_F is the uniformly varying shear force acting on each flange section and h is the distance
between them. The resolved direct force P_1 is restrained by the two web shears V_w, each equal to
$P/2$. The value of e is written most advantageously in terms of the dimension and physical
constants of the cross section as follows:

$$e = \frac{2V_F h}{P} \tag{7.10}$$

$$V_F = \tfrac{1}{2}s_s \times b \times t$$

But in § 7-12, the value of shearing stress in a
beam was found to be

$$s_s = \frac{V}{It} a\bar{y}$$

where the width of the area under shear has been
made equal to t in order to coincide with the presentation now being considered.

Figure 7-48

Substituting the last two equations into Eq. 7.10 there is obtained

$$e = \frac{\left(\dfrac{V}{It} a\bar{y}\right)bth}{P}$$

But $V = P/2$ and $a\bar{y}$ for shear stress at the junction of the flange and web
is equal to $bt \times h/2$. Further substitution yields

$$e = \frac{1}{4}\frac{b^2 h^2 t}{I} \tag{7.11}$$

Were the same beam to be loaded along the horizontal axis of symmetry,
balance between the shear forces would be obtained and no twisting would
result. The intersection of this axis of symmetry and the vertical line, on
which the load would have to be applied to overcome twisting, locates the

shear center. A load passing through this point on the beam would not produce a tendency to twist.

The value of I for a channel, if its thickness is small and uniform, may
be written as

$$I =_, 2bt\left(\frac{h}{2}\right)^2 + \frac{t \times h^3}{12} = \frac{th^2}{4}\left(2b + \frac{h}{3}\right) \qquad (7.12)$$

Placing this value in Eq. 7.11 gives

$$e = \frac{b^2}{2b + (h/3)} = \frac{b}{2 + (h/3b)} \qquad (7.13)$$

It is important to note that Eq. 7.13 is independent of the method
of loading or type of beam, i.e., simple cantilever, continuous. It consists of
dimensional values only and is a constant for any channel section. It
further reveals that e for a channel will never be greater than one half of the
width of the flange.

7-21. Shear center of angle cross section

An analysis similar to that used for the channel is employed for determining the shear center of an angle cross section. Let an angle be loaded as
a simple beam with its flanges tilted with respect to the horizontal (Fig.
7-49). By taking progressively larger free bodies from the legs of the angle,

Figure 7-49. All externally applied loads must pass through point
O to prevent twisting.

it is noted that the shear forces vary directly with the distance to the tips
and travel along the legs of the cross section from one end to the other.
Because the shear forces in the legs intersect at O, their moment about this
joint is zero. An applied force acting through point O will also have a zero
moment. There being a perfect balance between the moments of the external and internal forces, no twisting will occur. Point O is, therefore, the
shear center of the angle.

7-22. *Shear center — other rolled sections*

From previous statements made concerning the development of internal shearing forces, it follows that shear on any structural cross section which might be made by bending a single thin plate (i.e., a channel, Z beam, etc.)
flows from one end to the other without reversing itself. The flow of shear in a Z section, for example, is continuous, the direction of shear in each flange being the same (Fig. 7-50). If the flanges are of the same length, each will have the same shear force, and produce equal but opposite moments about the center of the web. Should the applied force pass through this point, no matter how directed, it could produce no twisting.

Figure 7-50

Frequently a beam cross section, consisting of two or more thin rectangular portions placed at right angles to one another, is formed in the shape of T, H, etc. with one axis of symmetry. If loads are applied perpendicular to the plane of symmetry, the internal shear force will be concentrated in the vertical portions of the cross section and directed parallel to their long axis. Any horizontal portion located on the neutral axis where the flexure stresses are zero has an insignificant amount of shear induced in it. The shear center of a T section is, therefore, located at the junction of the two sections (Fig. 7-51). That for the H section is located at the centroid of the shear forces, where

$$V_1 h_1 = V_2 h_2 \qquad (7.14)$$

Because both flanges have the same radius of curvature while being bent, their flexure stresses will reveal the same variation from the neutral axis. Thus $s_1/c_1 = s_2/c_2$. If now the flexure formulas $s_1 = M_1 c_1/I_1$ and $s_2 = M_2 c_2/I$ are substituted, there results

$$\frac{M_1}{I_1} = \frac{M_2}{I_2}$$

where M_1, I_1, and M_2, I_2 refer to the left and right-hand flanges respectively (Fig. 7-52).

Figure 7-51

Figure 7-52

Because $M_1 = V_1 x_1$ and $M_2 = V_2 x_1$, the previous equation may be modified to read

$$\frac{V_1}{I_1} = \frac{V_2}{I_2} \tag{7.15}$$

Substituting V_1 and V_2 with h_1 and h_2 from Eq. 7.14 yields the relationship

$$\frac{h_1}{h_2} = \frac{I_1}{I_2} \tag{7.16}$$

7-23. Shear center — solid sections

The exact location of the shear center of a solid cross section is much more difficult to find than those for the sections previously discussed. The reason for this difficulty is due mainly to the variation of the shear stresses in both direction and magnitude. For example, in a simple beam of solid *circular* cross section, it is impossible to apply the shear stress equations $s_s = \dfrac{V}{Ib}\, a\bar{y}$ to the determination of its shear center without introducing considerable error. The error is introduced where the assumption of a uniformly distributed horizontal shear stress made in its derivation is found to be in disagreement with actual conditions in a cylindrical beam. To have the assumed uniform distribution of horizontal shear would require the vertical shear on the abutting vertical section to be uniformly distributed also, and furthermore directed vertically. Thus the vertical shear stress at each end of a horizontal plane located a distance y from the neutral axis would have a component perpendicular to the circular periphery. To restrain this component stress would require the application of a resisting shear to the surface of the cylinder. Because this is an impossibility it can be deduced that the shear stress on a vertical section of a cylindrical beam can neither be uniformly distributed nor directed vertically. Instead, it will form a converging symmetrical pattern (Fig. 7-53)

Figure 7-53. Shear vector must act parallel to the surface, not vertically (except at A and B).

about the vertical axis of symmetry, the shear flowing tangentially at the periphery of the cross section. Because of the nonuniform pattern of the shear on the vertical section, it follows that the horizontal shear on any horizontal plane y distance from the neutral axis will also be nonuniformly distributed.

It is easy to see after this discussion that to find the shear center of any solid cross section is a difficult task. A complete analysis of this subject is beyond the scope of this text.

If, however, an axis of symmetry does exist, it is evident that the shear center will be in this axis. Furthermore, if two axes of symmetry exist, the shear center will be located at their intersection. The shear center of the circular cross section, previously discussed, will therefore be located at its centroid.

PROBLEMS

7-48. Locate the shear center of the channel sections shown in Fig. 7-54. Use Eq. 7.11, 7.12 or 7.13 or modification thereof to obtain the most accurate solution possible. *Answers:* (a) 1.00 in., (b) 0.40 in., (c) 0.65 in., (d) 2.88 in.

(a)   (b)   (c)   (d)

Figure 7-54

7-49. Draw a curve showing the change in location of the shear center as the flanges of the channel shown in Fig. 7-54(a) vary in length. Use Eq. 7.13.

7-50. Draw a curve showing the change in location of the shear center as the web of the channel shown in Fig. 7-54(a) changes in thickness. Use Eq. 7.12.

7-51. Determine the shear center of the cross section shown in Fig. 7-55. *Answer:* 10.25 in.

Figure 7-55

Chapter Eight

THE DEFLECTIONS OF STATICALLY
DETERMINATE BEAMS

8-1. *The reason for finding deflections*

Quite frequently, the design of a beam is governed by the amount of its permissible deflection. For example, beams that carry plaster ceilings are generally limited to a deflection of $\frac{1}{360}$ of their length. To exceed this value would encourage the formation of cracks. Various parts of accurate metal-shaping equipment, such as milling machines, lathes, boring tools, and so forth, would, if designed solely on the basis of strength, fail to function properly. The resulting deflections would allow distortions of such magnitude as to make precision work an impossibility.

8-2. *Fundamental considerations in determining deflections*

As previously revealed, a loaded beam must bend. The degree of bending thus incurred varies with the intensity of the internal stresses produced. Because shear and flexure stresses are generally present on every cross section of a beam, both contribute to its deflection. Except for short stubby beams, however, the deflection due to shearing stresses is so small that it is ordinarily neglected. This discussion of the deflection of loaded beams will, therefore, include only that portion produced by flexure stresses.

8-3. *Determination of the radius of curvature of a beam*

When a beam deflects, the vertical projection of the neutral plane assumes a curved position, which is known as the *elastic curve*. The radius of curvature at any point on the elastic curve is equal to the radius of that circle whose circumference conforms to the shape of the elastic curve at that point.

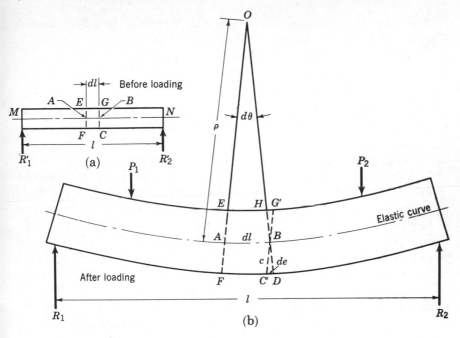

Figure 8-1

In the beam of Fig. 8-1, the length dl represents a minute portion of the elastic curve included in an imaginary circle of which OA and OB are radii. Prior to loading, the beam was straight, and cross sections EF and GC were parallel to each other and perpendicular to the longitudinal axis of the beam (Fig. 8-1a). When the loads were applied, section GC rotated with respect to section EF and assumed the position HD. During this rotation, sections EF and HD remained perpendicular to the elastic curve.

Line $G'C'$ drawn parallel to EF locates, therefore, the terminal position of the fibers included in the dl section before bending took place. The small triangles $HG'B$ and $BC'D$ represent the deformation of the fibers that took place during the bending of the beam.

Considering, now, the similar triangles OAB and $BC'D$, we may write the following proportion

$$\frac{de}{dl} = \frac{BC'}{OA}$$

But de/dl is equal to the unit strain ϵ incurred in fiber FC' while elongating to length FD. Moreover BC' equals c by observation, and OA equals ρ, the radius of curvature at A and B. Inserting these values in the equation above, we obtain

$$\epsilon = \frac{c}{\rho} \qquad (8.1)$$

The value of ϵ is also equal to s/E from our study in axially loaded members, and from the flexure equation, $c = sI/M$.

The substitution of these values in Eq. 8.1 yields

$$\frac{1}{\rho} = \frac{M}{EI} \tag{8.2}$$

where ρ = radius of curvature, in inches, M = bending moment at sections where ρ is desired, in in.-lb, E = modulus of elasticity, in psi, I = moment of inertia, in in.[4]

This equation is known as the *elastic-curve equation expressed in terms of the radius of curvature*. Besides being a basic equation in the development of deflection formulas, it has considerable value in analyzing moment-deflection relationships. For instance, if a beam of uniform cross section (I being constant) made of a homogeneous material (E being constant) were to have a constant value of bending moment M applied to any portion of its length, the value of ρ for such a portion would have to be a constant value, and because a constant value of ρ pertains to the radius of a circular curve, the elastic curve of each constant moment section must be a circular segment (Fig. 8-2). On the other hand, any portion of the

Figure 8-2

Figure 8-3. The resisting moment at each point on the ring equals M_0.

member bent into a circular curve would necessarily be subjected to a constant bending moment. For instance, if a steel band-saw blade were bent into a circular curve as shown in Fig. 8-3, the bending moment at every section would be equal. A special case to consider in this discussion is that obtained when $M = 0$, i.e., in the development of an *inflection point* (§ 6-12). Here the value of ρ equals infinity and indicates that the beam is perfectly straight at that point.

PROBLEMS

In the following problems, $E = 30 \times 10^6$ psi for steel.

8-1. A high-strength steel wire $\frac{1}{8}$ in. in diameter is coiled on a drum 4 ft in diameter. What is the extreme fiber unit stress in this wire?

8-2. A piece of spring steel $\frac{1}{2}$ in. thick, 1 in. wide, and 20 ft long is bent and fastened alongside a piece of circular track having a radius of 15 ft. If the 1-in. side is placed against the track, what is the maximum flexural stress in the steel? *Answer:* 41,700 psi.

8-3. A band saw blade $\frac{1}{16}$ in. thick and 1 in. wide moves on the periphery of a circular pulley 24 in. in diameter. What is the maximum flexural stress in the saw blade?

8-4. What value of I would the steel beam in Fig. 8-4 require to maintain its center portion at a radius of 500 ft? Of what importance is the induced maximum flexural stress to the computations of this problem? *Answer:* 48 in.[4]

Figure 8-4

8-4. *The double integration method of finding slopes and deflections*

A classical method for determining slopes and deflections of loaded beams is the double integration method   Its basic equation is derived from the elastic curve equation expressed in terms of the radius of curvature.

Figure 8-5

In a slightly more detailed drawing of Fig. 8-1, shown in Fig. 8-5, *dl* is approximately equal to *dx*. Thus we may write without inducing any appreciable error:

$$dx = dl = \rho \, d\theta, \quad \text{from which} \quad \frac{1}{\rho} = \frac{d\theta}{dx} \tag{8.3}$$

but
$$\theta = \frac{dy}{dx}, \quad \text{making} \quad \frac{d\theta}{dx} = \frac{d^2y}{dx^2} \tag{8.4}$$

By substituting Eq. 8.4 into Eq. 8.3 we obtain

$$\frac{1}{\rho} = \frac{d^2y}{dx^2} \tag{8.5}$$

With further substitution of Eq. 8.5 into the elastic curve equation expressed in terms of the radius of curvature, we get

$$\frac{M}{EI} = \frac{d^2y}{dx^2} \tag{8.6}$$

This equation is known as the *elastic curve equation expressed in rectangular coordinates* and forms the basis of the double integration method. The name of this method is apparent from the fact that two successive integrations of Eq. 8.6 yield the equation of the elastic curve in x and y. From this equation the exact deflection at any point x along that portion of the beam for which M is applicable can be obtained by substituting the value of x and solving for y.

In a similar manner the slope of the elastic curve at any point along this portion of the beam can be obtained from its value of dy/dx produced after one integration.

Illustrative Problem 1. Determine the slope and deflection equations for the simple beam shown in Fig. 8-6 having a concentrated load at its center.

Figure 8-6

SOLUTION. Because the x and y axes were chosen as indicated, d^2y/dx^2 will be positive as x increases. The bending moment equation for any point on the left-hand side of the beam can be expressed as

$$M = \frac{P}{2}x$$

When substituted into the elastic curve equation it gives

$$EI \frac{d^2y}{dx^2} = \frac{P}{2}x$$

Integration of this expression yields

$$EI \frac{dy}{dx} = \frac{Px^2}{4} + C_1$$

To obtain the value of C_1, substitute in the foregoing equation simultaneously known values of dy/dx and x occurring on the left-hand portion of the beam.* The only such point on the left-hand portion of the beam is at $x = l/2$ where $dy/dx = 0$.

Inserting these values in the previous equation and solving for C_1 makes C_1 equal to $-Pl^2/16$.

The dy/dx or *slope equation* for the left-hand portion of the beam is then equal to

$$EI \frac{dy}{dx} = \frac{Px^2}{4} - \frac{Pl^2}{16} \tag{8.7}$$

An additional integration gives

$$EIy = \frac{Px^3}{12} - \frac{Pl^2x}{16} + C_2$$

Using the same portion of the beam, the two simultaneously known values of y and x are found at $x = 0$ where y is also equal to zero. Substituting these values into the above equations makes $C_2 = 0$. Hence, *the deflection equation* for the left portion of the beam is

$$EIy = \frac{Px^3}{12} - \frac{P^2x}{16} \tag{8.8}$$

The maximum deflection of the beam occurs at the center where $x = l/2$. Thus, by substituting $l/2$ for x in Eq. 8.8 there results a deflection

$$\Delta = \frac{1}{48} \frac{Pl^3}{EI} \tag{8.9}$$

The deflection at any other point on the left-hand portion of the beam can be determined by inserting its corresponding value of x in terms of l

---

* Only the left-hand portion of the beams may be used in determining C_1, as the initial d^2y/dx^2 equation was formulated from the equation of moment pretaining to that portion of the beam.

into the elastic curve equation. Similarly, the slope at any point can be obtained by inserting corresponding values of x into the general slope equation. For instance, the slope at the quarter point may be obtained by inserting the value of $l/4$ for x in Eq. 8.7, resulting in

$$\left(\frac{dy}{dx}\right)_{l/4} = \theta_{l/4} = \frac{1}{EI}\left[\frac{P}{4}\left(\frac{l}{4}\right)^2 - \frac{Pl^2}{16}\right] = -\frac{3}{64}\frac{Pl^2}{EI} \qquad (8.10)$$

PROBLEMS

8-5. Determine by the double integration method the slope and deflection at the free end of a cantilever beam l ft long loaded uniformly with w lb per ft. Assume E and I constant. *Answers:* $\dfrac{wl^3}{6EI}, \dfrac{wl^4}{8EI}$.

8-6. Determine by double integration the slope and deflection at the free end of a cantilever beam l ft long with a concentrated load P at the free end. Assume E and I constant. *Answers:* $\dfrac{Pl^2}{2EI}, \dfrac{Pl^3}{3EI}$.

8-7. Determine by the double integration method the slope and elastic curve equations for a simple beam uniformly loaded. Also find the maximum deflection. Assume E and I constant.

Answer: $\Delta = \dfrac{5}{384}\dfrac{wl^4}{EI}$.

8-8. In Illustrative Problem 1, determine the exact slope and deflection at a point $\frac{3}{8} l$ from the left support if $P = 10,000$ lb, $l = 10$ ft, and the section used is 10 in. WF 25.4 lb.

8-9. Develop the procedure involved in using the double integration method for finding the elastic curve equation of a simple beam which restrains a concentrated load located off center.

8-5. Important relationships

We have seen the importance of the expressions obtained by the successive integration of the $\dfrac{M}{EI} = \dfrac{d^2y}{dx^2}$ equation. Considerable importance is also attached to the expressions obtained by the *successive differentiation* of the same equation. Thus

$$EI\frac{d^2y}{dx^2} = M$$

by one differentiation $= EI\dfrac{d^3y}{dx^3} = \dfrac{dM}{dx} = V$ \qquad (8.11)

by two differentiations $= EI\dfrac{d^4y}{dx^4} = \dfrac{d^2M}{dx^2} = \dfrac{dV}{dx} = w$ \qquad (8.12) where w is the intensity of the distributed load at the point x distance from the origin.

Although exploitation of these relationships will not be attempted in this book, they are of great use in the study of advanced stress problems.

8-6. Comments on double integration method

The double integration method of obtaining slopes and deflections of beams is academically proficient and is the basis for most of our modern methods of deflection analysis. However, it is cumbersome to use even in dealing with relatively simple practical problems. For this reason, the following pages of this chapter offer a more simple and direct method of obtaining slopes and deflections of beams, namely, the moment-area method.

8-7. The moment-area method of finding slopes and deflections

A simple revision of the elastic curve equation

$$\frac{M}{EI} = \frac{1}{\rho}$$

forms the basis of the *moment-area method* of determining slopes and deflections. Although other methods are available for finding deflections, the simplicity and range of usefulness of the moment-area method makes it one of the most popular.

Derivation. In Fig. 8-7(b) is shown the elastic curve of a loaded beam whose deflection is grossly exaggerated for clarity. An infinitesimal length dl (also shown exaggerated) is laid off on the elastic curve. At its extremities A and B are erected perpendiculars that intersect at point O with an angle $d\theta$. Because of the very small distance between points A and B, the value of ρ and the bending moment M for each point may be considered identical.

In an ordinary beam, the deflections are relatively small and the length of the elastic curve is very nearly equal to its horizontal projection. Thus, the value of dl is, for all practical purposes, equal to its horizontal projection dx, and we may write from our knowledge of radian measurement

$$d\theta = \frac{dx}{\rho}$$

By substituting for ρ its value obtained in the elastic-curve equation $1/\rho = M/EI$ we obtain

$$d\theta = \frac{M}{EI}\,dx \tag{8.13}$$

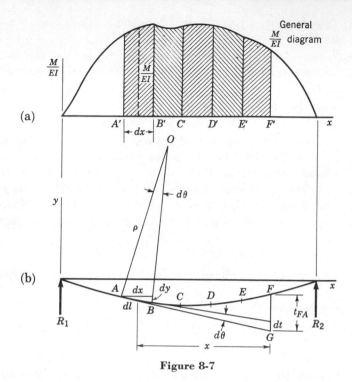

Figure 8-7

Now, $d\theta$ is also equal to the change in slope from A to B by construction. Therefore, if the change in slope from A to B is equal to $(M/EI)dx$, the changes in slope from B to C, C to D, D to E, and E to F are also equal to the same general expression. We may, therefore, sum up these individual changes in curvature to obtain the total change in slope from A to F by writing

$$\int_A^F d\theta = \int_A^F \frac{M}{EI}\, dx \qquad (8.14)$$

This expression could, of course, apply equally well to any other two points.

Proposition 1: Moment-area method for finding slopes. Let us now investigate the expression on the right-hand side of the equation. The value of M is the general expression of bending moment for any dx located between A and F and is obtainable from the bending moment equation applicable to the dx section under consideration. Because of the infinitesimal length of dx, M can be considered a constant value for each such increment.

Equation 8.14 further indicates that each ordinate, M, of the bending-moment diagram is divided by its corresponding value of EI. To simplify the incorporation of this division of M by EI into moment-area problems,

computations are based on the so-called *M/EI diagram*. For a homogeneous, uniform cross-sectioned beam, such a diagram would be reduced in
height when compared to the bending-moment diagram but would retain
exact similarity. Drawn to a new scale EI times the one previously used,
however, would make the *M/EI* diagram identical to the initial moment
curve.

Proceeding further, we note that the product of *M/EI* times the
length over which it occurs, dx, is equivalent to the area of a rectangle
(Fig. 8-7a) and also to the change in slope over dx. If, therefore, every
rectangle of base dx between points A and F were added together, the
total area would be equivalent to the change in slope between the same
limits. Accordingly, we may state as Proposition 1 of the moment-area
method of beam deflection, the following:

*The change in slope expressed in radians between any two points A and B
on a loaded beam is equal to the algebraic sum of the M/EI area between those
two points.*

This proposition may also be expressed for added convenience in terms
of finite values of slope and area:

$$\sum_{A}^{F} \Delta\theta = \sum_{A}^{F} \frac{M}{EI} \Delta x$$

Because most *M/EI* diagrams consist
of rectangles, triangles and parabolic
areas, the areas of which are easily ascertained, the equation above is very
useful.

Illustrative Problem 2. Determine the slope at the free end of the
cantilever beam shown in Fig. 8-8.
Note. Since the fixed end of a cantilever beam is generally considered
horizontal, the terms *slope* and *change
in slope* will be synonymous. $E =$
2×10^6 psi and $I = 100$ in.^{4}

SOLUTION.

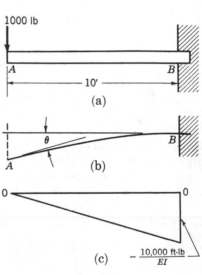

1000 lb

|A
— 10′ —
(a)

θ B
(b)

0   0
(c) $-\frac{10,000 \text{ ft-lb}}{EI}$

Figure 8-8

$$\sum_{A}^{B} \Delta\theta = \theta_A = \sum_{A}^{B} \frac{M}{EI} \Delta x = \frac{10,000 \times 12 \times 10 \times 12}{2 \times 2 \times 10^6 \times 100} = 36 \times 10^{-3}$$

$$= 0.036 \text{ radian}$$

Proposition 2: Moment-area method for finding deflections. Proposition 2 of the moment-area method involves the determination of *tan-*

gential deviations. By definition, *a tangential deviation is the vertical distance between any point A on the elastic curve of a beam and the tangent drawn from any other point B located on the same curve.* It is designated by the letter t with two subscripts: the first indicating the point of tangential deviation, the second the point from which the tangent is drawn. Several illustrations of tangential deviations are shown in Fig. 8-9.

(a)   (b)

Figure 8-9

Referring once again to Fig. 8-7b, let us draw the tangents to points A and B intercepting a vertical line drawn through point F. The intercept dt, located an average distance x from dx, is a small portion of the total distance FG — a tangential deviation at F between points A and F. Because all practical beams suffer no great sag even when stressed to their maximum allowable limit, the length of the sloping tangents just drawn may be set equal to x without incurring any appreciable amount of error. We may, therefore, state through the use of radian measurement that

$$dt = x\, d\theta$$

or, by substituting the equation included in Proposition 1,

$$dt = x\, \frac{M}{EI}\, dx \tag{8.15}$$

Although this expression for dt was derived using the tangents at A and B, it is not difficult to see that it also pertains to any two adjacent points. Thus, if we were to extend other tangents from points C, D, and E on the elastic curve (Fig. 8-7b), the value of each incremental intercept between points G and F would equal the same general expression given in Eq. 8.15. Furthermore, the sum of these individual intercepts would equal the tangential deviation at F taken between A and F. Expressed in equation form, the tangential deviation at F between A and F equals

$$\int_A^F dt = \int_A^F x\frac{M}{EI}\, dx = t_{FA} \qquad (8.16)$$

By scrutinizing this equation carefully, we again recognize the expression $(M/EI)dx$ as the rectangular area used in obtaining Proposition 1. The value of x is the distance between this area and the tangential deviation. The product of the $(M/EI)dx$ area and the value x is, therefore, the moment of an incremental portion of the M/EI diagram taken about the tangential deviation. Thus, the integration of all the products of x and $(M/EI)dx$ indicates that the tangential deviation between A and F is equal to the sum of the moments of the individual $(M/EI)dx$ areas between the limits A and F, taken about FG, the desired tangential deviation. Proposition 2 of the Moment Area Method is therefore expressed as follows:

The tangential deviation at A between any two points A and B on a loaded beam is equal to the algebraic sum of the moments of the M/EI area between these two points taken about point A, i.e., the point where the tangential deviation is desired.

In the solution of ordinary problems, the M/EI diagrams consist of groupings of triangles, rectangles, parabolas and so forth, whose centroids are generally known. Under such circumstances, Eq. 8.16 may be simplified to indicate a finite summation

$$t_{FA} = \sum_A^F \Delta t = \bar{x} \sum_A^F \frac{M}{EI} \Delta x \qquad (8.17)$$

8-8. Signs

When moments of M/EI areas are taken, the sign of the M/EI area under consideration shall be ascribed to its moment. The moment of negative areas shall, therefore, be negative and the moment of positive areas, positive.

It is important to note further that a negative tangential deviation implies a location above the elastic curve and a positive tangential deviation implies a location below the elastic curve.

Illustrative Problem 3. Determine the tangential deviation at the free end of the cantilever beam taken over its entire length — that is, from A to B (see Fig. 8-10). $E = 2 \times 10^6$ psi and $I = 100$ in.[4]

SOLUTION. Taking moments of the M/EI diagram between points A and B about CA — that is, the desired tangential deviation — we obtain

$$t_{AB} = -\frac{10,000 \times 12}{2 \times 10^6 \times 100} \times \frac{10 \times 12}{2} \times 6.67 \times 12 = -2.88 \text{ in.}$$

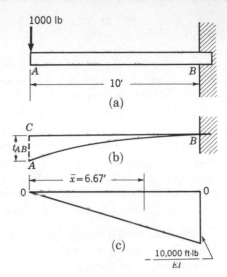

Figure 8-10

But the tangential deviation at the free end of a cantilever taken over its entire length is also equal to its maximum deflection. Thus, we may write

$$\Delta = -2.88 \text{ in.}$$

WARNING. In Illustrative Problems 1, 2 and 3, no account was taken of the stress developed in the beam. Since the flexure equation was used in the development of the elastic-curve equation, all of its assumptions and limitations apply to the moment-area equations. Thus, should the maximum flexural stress exceed the proportional limit stress, the computations of deflection and change in slope would be erroneous.

If the beam in Illustrative Problems 2 and 3 was made of yellow pine and had a depth of 8 in., the maximum flexural stress would be

$$s = \frac{Mc}{I} = \frac{10,000 \times 12 \times 4}{100} = 4800 \text{ psi}$$

Although this value exceeds the usual allowable flexural stress for this type of wood, it does not exceed the proportional limit stress of approximately 7000 psi.

The calculations of the deflection characteristics of the beam are, therefore, within the limitations of the previously derived equations and are theoretically correct.

8-9. *Further instructions on use of Propositions 1 and 2 of moment area*

Proposition 1 of the moment-area method finds its greatest use in determining the slopes at various points on a beam after some point of known slope has been established. In problems entailing cantilever beams and simple beams with symmetrical loadings, the establishment of a known slope is merely a matter of observation. On unsymmetrically loaded beams, however, the establishment of the point of reference slope takes place, generally, at the ends of the beam, or at the point of maximum deflection where the slope is horizontal. In the former case, the slope is established by dividing the tangential deviation between the two ends of the beam by its length. In the latter case, the tangential deviations from the point of zero slope to the ends of the beam are set equal to each other to determine the location of the point of tangency, or zero slope.

The application of Proposition 2 of the moment-area method to beam-deflection problems calls for nothing more than the judicious use of tangential deviations and similar triangles. Although some deflections may be determined directly from a computed tangential deviation, generally the addition or subtraction of tangential deviations and vertical sides of similar triangles is required. This simple procedure, once mastered, affords solutions of deflections for the most difficult problems.

Several of the more classical problems of beam deflection will now be solved to illustrate the use of the moment-area method.

GENERAL APPLICATIONS OF MOMENT-AREA PROPOSITIONS FOR BEAMS SUBJECTED TO CONCENTRATED LOADS

8-10. *Deflection characteristics of a simple beam — concentrated load at center*

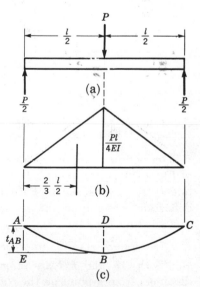

The simple beam shown in Fig. 8-11(a) is acted upon by load P at its mid-point. Its bending-moment diagram is shown in Fig. 8-11(b). Since the load is symmetrically placed, the maximum deflection occurs at the center of the beam.

Maximum deflection. To determine the magnitude of the maximum deflection requires the construction of a tangent to the elastic curve in such a position that will permit its calculation with the fewest number of tangential deviations and similar triangles.

If, therefore, on the elastic curve of the beam shown in Fig. 8-11(c), a tangent is drawn at the point of zero

Figure 8-11

slope — that is, maximum deflection, the intercept AE on the vertical line passing through point A will be equal to the maximum deflection DB. Moreover, AE is also the tangential deviation at A between points A and B. The maximum deflection Δ may thus be found by taking the moment of the M/EI diagram between points A and B about the tangential deviation AE, as indicated in Eq. 8.17.

$$\Delta = t_{AB} = \bar{x} \sum_{A}^{B} \frac{M}{EI} \, \Delta x$$

Since the center of gravity of a triangle is located a distance equal to one-third of its altitude from the base as shown in Fig. 8-12, we may substitute as follows:

$$\Delta = t_{AB} = \frac{2}{3} \times \frac{l}{2} \times \frac{1}{2} \times \frac{Pl}{4EI} \times \frac{l}{2} = \frac{Pl^3}{48EI} \tag{8.18}$$

Figure 8-12. Look at this diagram from the right.

Figure 8-13

Deflection at any point on a beam. The deflection of the beam shown in Fig. 8-13(a) at a point x feet away from the left reaction can be determined in various ways. Perhaps the easiest method of obtaining this deflection is to employ the previous horizontal tangent at B. Thus,

$$y_F = GF = GH - FH$$
$$= AE - FH$$

But both AE and FH are tangential deviations, since they are vertical distances from a point on the elastic curve to a tangent drawn from some other point on the elastic curve. Accordingly, we may write

$y_F = t_{AB} - t_{FB}$ = moment of area JLM about AE
$$- \text{ moment of area } KLMN \text{ about } FH$$

But since

moment of area $KLMN$ = moment of area KLM about FH
$$+ \text{ moment of area } KNM \text{ about } FH$$

y_F = moment of area JLM about AE $-$ moment of area KLM about FH
$$- \text{ moment of area } KNM \text{ about } FH$$

$$y_F = \frac{1}{2} \times \frac{Pl}{4EI} \times \frac{l}{2} \times \frac{2}{3} \times \frac{l}{2} - \frac{1}{2} \times \frac{Pl}{4EI}\left(\frac{l}{2} - x\right)\frac{2}{3}\left(\frac{l}{2} - x\right)$$
$$- \frac{1}{2} \times \frac{Px}{2EI}\left(\frac{l}{2} - x\right)\frac{1}{3}\left(\frac{l}{2} - x\right)$$

$$= \frac{Pl^3}{48EI} - \frac{Pl}{12EI}\left(\frac{l}{2} - x\right)^2 - \frac{Px}{12EI}\left(\frac{l}{2} - x\right)^2$$

$$= \frac{Pl^3}{48EI} - \frac{Pl^3}{48EI} + \frac{Pl^2x}{12EI} - \frac{Plx^2}{12EI} - \frac{Pl^2x}{48EI} + \frac{Plx^2}{12EI} - \frac{Px^3}{12EI}$$

$$= + \frac{1}{16}\frac{Pl^2x}{EI} - \frac{1}{12}\frac{Px^3}{EI} \qquad (8.19)$$

Maximum slope. The greatest slope on the beam is, of course, at the reaction points. Since all slopes are referred to a horizontal datum, we must determine the *change in slope* from the horizontal tangent at the center to the ends of the beam. By Proposition 1, this is equal to the area JLM.

$$\theta_A = \frac{1}{2} \times \frac{Pl}{4EI} \times \frac{l}{2} = \frac{Pl^2}{16EI} \text{ radians} \qquad (8.20)$$

Slope at any point. The slope at any point x distance from the left reaction is equal to the area $KLMN$, since its right-hand boundary is located at the point of tangency of the horizontal tangent.

$$\theta_x = \frac{1}{2}\frac{Pl}{4EI}\left(\frac{l}{2} - x\right) + \frac{1}{2}\frac{Px}{2EI}\left(\frac{l}{2} - x\right)$$

$$= \frac{Pl^2}{16EI} - \frac{Plx}{8EI} + \frac{Plx}{8EI} - \frac{Px^2}{4EI} = \frac{Pl^2}{16EI} - \frac{Px^2}{4EI} \qquad (8.21)$$

8-11. Simple beams — any symmetrical loading

The approach used in the preceding problem may be followed when computing the slopes and deflections of any symmetrically loaded simple beam. Although the M/EI diagram may be more complex and entail more moments of areas than already illustrated, the technique is exactly the same.

8-12. Cantilever beam — concentrated load at free end

Maximum deflection. As previously shown, the maximum deflection is equal to the tangential deviation at the free end taken over the entire length of the beam (Fig. 8-14).

Figure 8-14

$$\Delta = t_{AB} = \text{moment of } M/EI \text{ diagram about } FA$$

$$= -\frac{Pl}{EI} \times \frac{l}{2} \times \frac{2}{3}l = -\frac{Pl^3}{3EI} \qquad (8.22)$$

Deflection at any point. The deflection of this beam at any other point G located x distance from the fixed end is by observation equal to the tangential deviation at G between B and G. Taking the moment of area $CJKE$ or, more conveniently, its component areas CJK and ECK, about HG, we obtain

$$y_G = t_{GB} = \frac{-P(l-x)}{EI} \times \frac{x}{2} \times \frac{x}{3} - \frac{Pl}{EI} \times \frac{x}{2} \times \frac{2}{3}x$$

$$= +\frac{Px^3}{6EI} - \frac{Plx^2}{2EI} = \frac{Px^2}{6EI}(x - 3l) \qquad (8.23)$$

Maximum slope. Stated in general terms, the maximum slope is equal to

$$\theta_A = \text{area } CDE = \frac{-Pl}{EI} \times \frac{l}{2} = -\frac{Pl^2}{2EI} \qquad (8.24)$$

Slope at any point. Finding the slope at any point G requires the determination of the change in slope from the point of horizontal slope B to point G. This is, of course, equal to the area of the M/EI diagram between these two points.

$$\theta_G = \frac{-P(l-x)}{EI} \times \frac{x}{2} - \frac{Pl}{EI} \times \frac{x}{2}$$

$$= \frac{-Plx}{2EI} + \frac{Px^2}{2EI} - \frac{Plx}{2EI} = \frac{Px}{2EI}(x - 2l) \qquad (8.25)$$

8-13. Cantilever beam — any loading

The method of obtaining slopes and deflections of cantilever beams subjected to any loading follows that used in the preceding problem.

8-14. Simple beam — concentrated load not at center

When a concentrated load acts off center on a simple beam, the maximum deflection and point of horizontal slope of the beam are no longer located either at its mid-point or under the concentrated load. In the light of this information, the technique necessary for slope and deflection determinations must be modified.

Deflection under load P. Referring to the beam shown in Fig. 8-15(a), let us obtain the deflection under load P.

Because this deflection, DC, is not by itself a tangential deviation, it must become affiliated with one or more of them in such a way that its solution may be ascertained. The most common method of affiliating tangential deviations with deflections is

Figure 8-15

through the use of similar triangles. Let us, therefore, draw a tangent at A intersecting the verticals passing through points B and D. The deflection DC may then be written as

$$DC = DE - CE$$

But by similar triangles, ADE and ABF,

$$DE = BF \times \frac{a}{l}$$

By substitution, then,

$$DC = BF \times \frac{a}{l} - CE$$

But BF is the tangential deviation, t_{BA}, at B between A and B, and CE is the tangential deviation, t_{CA}, at C between A and C. Thus, it follows that

$$DC = t_{BA} \times \frac{a}{l} - t_{CA} \qquad (8.26)$$

Computing t_{BA}. To compute the value of t_{BA}, the moment of the entire M/EI diagram (that is, between A and B) must be taken about BF. Thus,

$$t_{BA} = \frac{Pab}{EIl} \times \frac{b}{2} \times \frac{2}{3}b + \frac{Pab}{EIl} \times \frac{a}{2}\left(b + \frac{a}{3}\right)$$

$$t_{BA} = \frac{Pab^3}{3EIl} + \frac{Pa^2b^2}{2EIl} + \frac{Pa^3b}{6EIl}$$

Computing t_{CA}. The value of t_{CA} is obtained by taking the moment of the M/EI diagram between A and C about CE.

$$t_{CA} = \frac{Pab}{EIl} \times \frac{a}{2} \times \frac{a}{3} = \frac{Pa^3b}{6EIl} \qquad (8.27)$$

The deflection DC. By substituting and rearranging the foregoing values in Eq. 8.26, we obtain

$$DC = \left(\frac{Pab^3}{3EIl} + \frac{Pa^2b^2}{2EIl} + \frac{Pa^3b}{6EIl}\right)\frac{a}{l} - \frac{Pa^3b}{6EIl} = \frac{Pa^2b^3}{3EIl^2} + \frac{Pa^3b^2}{2EIl^2} + \frac{Pa^4b}{6EIl^2} - \frac{Pa^3b}{6EIl}$$

$$= \frac{Pa^2b}{6EIl}\left(\frac{2b^2}{l} + \frac{3ab}{l} + \frac{a^2}{l} - a\right) = \frac{Pa^2b}{6EIl}\left(\frac{(2b + a)(b + a)}{l} - a\right)$$

$$= \frac{Pa^2b^2}{3EIl} \qquad (8.28)$$

Deflections to either side of load P. The computation of the deflection at any point on the beam off the action line of load P follows the same pattern used in the preceding analysis.

Thus, the deflection x distance from the left reaction is equal to

$$GH = t_{BA} \times \frac{x}{l} - t_{HA} \qquad (8.29)$$

The value of t_{HA} is the moment of triangle RST of the M/EI diagram taken about ST.

Although the value of the deflection x' distance from the right reaction could be obtained in the same manner using the tangent at A, it is more convenient to use a tangent drawn at B. Thus, the deflection at this point is equal to

$$LM = t_{AB} \times \frac{x'}{l} - t_{MB}$$

Maximum deflection. To determine the maximum deflection of a simple beam by the moment-area method, one needs to recall the fact that the tangential deviations developed at the reactions by extending the horizontal tangent from the point of maximum deflection (Fig. 8-16) are equal to each other. When these two tangential deviations are properly equated in general form, using an assumed point of horizontal tangency, the exact location of the point of maximum deflection may be found. Having once located the position of maximum deflection, its magnitude is found as previously illustrated.

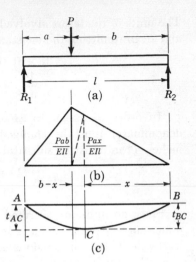

Figure 8-16

Slope at any point on a beam. Having established the location of the maximum deflection or, in other words, the point where the slope of the beam is horizontal, the slope at any point on a beam as determined by the moment-area method is a relatively simple matter.

This can be accomplished by summing algebraically the M/EI area from the point of horizontal slope to the point where the slope is desired.

The slope at any point may be established in an even more direct manner by determining the slope at either end of the beam. For instance, in Fig. 8-15, t_{BA} divided by l would provide the slope at A. With a slope thus established, other slopes can be found by adding algebraically the intervening M/EI area.

8-15. Consideration of units in calculating slopes and deflections

When slopes and deflections are calculated from the previously derived equations, it is important that the units of the various terms be carefully employed. Because these terms are not ordinarily expressed in similar units, a correction factor must be employed. Equations 8.23 and 8.25 for the *slope and deflection at any point* on a cantilever beam with a concentrated load at its free end will be used to illustrate the computation of the correction factor.

Substituting in the general slope equation 8.25,

$$\theta_G = \frac{Px(x - 2l)}{2EI}$$

The units of the terms involved are: E, lb per sq in.; I, in.⁴; x and l, ft; and P, lb (omitting the constants),

$$\theta_G = \frac{\text{lb} \times \text{ft}(\text{ft} - \text{ft})}{\dfrac{\text{lb}}{\text{in.}^2} \times \text{in.}^4} = \frac{\text{lb} \times \text{ft}^2}{\text{lb} \times \text{in.}^2} = \frac{\text{ft}^2}{\text{in.}^2}$$

In order to assign to θ_G one specific unit, either the numerator or denominator must be changed. Choosing to change the numerator to inches, 12 in. must be substituted for each foot. Thus,

$$\theta_G = \frac{(12 \text{ in.})^2}{\text{in.}^2} = \frac{144 \text{ in.}^2}{\text{in.}^2} = 144$$

Since no units are ascribed to the factor 144, the slope θ_G becomes a dimensionless term, which is in agreement with its use as a radian angle in the derivation of the slope equation. Therefore, if the above units are used, the substituted values must be multiplied by a factor 144 to obtain an answer expressed in radians.

The deflection equation 8.23,

$$y_G = \frac{Px^2}{6EI}(x - 3l)$$

which expresses the deflection at any point G on the same cantilever beam, may be examined for a proper correction factor in a manner like that used for the slope equation. Assuming the terms to have the same units as previously ascribed, the substitution proceeds as follows:

$$y_G = \frac{\text{lb} \times \text{ft}^2}{\dfrac{\text{lb}}{\text{in.}^2} \times \text{in.}^4}(\text{ft} - \text{ft}) = \frac{\text{ft}^3}{\text{in.}^2}$$

Desiring the deflection to be calculated in inches, let us substitute 12 in. for each foot term in the numerator. Thus,

$$y_G = \frac{(12 \text{ in.})^3}{\text{in.}^2} = 1728 \text{ in.}$$

Therefore, if numerical values bearing the units used above are substituted in this deflection equation, a multiplier of 1728 must be used to obtain the answer in inches.

Illustrative Problem 4. Find the deflection and slope at the midpoint of a steel cantilever beam 12 ft long, loaded at its free end with a 10-kip load (Fig. 8-17). It is assumed that the maximum flexural stress does not exceed the proportional limit. $E = 30 \times 10^6$ psi and $I = 200$ in.⁴

SOLUTION. The slope at point M is equal to the value of the portion of the M/EI diagram between D and E, since this area is by definition the

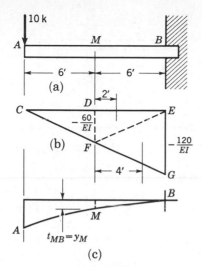

Figure 8-17

change in slope from point B to point M.

$$\theta_M = \frac{1}{30 \times 10^6 \times 200}\left(\frac{-60 - 120}{2}\right) \times 6 \times 144 \times 1000$$
$$= -0.01296 \text{ radians, or } 0°44'31.2''$$

The deflection at the mid-point is equal to the tangential deviation at M between points M and B. Thus, by taking the moment of the area $DEGF$ (divided into two triangles) about the tangential deviation t_{MB}, the deflection y_M becomes

$$y_M = \frac{1728}{30 \times 10^6 \times 200}\left(\frac{-60}{2} \times 6 \times 2 - \frac{120}{2} \times 6 \times 4\right) \times 1000$$
$$= -\frac{1728 \times 1800}{30 \times 10^3 \times 200} = -0.518 \text{ in.}$$

Illustrative Problem 5. Find the deflection at point A of the beam shown in Fig. 8-18. Calculate also the position of maximum deflection. $E = 30 \times 10^6$ psi and $I = 250$ in.^{4}

SOLUTION. From the discussion of Eq. 8.29 on page 240, we may write

$$y_A = FD - AD = \tfrac{5}{15}t_{CB} - t_{AB}$$

Computing t_{CB} as the moment of the entire M/EI diagram about CE, there results

$$t_{CB} = \left(\frac{50 \times 10}{2EI} \times \frac{25}{3} + \frac{50 \times 5}{2EI} \times \frac{10}{3}\right) \times 1728 \times 1000$$

Figure 8-18

$$= \frac{2500}{EI} \times 1728 \times 1000$$

The value of t_{AB} is now found by taking moments of triangle GLM about AD. Thus,

$$t_{AB} = \left(\frac{25 \times 5}{2EI} \times \frac{5}{3} \right) 1728 \times 1000 = \frac{625 \times 1728}{6EI} \times 1000$$

Substituting the values of t_{AB} and t_{CB} in the general equation above, we have

$$y_A = 1728 \left(\frac{1}{3} \times \frac{2500}{EI} - \frac{625}{6EI} \right) \times 1000 = 0.168 \text{ in.}$$

Position of maximum deflection. From experience we know that the point of maximum deflection is located somewhere to the left of load P (Fig. 8-19). Since the slope of the elastic curve at that point must be horizontal, the tangential deviations t_{BH} and t_{CH} located at right and left ends of the beam, respectively, must be equal. Thus, we may write

Figure 8-19

$$t_{BH} = t_{CH}$$

$$\frac{5x}{EI} \times \frac{x}{2} \times \frac{2x}{3} = \frac{5x}{2EI} (10 - x) \left[5 + \frac{2}{3} (10 - x) \right]$$

$$+ \frac{50}{2EI} (10 - x) \left[5 + \frac{10 - x}{3} \right] + \frac{50}{2EI} \times 5 \times \frac{10}{3}$$

$$10x^3 = 1750x - 275x^2 + 10x^3 + 12{,}500 - 1750x + 50x^2 + 2500$$

from which
$$225x^2 = 15{,}000 \quad \text{and} \quad x = \pm\, 8.17 \text{ ft}$$

The negative value of this answer is, of course, meaningless and should be omitted.

PROBLEMS

8-10. A steel cantilever beam 9 ft long carries a concentrated load of 4 kips at its free end. What is the maximum slope and deflection? $I = 100$ in.^{4} *Answer:* 0.0077 radians; 0.560 in.

8-11. A timber cantilever beam 6 ft long is to be so designed that it will deflect exactly 0.3 in. at its free end. Determine the concentrated load required at its free end if $E = 2 \times 10^6$ psi and $I = 500$ in.^{4}

8-12. Placed at the mid-point of a simple beam 12 ft long is a load of 6 kips. Determine the slope and deflection at one of the quarter points. $E = 30 \times 10^6$ psi and $I = 100$ in.^{4} *Answer:* 0.001945 radian; 0.085 in.

8-13. A simple timber beam 9 ft long is acted upon by a concentrated load of 10 kips placed at its mid-point. What is the slope and deflection at a point 3 ft from one of the reactions? $E = 2 \times 10^6$ psi and $I = 300$ in.^{4}

8-14. A steel I beam 12 ft long is used as a simple beam carrying a load of 15 kips at one of its quarter points. What is the deflection at the other quarter point? $I = 100$ in.^{4} *Answer:* 0.136 in.

8-15. A 6-ft steel shaft 3 in. in diameter is supported as a simple beam on adjustable-pillow block bearings. If a load of 4 kips is applied at one of the third points, determine the deflection at the other third point.

8-16. Find the location and magnitude of the maximum deflection of the beam in Problem 8-14. *Answer:* 6.70 ft from the right reaction; 0.218 in.

8-17. Find the location and magnitude of the maximum deflection of the beam of Problem 8-15.

8-18. A cantilever beam 9 ft long has loads of 2 kips applied to its free end and mid-point. What is the deflection and slope at the free end of the beam? $E = 2 \times 10^6$ psi and $I = 300$ in.^{4} *Answer:* 1.838 in., 0.0243 radians.

BEAMS SUBJECTED TO UNIFORM LOADS

8-16. Introduction

The method of calculating the deflections of uniformly loaded beams is identical in principle to that used for beams carrying concentrated loads.

The curved M/EI diagrams, however, present the problem of locating the proper centers of gravity of the various areas concerned. To prevent any later difficulty, the student would do well to memorize the location of the centers of gravity and the area of the two parabolic segments found in Table 13. The position of the center of gravity with respect to the vertex of the parabola is of special importance.

8-17. Cantilever beam — uniform load

Maximum deflection. The maximum deflection is equal to the tangential deviation at A between A and B (Fig. 8-20). Thus,

$$\Delta = \frac{1}{3} \times \frac{wl^2}{2EI} \times l \times \frac{3}{4}l = \frac{1}{8}\frac{wl^4}{EI} \tag{8.30}$$

Figure 8-20

Maximum slope. The maximum slope is, of course, located at A. Since the slope at B is zero, it must be equal to the area of the entire M/EI diagram between A and B.

$$\theta_A = \frac{1}{3} \times \frac{wl^2}{2EI} \times l = \frac{1}{6}\frac{wl^3}{EI} \tag{8.31}$$

Deflection at any point. Finding the deflection at any point x on a uniformly loaded cantilever beam offers some difficulty, since the M/EI area $DEFG$ that must be used in its calculation is not regular. But the moment of this area will be obtained in the process of finding tangential deviation t_{xB} if we subtract the moment of portion CFG, whose center of gravity is known, from the entire parabolic area taken about FG. This procedure is merely an application of the principle, "The moment of a resultant is equal to the algebraic sum of the moments of its components." A more detailed explanation follows.

Explanation. If, in Fig. 8-21(a), the moment of force A_2 is desired about point F in terms of the resultant ΣA and force A, we may write that

$$\Sigma A \times b = -A_1 a + A_2 c$$

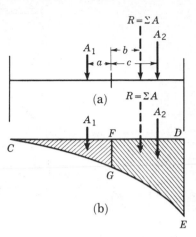

Solving for the moment of force A_2, we obtain

$$A_2 c = \Sigma A \times b + A_1 a$$

Note the plus sign! Errors may easily be involved at this point.

If, now, we assume the segments of the parabolic area shown in Fig. 8-21(b) to represent the forces A_1 and A_2, we may write an identical equation to that written above.

Figure 8-21

Proceeding with the calculation of the deflection at point F, any point x distance from the free end where x is less than $\frac{3}{4}l$, we have

$$y_x = t_{xB} = \text{moment of } CDE \text{ about } FG + \text{moment of } CFG \text{ about } FG$$

$$= \frac{1}{3}\frac{wl^2}{2EI} \times l\left(\frac{3}{4}l - x\right) + \frac{1}{3}\frac{wx^2}{2EI} \times x \times \frac{1}{4}x$$

$$= \frac{1}{8}\frac{wl^4}{EI} - \frac{1}{6}\frac{wl^3 x}{EI} + \frac{1}{24}\frac{wx^4}{EI} \tag{8.32}$$

A change of signs in the equation above should be noted when x becomes greater than $\frac{3}{4}l$.

Slope at any point. Since the slope at any point F on the cantilever beam is equal to its change in slope from point B, we may write

$$\theta_x = \frac{1}{3} \times \frac{wl^2}{2EI} \times l - \frac{1}{3} \times \frac{wx^2}{2EI} \times x = \frac{w}{6EI}(l^3 - x^3) \tag{8.33}$$

8-18. Simple beam — uniform load

Maximum deflection. The maximum deflection for a uniformly loaded simple beam is equal to the tangential deviation formed at one of the reactions by drawing of the tangent at the mid-point (Fig. 8-22). Taking, therefore, the moment of area DES about the tangential deviation t_{AC}, we obtain

$$\Delta = t_{AC} = \frac{2}{3} \times \frac{wl^2}{8EI} \times \frac{l}{2} \times \frac{5}{8} \times \frac{l}{2} = \frac{5}{384}\frac{wl^4}{EI} \tag{8.34}$$

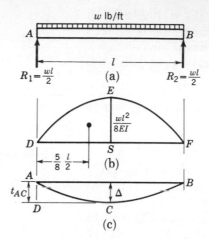

Figure 8-22

Deflection at any point. The deflection at any point K on a uniformly loaded beam can be obtained in several ways, some of which are:

(1) By drawing a tangent at B and obtaining the tangential deviation t_{AB}. Then by similar triangles finding the intercept JL between the tangent and the line AB at K. The subtraction of t_{KB} from JL will give y_K.

(2) By following a solution similar to method (1) but drawing the tangent at A and obtaining the tangential deviation at B.

(3) By determining the maximum deflection of the beam at its midpoint C and subtracting the tangential deviation at K between points C and K.

Contrasting methods (1) and (2), as applied to Fig. 8-23(b), it is found best to draw the tangent from that reaction on the opposite side of the beam from which the deflection is desired. In so doing, the component moments of areas are added. Were the deflection at K to be found by method (2), using the same figure, a subtraction of moment areas would be required. The use of a separated moment diagram (Fig. 8-23c) eliminates the latter objection.

Method (3) offers the most simple solution if the general expression for maximum deflection is known. If it is not known, methods (1) and (2) are equally expeditious and present a more general solution. Method (1), which was previously presented in § 8-14, will be used in the following solution.

Referring to Fig. 8-23(b), the deflection at any point K is obtained by writing the expression

$$y_K = \frac{x}{l} t_{AB} - t_{KB}$$

The determination of t_{AB} offers no difficulty, being equal to the moment of the entire M/EI area between A and B taken about A. The value of

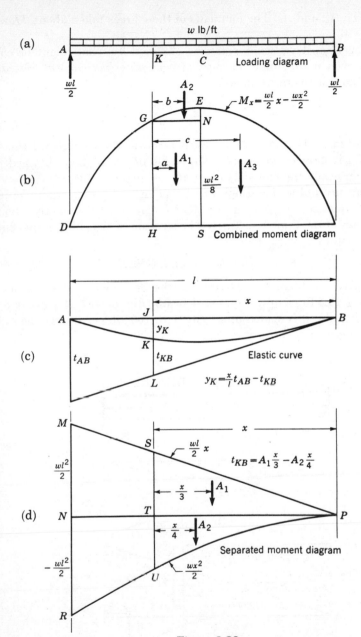

Figure 8-23

t_{KB} is more difficult to obtain. Because it is equal to the moment of a portion of the entire parabolic area (Fig. 8-23b), that portion must be split
into sections whose centers of gravity are known. In this sketch these areas

are called A_1, A_2, and A_3. The moments of these areas taken about JL will equal t_{KB}.

The tangential deviation t_{KB} can be obtained by what might be considered an even more simple method of *separating the moment diagram*. In this method the moment equation

$$M_x = \frac{wl}{2} x - \frac{wx^2}{2}$$

is considered in parts (Fig. 8-23d). Each term on the right hand side of the equation is drawn separately. The value of t_{KB} is then obtained by adding algebraically the moments of A_1 and A_2 taken about JL.

Slope at any point. The slope at any point x distance from the left reaction is equal to the area of the M/EI diagram between that point and the center of the beam — namely, the location of the point of tangency of the horizontal tangent. Thus

$$\theta_x = \text{area } GEN + \text{area } GNSH$$

Illustrative Problem 6. Determine the deflection and slope of an 18 ft, 10 in. I 25.4 lb, simply supported beam (Fig. 8-24a) at a point 6 ft from the left end if it is loaded uniformly with 1000 lb per ft over the right half of its length. $I = 122.1$ in.^{4}, $E = 30,000,000$ psi.

Figure 8-24. All ordinates are to be divided by EI.

SOLUTION. *Deflection of point D.* The use of a separated moment diagram is again desirable (Fig. 8-24c). This time, however, it is better to draw the separated moment curves from the left because of the simple calculations required.

The fundamental equation for y_D obtained from Fig. 8-24(b) is

$$y_D = \frac{6}{18} t_{BA} - t_{DA}$$

The values of t_{BA} and t_{DA} are now determined for insertion into this equation:

$$t_{BA} = \frac{40,500}{EI} \times \frac{18}{2} \times 6 - \frac{40,500}{EI} \times \frac{9}{3} \times 2.25$$

$$= \frac{2,187,000}{EI} - \frac{274,000}{EI} = \frac{1,913,000}{EI}$$

$$t_{DA} = \frac{13,500}{EI} \times \frac{6}{2} \times 2 = \frac{81,000}{EI}$$

The exact value of y_D is therefore

$$y_D = \frac{6}{18}\left(\frac{1,913,000}{EI}\right) - \frac{81,000}{EI} = \frac{556,000}{EI}$$

$$= \frac{556,000 \times 1728}{30,000,000 \times 122.1} = 0.262 \text{ in.}$$

Slope at D. The equation for slope at D may be written as

$$\theta_D = \theta_A - \left[\Delta\theta\right]_A^D = \frac{t_{BA}}{18} - \text{area } AEF = \frac{1,913,000}{18EI} - \frac{13,500}{EI} \times \frac{6}{2}$$

$$= \frac{65,700}{EI} = \frac{65,700 \times 144}{30,000,000 \times 122.1} = 0.00258 \text{ radian}$$

Illustrative Problem 7. Determine the deflection of the free end of the overhanging beam shown in Fig. 8-25 in terms of E and I.

SOLUTION. The ordinary M/EI diagram as shown in Fig. 8-25(b) would tend to present discouraging complications if used for finding deflections by the moment-area method. But if the M/EI diagram were separated into its several components, as shown in Fig. 8-25(c), the computations would be simplified, since each component area is regular and has a known center of gravity.

The M/EI diagram is separated into its component areas by writing the bending-moment equation for a point on the beam x feet to the right of reaction R_1.

$$M_x = -2000(4 + x) + 4800x - \frac{400x^2}{2} \tag{8.35}$$

Figure 8-25

If these terms are plotted individually as they appear in Eq. 8-35 divided by EI, the separated M/EI diagram of Fig. 8-25(c) results. It naturally follows that the sum of the M_1, M_2, and M_3 ordinates of the separated diagram must add up to the M ordinate of the composite diagram.

Proceeding to the computation of the deflection of the free end of the beam, let us draw a tangent to the assumed elastic curve at reaction R_1. From the geometry of the figure, we may write

$$y_A = t_{AC} - \tfrac{4}{10}t_{BC}$$

The character of the algebraic signs of this equation is doubtful because the slope of the elastic curve (and the tangent) at R_1 was assumed. The correct slope of the tangent can be found by the computation of t_{BC} (see § 8-8). If t_{BC} is positive, it must lie below the elastic curve, thereby verifying the assumed position of Fig. 8-25(d). If the numerical value of t_{BC} were negative, the shape of the beam would appear as shown in Fig. 8-25(e), making

$$y_A = t_{AC} + \tfrac{4}{10}t_{BC} \tag{8.36}$$

The computations follow:

$$t_{AC} = -\frac{4 \times 8000}{2EI} \times 2.67 \qquad = \qquad -\frac{42{,}700}{EI}$$

$$t_{BC} = -\frac{8000}{EI} \times 10 \times 5 \qquad = -\frac{400{,}000}{EI}$$

$$= -\frac{20{,}000 \times 10 \times 3.33}{2EI} \qquad = -\frac{333{,}000}{EI}$$

$$= -\frac{1}{3} \times 10 \times 20{,}000 \times \frac{10}{4} = \qquad -\frac{166{,}700}{EI}$$

$$= \frac{48{,}000 \times 10}{2} \times 3.33 \qquad = +\frac{800{,}000}{EI}$$

$$t_{BC}= \qquad\qquad\qquad\qquad -\frac{99{,}700}{EI}$$

Since the algebraic sign of t_{BC} is negative, it must lie above the elastic curve. Therefore, it substantiates the assumed position of Fig. 8-25(e) and renders Fig. 8-25(d) incorrect. Once the correct position of the tangent is ascertained, the values of t_{AC} and t_{BC} might be handled as abstract values to avoid confusion in signs.

Substitution of the numerical values in Eq. 8.36 gives

$$y_A = \frac{42{,}700}{EI} + \frac{4}{10}\left(\frac{99{,}700}{EI}\right) = \frac{82{,}600}{EI}$$

If E is in lb per sq in., I in in.^{4}, and y is desired in inches,

$$y_A = \frac{82{,}600}{EI} \times 1728 = \frac{1.43 \times 10^8}{EI} \text{ in.}$$

Note. Investigation of the uniform and concentrated loads with respect to their contribution to the total deflection of the free end of the beam would reveal that their individual effects, when added, give the total deflection. Moreover, any beam loaded with a complicated system of concentrated and distributed loads can be studied for deflection by considering the various loads or groups of loads separately and adding their individual deflections to give the total deflection at any desired point.

These statements are an outgrowth of the *principle of superposition*, which states that the resultant effect is the sum of the individual effects. For beams, this principle holds true as long as the assumptions and limitations of the theory used are not violated and as long as one effect (deflection) does not magnify or interfere with the development of any other effect.

8-19. *Separated moment diagrams*

The solution of deflection problems is frequently simplified through the proper use of separated moment diagrams. However, there are usually several possible separated moment diagrams which can be drawn for the

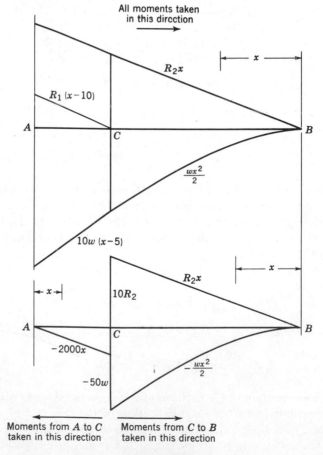

Figure 8-26

solution of any one problem. Moreover, not every separated moment diagram is equally suited for any one solution. Therefore, familiarity with the construction of all the possible diagrams will save valuable time.

Two additional separated moment diagrams for the overhanging beam of Illustrative Problem 7 are shown in Fig. 8-26. The difference in diagrams is readily explained when one remembers that the bending moment at any point on a beam is equal to an algebraic summation of moments *to the left or to the right* of the point. In either diagram, the algebraic sum of the ordinates at any one section is equal to the corresponding ordinate on the composite bending moment diagram.

PROBLEMS

8-19. Determine the deflection at the free end of a steel cantilever beam 12 ft long if it is loaded with a uniform load of 1000 lb per ft over the outermost half of its length (Fig. 8-27). $I = 200$ in.^{4} *Answer:* 0.637 in.

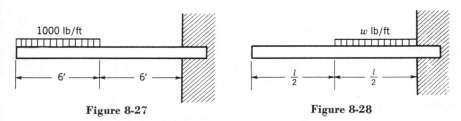

Figure 8-27   Figure 8-28

8-20. Determine the deflection at the free end of a steel cantilever beam if it is loaded with a uniform load of 1000 lb per ft over the innermost half of its length (Fig. 8-28). $I = 200$ in.^{4}

8-21. Determine the deflection at the quarter points of a uniformly loaded cantilever beam l ft long. Place the answer in terms of w, l, E, and I.

Answer: $\dfrac{513}{6144}\dfrac{wl^4}{EI}$, $\dfrac{27}{2048}\dfrac{wl^4}{EI}$.

8-22. A simple beam is loaded as shown in Fig. 8-29. Find the deflection at the center in terms of w, l, E, and I. *Hint.* Draw the moment diagram in its component parts.

Answer: $\dfrac{5}{768}\dfrac{wl^4}{EI}$.

Figure 8-29

Figure 8-30

8-23. Determine the deflection at the third points of the beam shown in Fig. 8-30 in terms of w, l, E, and I.

8-24. Find the maximum deflection of the beam shown in Fig. 8-30, in terms of w, l, E, and I.

Answer: $0.0064 \dfrac{wl^4}{EI}$.

8-25. Find, by the principle of superposition, the deflection at the free end of the cantilever shown in Fig. 8-31. $E = 10,000,000$ psi and $I = 200$ in.[4] *Answer:* 0.145 in.

Figure 8-31   Figure 8-32

8-26. Determine the deflection at point A on the overhanging beam shown in Fig. 8-32. $E = 10,000,000$ psi and $I = 600$ in.[4]

8-27. Determine the deflection at point A on the overhanging beam shown in Fig. 8-33. $E = 30,000,000$ psi and $I = 500$ in.[4] *Answer:* 0.0149 in.

Figure 8-33

8-28. A couple of M ft-lb is placed at the free end of a cantilever beam l feet in length. Determine the deflection of the free end in terms of M, l, E, and I.

8-29. A clockwise moment of M ft-lb is placed at the center of a simple beam. Determine the deflection at $l/4$ from the left reaction, placing the answer in terms of M, l, E and I.

Answer: $\dfrac{3}{384} \dfrac{Ml^2}{EI}$.

GRAPHICAL DETERMINATION OF SLOPE AND DEFLECTION OF BEAMS

8-20. General considerations

Occasionally, it is desirable to represent graphically the deflected position of a shaft or beam in order that the clearances of gears, pulleys, or other attached appurtenances may be determined. This desire for graphical representation is usually prompted by the tediousness of conducting the many mathematical solutions necessary to determine an accurate picture of the elastic curve.

The method is based on a graphical representation of the two fundamental equations of moment area given in § 8-7. The first of these equations,

$$\int_A^B d\theta = \int_A^B \frac{M}{EI}\,dx \tag{8.37}$$

indicates that the change in slope between any two points A and B is equal to the *accumulated* sum of the $(M/EI)\,dx$ areas obtained from the M/EI diagram between A and B. If the partial sums from point A were plotted as ordinates to a graph whose base and reference line were equal to the length of beam AB, the ordinate at any intermediate point would represent the change in slope between that point and point A.

By changing the position of the reference line to some parallel position crossing the $(M/EI)\,dx$ curve, the new ordinate at any point would present the change of slope from the intersection point to the point in question. Were the point of intersection to coincide with the point of zero slope (i.e., maximum deflection on the beam), the ordinates would represent actual slopes.

Because the integration of the right hand portion of Eq. 8-37 is equal to

$$\frac{M}{EI}\,x \;\Big]_A^B$$

which can be plotted as an accumulative curve, the second fundamental equation of moment area

$$\int_A^B dt = \int_A^B \frac{M}{EI}\,x\,dx \tag{8.38}$$

can also be expressed graphically as an accumulative sum of the $(M/EI)\,dx$ (slope) curve. Were the partial sums of incremental $(M/EI)x\,dx$ areas plotted as previously, the ordinate to any point of the resulting graph would be equal to the tangential deviation between that point and point A. Assuming now that the slope curve for the entire beam had been plotted with reference to the zero slope line, the sum of the $(M/EI)x\,dx$ areas on either side of the zero slope point would have had to balance, inasmuch as they represent tangential deviations and the tangential deviations at the ends of a simple beam created by a horizontal tangent to the elastic curve must be equal.

Therefore, to obtain the zero slope line for the solution to the type of problem described above, one must obtain the average ordinate to the slope curve drawn with respect to the slope at one end.

The deflection curve results from plotting the accumulative sums of the $(M/EI)x\,dx$ areas taken from the slope curve plotted with reference to the zero slope line.

Figure 8-34

Illustrative Problem 8.   Suppose it is required to obtain the deflection curve of the 3-in. diameter steel shaft loaded as shown in Fig. 8-34.

SOLUTION.   As the first step toward obtaining the deflection curve of the beam, let us draw an accumulated area curve of the M/EI diagram as we proceed from A to B on the beam. The segmental areas of the M/EI diagram over each of the nine 1-ft intervals are recorded in Fig. 8-34(b). If the magnitude of area A_1 is placed as an ordinate at the 1-ft mark of an x axis equal in length to the beam, we have the start of the curve shown in Fig. 8-34(c). It should be recalled that area A_1 is the change in slope between points 0 and 1 on the beam. Following the recording of the A_1 ordinate, the magnitude of areas A_1 and A_2 is recorded at point 2. When the other segmental areas are in turn added accumulatively and plotted as ordinates at their respective end points, curve Fig. 8-34(c) is obtained.

The value of the ordinate at any point on this curve is the difference in slope between that point and the left end of the beam. *To obtain the exact slope of any point on the beam from this curve requires that the point of zero slope or maximum deflection be located.* When area EFG is divided by the length of the beam, an average ordinate is obtained that intersects the slope curve at the point of zero slope. Using HJ, the average ordinate line, as a new axis, any ordinate to the curve now becomes equal to the actual slope at that point. Point k, at the very center of this particular beam, is the point of zero slope.

The deflection curve is obtained by performing a similar accumulated sum operation on the change in slope curve (Fig. 8-34c) just constructed. If these N areas are progressively and algebraically accumulated from point E to F and the intermediate sums plotted as ordinates at their respective points on still another x axis equal to the length of the beam, the actual deflection curve of the beam will result (Fig. 8-34d).

The maximum deflection resulting from this progressive summation, corrected for units, is

$$\Delta = \frac{77,625}{3EI} \times 1728 \text{ in.} = \frac{25,875}{EI} \times 1728 \text{ in.}$$

Theoretically, the maximum value of deflection is computed to be

$$\frac{Pa}{12EI}\left(\frac{3}{4}l^2 - a^2\right)$$

where P = the sum of both concentrated loads, a = the distance from a load to the nearest reaction, l = length of the beam.

Substituting the proper values in this equation, we obtain

$$\Delta = \frac{2000 \times 3}{12EI}\left(\frac{3}{4} \times 9^2 - 3^2\right) = \frac{500}{EI} \times \frac{207}{4} = \frac{103,500}{4EI} = \frac{25,875}{EI}$$

Assuming the units of E to be in lb per sq in. and I to be in in.[4], this deflection becomes

$$\Delta = \frac{25,875}{EI} \times 1728 \text{ in.}$$

which is exactly equal to that found by graphical integration

The method of graphical determination of deflection as illustrated in the foregoing problem is applicable to all statically determinate beams under any conditions of loading. Should the areas under the slope curve become difficult to determine theoretically, they can be approximated with sufficient accuracy for most purposes by the use of triangles, rectangles, and trapezoids or by the use of a planimeter.

PROBLEMS

8-30. Draw the deflection curve of the beam shown in Fig. 8-35. Use as large a scale as is possible for accuracy. $E = 2 \times 10^6$ psi and $I = 800$ in.[4] *Answer:* $\Delta = 1.48$ in.

Figure 8-35   Figure 8-36

8-31. Draw the deflection curve for the beam shown in Fig. 8-36. Determine the deflection under the 3-kip load. $E = 2 \times 10^6$ psi and $I = 500$ in.[4]

8-32. Obtain from the deflection curve, drawn for the beam shown in Fig. 8-37, the location and magnitude of the maximum deflection. $E = 30 \times 10^6$ psi. *Answer:* 25.6 in. from left reaction, 0.009 in.

Figure 8-37   Figure 8-38

8-33. From the slope and deflection curve drawn for the beam shown in Fig. 8-38, determine the location, the magnitude of maximum deflection, and the slope under the 4- and 2-kip loads. $E = 30 \times 10^6$ psi.

Chapter Nine

STATICALLY INDETERMINATE BEAMS

9-1. *Restraining moments, reactions, and deflections*

Problems involving statically indeterminate beams are generally best solved by the calculation of *restraining moments*. These restraining moments are not directly applied, but *are induced whenever the normal deflection of a simply supported beam is hindered.*

For instance, consider a beam having both ends cemented into a stone wall (Fig. 9-1a). The complicated nature of the restraint offered by the

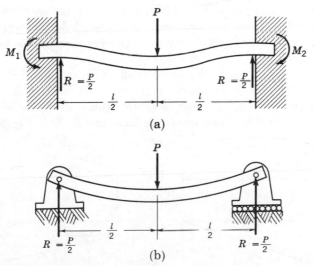

(a)

(b)

Figure 9-1

walls may be resolved into reactions R_1 and R_2, which maintain vertical balance and the restraining moments, i.e., couples M_1 and M_2. The induced development of M_1 and M_2 causes a reduction in deflection and imposes upon the beam a statically indeterminate condition. From inspection, the only difference between the loading diagram of the statically indeterminate beam of Fig. 9-1(a) and the statically determinate beam of Fig. 9-1(b) is the presence of these two restraining couples.

Restraining moments are also induced at the supports of continuous beams, as shown in Fig. 9-2. Obviously, the elastic curve of each span

Figure 9-2

would change if the beam were to be cut into three simple beams of lengths l_1, l_2, and l_3. The restoration of continuity to the beam could be accomplished only by the restoration of the internal-resisting moments at each interior reaction.

9-2. What happens when end moments act alone on a beam

One of the effects of applying the counterclockwise couple M_1 to the left end of the beam shown in Fig. 9-3(a) is to cause the reaction R'_2 to act downward. The beam is, therefore, forced to deflect upward, creating negative bending over its entire length. The variation of this bending moment is triangular, as shown in Fig. 9-3(b).

If, on the other hand, the same beam were to be acted upon by a clockwise couple M_2 located at its right end, the reaction R''_1 would act down and the bending moment diagram would again be of triangular shape, zero bending moment occurring this time at R''_1 (Fig. 9-4b).

Figure 9-3   **Figure 9-4**

Should both M_1 and M_2 happen to act simultaneously on the same beam, the bending-moment diagram would by virtue of the law of superposition be a combination of Figs. 9-3(b) and 9-4(b). If, as shown in Fig. 9-5, M_2 is smaller than M_1, the composite-moment diagram is a trapezoid, having its greatest ordinate at M_1. Note that that portion

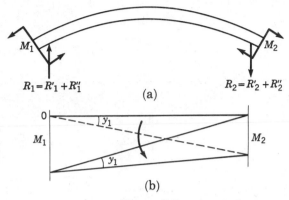

Figure 9-5

created by M_2 is not left in an overlapping position with respect to moment diagram created by M_1, but in a complementary position where the ordinates of each are additive. If M_2 were greater than M_1, the slope of the lower boundary line would be reversed. Having M_1 equal to M_2 would produce a negative rectangular bending-moment diagram.

9-3. What happens when end restraints act on a loaded beam

When restraining moments, such as M_1 and M_2, are added in turn to a loaded simple beam, their effect is to rotate the end upon which they act in a direction opposite to that produced by the load. In doing so, they impose upon the bending-moment diagram of the simple beam through the application of the principle of superposition negative bending-moment diagrams of the types shown in Figs. 9-3(b) and 9-4(b). When the magnitudes of restraining moments are such as to rotate the ends of beams on which they act into a horizontal position, they are said to produce ends that are *completely fixed.* The addition of these negative diagrams to the bending-moment diagram of a loaded simple beam is shown in Figs. 9-6 and 9-7.

To convey more clearly the rotational effect of a couple, an ordinary *monkey wrench* has been substituted for the more conventional couple representation. The application of a restraining force to the handle of the wrench will:

(1) Increase the value of the negative bending moment and the reaction at its point of application in exact proportion to the pull or moment applied to the wrench.

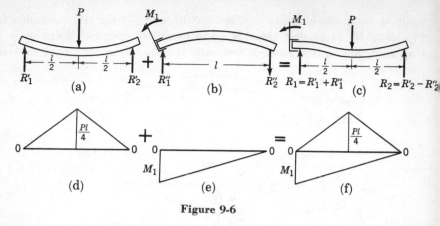

Figure 9-6

Figure 9-7

(2) Decrease the magnitude of the opposite reaction.

(3) Decrease and change the location of the maximum deflection of the beam.

(4) Impart a reversed curvature to the elastic curve of the beam in the vicinity of its point of application.

If an end restraining moment acting on a beam is incapable of rotating its end to a horizontal position, that end is said to be *partially fixed*. Whether an end moment creates complete or partial fixity, it is represented by an equivalent couple acting in the direction of the restraint.

9-4. The use of the law of superposition

As shown in Figs. 9-6 and 9-7, the bending-moment diagram of a loaded beam with end restraints may be compiled by adding thereto the separate bending-moment effects induced by the applied loads and couples. This important principle, made possible by the law of superposition, is used extensively in the study of statically indeterminate beams.

For instance, if a beam with completely fixed ends were acted upon by a uniform load, the bending-moment diagram (Fig. 9-8) would be

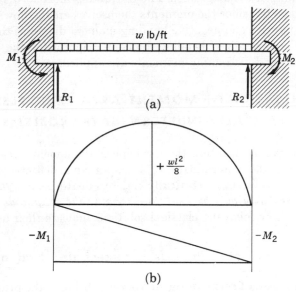

Figure 9-8

constructed by first drawing the positive parabolic-moment diagram for the simple beam and then adding the two equal negative triangular restraining-moment diagrams below the axis. The composite negative portion of the diagram would then be a rectangle, since no diagrams are overlapped. Should one of the ends of the beam be only partially restrained, the bending moment at that point would be reduced with the result that the negative portion of the composite diagram would become a trapezoid.

As a general rule, the drawing of a generalized bending-moment diagram for a statically indeterminate beam proceeds according to the following steps:

(1) Assume the beam to be statically determinate by relaxing the end restraints. In case of a continuous beam each span is to be similarly regarded — the relaxation of the restraining moments at each support making each span a simple beam.

(2) Draw the bending-moment diagram for the relaxed simple beam either in the combined or separated form, depending on which is more convenient.

(3) Remove the loads applied to the simple beam considered above, and reapply all previously relaxed restraining moments.

(4) Draw successively the bending-moment diagram for each reapplied restraining moment on the negative side of the axis used in step 2. Avoid any overlapping of the diagrams. The restraining-moment diagrams are of a general character, since the moments themselves are unknown quantities.

(5) The positive and negative bending-moment diagrams thus obtained constitute the generalized bending-moment diagram for the given beam when all loads and restraining moments are applied.

APPLICATION OF MOMENT-AREA PRINCIPLES TO STATICALLY INDETERMINATE PROBLEMS

In the previous chapter, the principles of moment area were used exclusively for the determination of slopes and deflections of simple beams. In the solution of statically indeterminate beams, *the principles of moment area may also be used to determine the magnitude of restraining moments*. The following classical solutions indicate their use.

9-5. Beam fixed* at both ends — concentrated load at mid-span

Determination of restraining moments. Owing to the presence of two unknown end restraints, two unknown reactions, and the adaptability of only two equilibrium equations, the beam shown in Fig. 9-9 is statically indeterminate. In accordance with the first principle for drawing the bending-moment diagram of statically indeterminate beams, let us relax the end restraints. In other words, temporarily remove M_1 and M_2. The beam will then be a simple beam having a positive isosceles-triangle bending-moment diagram with a maximum ordinate of $Pl/4$. Now, remove the load P and reapply in turn the restraining moments M_1 and M_2. Their bending-moment diagrams are represented by triangles I and II, respectively. Because of the symmetrical loading condition imposed upon the beam, M_1 and M_2 are equal, making triangles I and II congruent. Having now completed the drawing of the bending-moment diagram, let us turn our attention to the application of the principles of moment area.

From a perusal of Fig. 9-9(b), it is evident that *the change in slope from A to B is equal to zero*, since both ends are completely fixed. Thus, by applying Principle (1) of moment areas, it follows that *the algebraic sum of the M/EI diagram between points A and B must also equal zero*. Considering M_1 and M_2 to be positive until proven otherwise, the summation equals

* When the term *fixed beam* is used without any qualifying adjective it is understood to mean *completely fixed*.

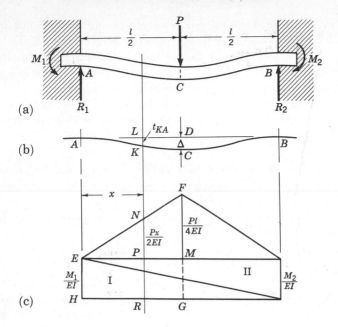

(a)

(b)

(c)

Figure 9-9. E and I are constant values.

$$\frac{Pl}{4EI} \times \frac{l}{2} + \frac{M_1}{EI} \times l = 0, \qquad M_1 = -\frac{Pl}{8} \tag{9.1}$$

and because $M_1 = M_2$, $\qquad M_2 = -\dfrac{Pl}{8}$ $\tag{9.2}$

Algebraic sign of restraining moments. In the computation of M_1 and M_2, their algebraic signs were assumed to be *positive*, even though the bending-moment diagrams representative of their effect were drawn below the axis. Although this may seem contradictory, it is actually a very convenient procedure. Let us see how it works.

Whenever restraining moments such as M_1 and M_2 are assumed positive and become negative upon computation, the assumption is shown to have been wrong. This is a purely algebraic deduction. If, however, the negative sign obtained by calculation corresponds to the standard moment criterion, the restraining moment is actually a negative moment producing tension on the upper fibers of the beam. No further adjustment of sign is necessary. Moreover, if the positively assumed moments M_1 and M_2 are verified as such by a plus sign, the assumption is correct and its sign is again in conformity with the standard moment criteria. Regardless of the apparent inconsistency of the assumed sign, the computed sign will be in agreement with the actual moment present. This method is the one to be used in this text.

How much better is this method than that using the opposite approach! Suppose a negative moment were, in its computation, initially assumed negative. The answer would be positive, showing that the initial assumption was correct. And if it were actually a positive moment and initially assumed negative, the answer would be negative in contradiction to the initial assumption. There would be no conformity between the sign of the moment and the moment criterion. Moreover, this swift interchange of algebraic signs, although producing correct results, is also productive of numerous errors and should be avoided.

When computing restraining moments, therefore, it is recommended that the restraining-moment diagrams be drawn negatively for convenience. In this position, they will not interfere with any positive-moment diagram drawn for the simple beam and will, in ninety-nine cases out of a hundred, be in their correct general position. The unknown restraining moments should then be assumed positive, since the algebraic sign of the computed value will be the correct one.

The above method pertains only to the determination of restraining moments. Slopes and tangential deviations are computed solely on the basis of algebraic summations after the bending-moment diagram has been established.

Maximum deflection. Because of the symmetrical loading, the maximum deflection occurs at the center of the beam. To determine its method of computation, draw, first, the horizontal line AB. Since line AB is tangent to the beam at A, the maximum deflection is also made equal to the tangential deviation at the center taken between points A and C. Its computation, according to Principle (2) of moment areas, is equal to the moment of area $EFGH$ taken about DC or FG. But the moment of area $EFGH$ equals moment of area EFM minus moment of area $EMGH$; therefore,

$$\Delta = \frac{1}{2} \times \frac{Pl}{4EI} \times \frac{l}{2} \times \frac{1}{3} \times \frac{l}{2} - \frac{Pl}{8EI} \times \frac{l}{2} \times \frac{l}{4} = \frac{Pl^3}{96EI} - \frac{Pl^3}{64EI} = -\frac{1}{192} \frac{Pl^3}{EI}$$
$$(9.3)$$

This maximum deflection is one quarter of the corresponding deflection of a simple beam similarly loaded (see § 8-10).

Deflection at any point. Suppose the deflection is desired at any point on the beam of Fig. 9-9, located x distance from the left reaction. By observation, the deflection LK at that point is also equal to the tangential deviation t_{KA}. Thus, taking the algebraic sum of the moments of the M/EI areas between A and K about LK, we have

$$t_{KA} = LK = \frac{Px}{2EI} \times \frac{x}{2} \times \frac{x}{3} - \frac{Pl}{8EI} \times x \times \frac{x}{2} = \frac{Px^3}{12EI} - \frac{Plx^2}{16EI} \quad (9.4)$$

Slope at any point. The slope at any point on the beam of Fig. 9-9 located x distance from the left reaction is equal to the algebraic sum of the M/EI area between the point in question and the point of horizontal tangency at A. Thus,

$$\theta_x = \frac{Px}{2EI} \times \frac{x}{2} - \frac{Pl}{8EI} \times x = \frac{Px^2}{4EI} - \frac{Plx}{8EI} \tag{9.5}$$

9-6. Beam fixed at one end — freely supported at the other — concentrated load at center

Determining the restraining moment M_1. The analysis of this beam, Fig. 9-10, is initiated as before with the drawing of the M/EI diagram in

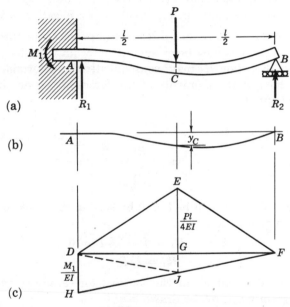

Figure 9-10

compliance with the principles previously explained in § 9-4. With the removal of the restraining moment M_1, the beam becomes a simple beam whose variation in moment is represented by the positively located isosceles triangle shown in Fig. 9-10(c). Removing load P and reapplying an unknown M_1, imposes a uniformly varying moment indicated by line FH placed below the axis line for convenience. The exact location of the line will remain in doubt until the sign and magnitude of M_1 are determined by computation. The simultaneous actions of both P and M_1 result in a combined M/EI diagram consisting of triangles DEF and DFH.

The principles of moment area may again be applied by extending the tangent at A through point B, thus making the tangential deviation at B between points A and B equal to zero. Expressing the tangential deviation at point B in equation form, assuming M_1 to be positive, we get

t_{BA} = moment of area DEF about vertical through B
$$+ \text{ moment of area } DHF \text{ about vertical through } B = 0$$

$$= \frac{Pl}{4EI} \times \frac{l}{2} \times \frac{l}{2} + \frac{M_1}{EI} \times \frac{l}{2} \times \frac{2}{3} \times l = 0$$

from which $$M_1 = - \tfrac{3}{16}Pl \qquad (9.6)$$

The negative sign resulting from this computation reveals that the positive assumption was incorrect. Because of its negative value, it also reveals that the upper fibers of the beam must be in tension and that, as a consequence, M_1 must act counterclockwise. The resulting M/EI diagram is, therefore, shown correctly in Fig. 9-10(c) in a negative position.

The determination of reaction R_1. Because one of the three unknowns acting on the beam has now been found, the beam is no longer statically indeterminate. Reaction R_1 may, consequently, be determined by taking the algebraic sum of the moments of the forces acting on the free body (Fig. 9-10a) about A.

Note. The restraining moment M_1 acts in the same direction as reaction R_2 about point A.

Therefore $$\Sigma M_A = R_2 l - \frac{Pl}{2} + \frac{3}{16} Pl = 0 \qquad (9.7)$$

$$R_2 = \tfrac{5}{16}P$$

The value of R_1 may then be found by setting the algebraic sum of the vertical forces equal to zero.

$$\Sigma V = R_1 - P + \tfrac{5}{16}P = 0$$

$$R_1 = \tfrac{11}{16}P$$

Having thus determined all the vertical forces acting on the beam, the shear diagram may now be drawn.

The deflection under the load. To obtain the deflection under load P compute the tangential deviation at C between points C and A. Thus

$y_C = t_{CA}$ = moment of area DEG about EJ
$$- \text{ moment of area } DGJH \text{ about } EJ$$

$$= \frac{Pl}{4EI} \times \frac{1}{2} \times \frac{l}{2} \times \frac{1}{3} \times \frac{l}{2} - \frac{3}{16}\frac{Pl}{EI} \times \frac{1}{2} \times \frac{l}{2} \times \frac{2}{3} \times \frac{l}{2}$$

$$- \frac{3}{32}\frac{Pl}{EI} \times \frac{1}{2} \times \frac{l}{2} \times \frac{1}{3} \times \frac{l}{2}$$

$$= \frac{Pl^3}{96EI} - \frac{6}{384}\frac{Pl^3}{EI} - \frac{3}{768}\frac{Pl^3}{EI} = - \frac{7}{768}\frac{Pl^3}{EI} \qquad (9.8)$$

The deflection at any point on the beam. The deflection of any point on the beam of Fig. 9-10 is obtained in the same manner as it is for the mid-point. Because the tangent at A is horizontal, any tangential deviation located between the elastic curve and the tangent is equal to the deflection at that point.

The maximum deflection. Inasmuch as only one restraining moment acts on the beam, the point of maximum deflection is forced off-center in a direction away from the restrained end — that is, on the right side of load P (Fig. 9-11). Arbitrarily choosing some point D as the point of

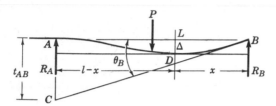

Figure 9-11

maximum deflection (or horizontal slope), one must equate the moments of the M/EI areas on either side of LD, about the verticals passing through A and B, since the tangential deviations thus obtained will be equal. Because the equation contains only one variable, x, its solution provides the location of the point of maximum deflection ($x = \frac{4}{9}l$, approximately). The location of the maximum deflection may also be found by differentiating the elastic curve equation of the beam between C and B and setting it equal to zero.

The slope at any point. To obtain the slope at any point on the beam shown in Fig. 9-10, the algebraic sum of the M/EI area is taken from the horizontally fixed end A to the point in question. Should the end at A be only *partially fixed*, the slope at any point would have to be referenced to the zero slope at the point of maximum deflection or to the slope at some point such as B, obtained by dividing the tangential deviation t_{AB} (Fig. 9-11) by the length of the beam.

9-7. The composite bending-moment diagram for restrained beams

In each of the foregoing discussions, the M/EI diagrams (pertains also to the bending-moment diagrams) were drawn in two parts showing the separate effects of the loads and the restraining moments. But by the law of superposition, these two separate effects may be algebraically added to obtain a composite M/EI (or bending-moment) diagram. Thus, the algebraic sum of the ordinates to the M/EI or bending-moment diagrams at any one point on the beam is the actual M/EI, or bending moment at the point.

Referring to Fig. 9-12, the bending-moment diagram for a fixed-ended beam loaded with a concentrated load at the center, we may perform the

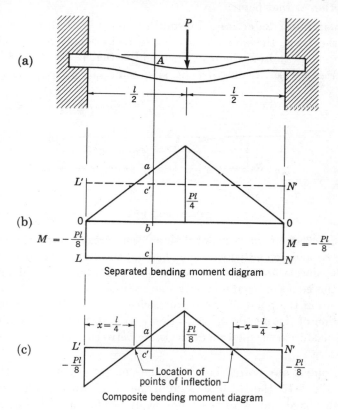

Figure 9-12

algebraic summation at any point A by subtracting the value of bc from ab to obtain the length ac'. The location of c' may also be found geometrically by rotating bc perpendicularly about the zero axis. In fact, this geometric subtraction may be performed for every ordinate in one step by rotating the entire negative moment diagram about the zero axis, locating LN in a new position $L'N'$. Any positive excess will lie above line $L'N'$. Algebraic summations resulting in negative values will be located below line $L'N'$. Line $L'N'$ is, therefore, the new zero-moment line and all magnitudes of M/EI in the composite-moment diagram must be referenced to it.

The points of zero moment or points of inflection determined by the superposition of the negative-moment diagram on the positive-moment diagram are easily computed. From an inspection of the resulting similar triangles, the distance from either end to the closest inflection point is $l/4$.

The composite bending-moment diagram for a beam fixed at only one end with a concentrated load at its center is shown in Fig. 9-13c. A somewhat more favored arrangement places $L'O$ in a horizontal position as shown in Fig. 9-13(d). Both Figs. 9-13(c) and (d) are equally correct.

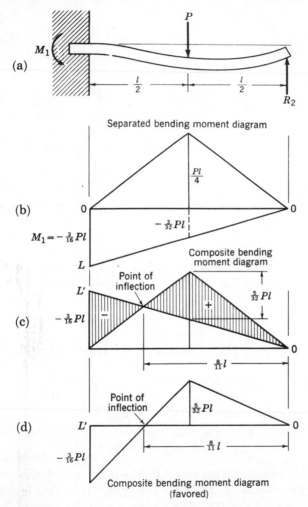

Figure 9-13

Illustrative Problem 1. Determine the slope and deflection at one of the quarter points of the completely restrained beam shown in Fig. 9-14, loaded with a concentrated load P at the other quarter point. Place the answer in terms of P, l, E, and I.

Figure 9-14

SOLUTION. The bending moment of the beam after eliminating the effects of the restraining moments M_1 and M_2 is shown as the positive triangle in Fig. 9-14(b). The moment diagram for the restraining moments M_1 and M_2 will be a trapezoid, since the beam is not symmetrically loaded. It is placed on the negative side of the axis until such time as M_1 and M_2 (assumed positive) can be definitely ascertained in both magnitude and sign.

Determination of restraining moments. Since the tangents at both A and B are horizontal and collinear, the change in slope from A to B must be zero. Thus, we may set the algebraic sum of the entire M/EI diagram equal to zero

$$\Delta\theta = \frac{3}{16}\frac{Pl}{EI} \times \frac{l}{2} + \frac{M_1 l}{2EI} + \frac{M_2 l}{2EI} = 0$$

whence

$$M_1 + M_2 = -\tfrac{3}{16}Pl$$

Still another equation is necessary for the solution of the above equation, since two unknowns M_1 and M_2 are involved. This may be obtained by equating the moments of the M/EI areas about the vertical line passing through B, since the tangential deviation at this point will be zero.

$$t_{BA} = \frac{3}{16}\frac{Pl}{EI} \times \frac{l}{4} \times \frac{1}{2} \times \frac{2}{3} \times \frac{l}{4} + \frac{3}{16}\frac{Pl}{EI} \times \frac{3}{4}l \times \frac{1}{2} \times \frac{l}{2} - \frac{M_1}{EI} \times \frac{l}{2} \times \frac{2}{3}l$$

$$- \frac{M_2}{EI} \times \frac{l}{2} \times \frac{l}{3} = 0$$

whence

$$2M_1 + M_2 = -\tfrac{15}{64}Pl$$

Solving for the unknown moments M_1 and M_2 gives

$$M_1 = -\tfrac{3}{64}Pl \tag{9.9}$$

$$M_2 = -\tfrac{9}{64}Pl \tag{9.10}$$

Deflection at quarter point D. $y_D = t_{DA}$ = algebraic sum of the moments of M/EI diagram between A and D taken about DG

$$= \frac{1}{2} \times \frac{1}{16}\frac{Pl}{EI} \times \frac{l}{4} \times \frac{1}{3} \times \frac{l}{4} - \frac{1}{2} \times \frac{9}{128}\frac{Pl}{EI} \times \frac{l}{4} \times \frac{1}{3} \times \frac{l}{4}$$

$$- \frac{1}{2} \times \frac{3}{64}\frac{Pl}{EI} \times \frac{l}{4} \times \frac{2}{3} \times \frac{l}{4}$$

$$= \left(\frac{Pl^3}{1536} - \frac{3}{4096}Pl^3 - \frac{Pl^3}{1024}\right)\frac{1}{EI} = -\frac{13}{12,288}\frac{Pl^3}{EI} \tag{9.11}$$

Slope at quarter point D. θ_D = algebraic sum of M/EI diagram between A and D

$$= \frac{1}{2} \times \frac{1}{16}\frac{Pl}{EI} \times \frac{l}{4} - \frac{1}{2} \times \frac{9}{128}\frac{Pl}{EI} \times \frac{l}{4} - \frac{1}{2} \times \frac{3}{64}\frac{Pl}{EI} \times \frac{l}{4}$$

$$= \frac{Pl^2}{128EI} - \frac{9}{1024}\frac{Pl^2}{EI} - \frac{3}{512}\frac{Pl^2}{EI} = -\frac{7}{1024}\frac{Pl^2}{EI} \tag{9.12}$$

PROBLEMS

9-1. A 10-in. I 25.4-lb steel beam, 12 ft long, is fixed at both ends. If it is subjected to a concentrated load of 5000 lb at the center, what will the deflection be directly under the load? *Answer:* 0.0212 in.

9-2. If the fixity at one end of the beam in Problem 9-1 were to be released, what would be the new deflection and slope under the load? Discuss briefly the effect on the bending-moment diagram caused by a gradual relaxation of the one restraining moment.

9-3. Determine the location and magnitude of the maximum deflection of the beam of Problem 9-2. *Answer:* 5.37 ft from simple support, 0.0380 in.

9-4. A steel I beam 20 ft long ($I = 100$ in.⁴) is fixed at one end. Located 8 ft from its freely supported end is a 10-ton load. Draw its shear- and bending-moment curves.

9-5. Determine the deflection of the beam of Problem 9-4 directly under the load. *Answer:* 0.903 in.

9-6. Determine the location and magnitude of the maximum deflection of the beam of Problem 9-4.

9-7. A 6 by 12-in. timber beam 18 ft long ($E = 1.2 \times 10^6$ psi) is fixed at both ends. It is subjected to a load of 4000 lb at a point 6 ft from one end. Draw the shear- and bending-moment diagram. *Answer:* Maximum moment = 10,680 ft-lb.

9-8. Select an American Standard I beam 15 ft long to carry a load of 10,000 lb located 10 ft from its fixed end. The other end is freely supported. Maximum allowable fiber stress is 20,000 psi. *Answer:* 8 in. I, 23.0 lb.

9-9. Draw the shear and bending moment diagram for a beam of a length l fixed at one end and freely supported at the other, and loaded at the third points with loads equal to P. *Answer:* $M_{\text{max.}} = -Pl/3EI$.

9-8. Uniformly loaded beam — fixed at each end

As indicated in the preceding chapter, uniformly loaded beams offer no difficulty in the applications of the principles of moment area, aside from the determination of the area moments themselves.

Consider the beam shown in Fig 9-15. As in all statically indeterminate beams, let us first determine the restraining moments M_1 and M_2.

Computation of restraining moments. With only the uniform load acting on the beam, the bending-moment diagram produced is entirely positive, and is shown as the parabolic curve in Fig. 9-15d. Immediately below the axis line is the rectangular bending-moment diagram produced by the action of the equal restraining moments M_1 and M_2. Because R_1 and R_2 are on the same elevation and the tangents at each end are horizontal, the change in slope, or the algebraic sum of the M/EI diagram between the ends, is equal to zero. Thus

$$\frac{2}{3} \times \frac{wl^2}{8EI} \times l + \frac{M_1}{EI} \times l = 0$$

$$M_1 = -\frac{wl^2}{12EI} \quad \text{and} \quad M_2 = -\frac{wl^2}{12EI} \qquad (9.13, 9.14)$$

Maximum deflection. The maximum deflection may be obtained by taking moments of the M/EI diagram between A and C about the vertical line passing through the center of the beam.

$$t_{CA} = \Delta = \frac{2}{3} \times \frac{wl^2}{8EI} \times \frac{l}{2} \times \frac{3}{8} \times \frac{l}{2} - \frac{wl^2}{12EI} \times \frac{l}{2} \times \frac{l}{4} = 0$$

$$\Delta = -\frac{1}{384} \frac{wl^4}{EI} \qquad (9.15)$$

Comparing this deflection with that for the uniformly loaded simple beam of Fig. 8-22 reveals that fixing the ends decreases the deflection to one-fifth of the simple beam value.

Figure 9-15

Deflection at any point. The determination of the deflection at any point D on the beam is simplified a great deal for two reasons: first, because each deflection is a tangential deviation, and, second, tangential deviations can be computed by taking the algebraic sum of the moments of the M/EI areas either to the right or left of their location. The latter simplification is made possible by the horizontal tangents located at each end of the beam.

Although the bending-moment diagram of Fig. 9-15(d) could be used for the determination of deflection at any point D, the separated diagram shown in Fig. 9-16 will prove to be more desirable. In this diagram, the

Figure 9-16

simple beam moment curve has been divided into two parts, one showing the effect of the uniform load, the other the reaction. The moments were taken to the left for all sections of the beam. The deflection at D is then equal to

$$y_D = t_{DA} = A_1\bar{x}_1 - A_2\bar{x}_2 - A_3\bar{x}_3 \quad \text{(areas divided by } EI\text{)}$$

$$= \frac{wl}{2EI} x \times \frac{x}{2} \times \frac{x}{3} - \frac{wx^2}{2EI} \times \frac{x}{3} \times \frac{x}{4} - \frac{wl^2}{12EI} \times x \times \frac{x}{2}$$

$$= \frac{2wlx^3 - wx^4 - wl^2x^2}{24EI}$$

9-9. Uniformly loaded beam — fixed at one end — freely supported at the other

Determination of restraining moment. The bending-moment diagram for the separate effects of the uniform load applied to the beam of Fig. 9-17 is shown in part (d). To obtain the value of the unknown restraining moment M_2, using the application of the principle of tangential deviations, requires the location of a point on the beam where the tangential deviation is known. Such a point is located at the left end where the tangential deviation is zero. Taking the moment of the M/EI areas about the vertical passing through A, assuming M_2 positive, provides the following equation:

$$\Sigma M = \frac{2}{3} \times \frac{wl^2}{8EI} \times l \times \frac{l}{2} + \frac{M_2}{EI} \times \frac{l}{2} \times \frac{2}{3}l = 0$$

from which

$$M_2 = -\tfrac{1}{8}wl^2 \tag{9.16}$$

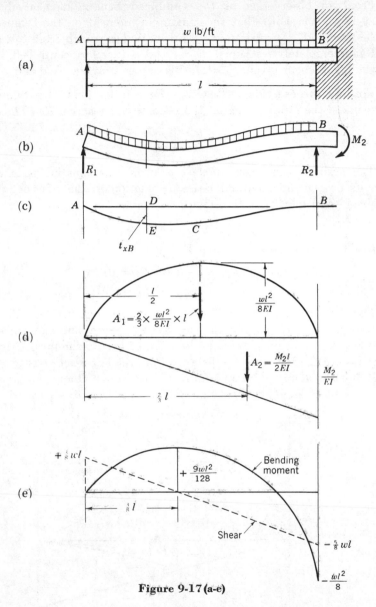

(a)

(b)

(c)

(d)

(e)

Figure 9-17 (a-e)

The presence of the negative sign reveals that the bending moment is opposite to the assumed positive direction. Moreover, it acts to create the effects of a negative moment, which are tensile stresses on the top, and compression stresses on the bottom of the beam. Obviously, the couple to produce these effects at the right-hand end must act clockwise.

From an observation of the combined bending-moment diagram, Fig. 9-17(e), it is shown that the maximum moment on the beam occurs at the fixed end. The design of all prismatic beams subjected to uniform load and completely restrained at one end is therefore controlled, insofar as bending moment is concerned, by the moment at the fixed end.

Finding the reactions. Reaction R_1 can be found by taking the moments of the forces acting on the beam about reaction R_2. Thus

$$R_1 l - \frac{wl^2}{2} + \frac{wl^2}{8} = 0 \tag{9.17}$$

The positive sign given the last term of this equation is in accord with its proven direction and bears no relation to the type of moment involved. The solution of this equation gives

$$R_1 = \tfrac{3}{8}wl \tag{9.18}$$

Reaction R_2 is computed using $V = 0$:

$$\Sigma V = \tfrac{3}{8}wl - wl + R_2 = 0$$
$$R_2 = \tfrac{5}{8}wl \tag{9.19}$$

The shear diagram for the beam is shown in Fig. 9-17(e). From the analysis of this diagram, it is shown that the restraining moment on the right end of the beam moved the location of the maximum positive moment toward the left end. Its distance from the left reaction is $\tfrac{3}{8}l$.

Deflection at any point on beam. The deflection at any point x is most advantageously obtained by using the more elaborate separated M/EI

(f)

Figure 9-17(f)

diagram shown in Fig. 9-17(f). In this diagram the moment due to the simple beam reaction R'_2 and the uniform load are shown separately. The deflection will then be found from the expression

$$t_{zB} = y_x = A_1\frac{x}{3} - A_2\frac{x}{4} - 2A_3\frac{x}{3} - A_4\frac{x}{3}$$

Illustrative Problem 2. A 12 in. I 35 lb beam 12 ft long, and fixed at the right end is loaded as shown in Fig. 9-18(a). Determine the reactions and the restraining moment at the right end. $I = 227.0$ in.^{4}

SOLUTION. A beam, fixed at one end and simply supported at the other is statically indeterminate to the first degree, meaning that there is one reaction component too many to make possible a solution using the equilibrium equations alone. This requires another equation to unlock the solution for any one or all the reaction components.

All individual moment diagrams are taken to the left

Figure 9-18

The one equation required can be determined most easily for the beam in question, by using a technique slightly different from that previously recommended. It is dependent upon the use of the moment diagram drawn with *both* applied loads and the restraining moment applied simultaneously. The separated moment diagram (Fig. 9-18c), obtained by taking moments to the left, will then involve the actual value of R_L as the sole redundant. By taking moments to the left, the use of M_B is avoided in drawing the moment diagram. Because all the reaction components and loads were acting on the beam simultaneously, the resulting moment diagram must present the actual moments acting on the given beam.

Since in Fig. 9-18(b) $t_{AB} = 0$, the moments of the M/EI diagrams between A and B taken about A must equal zero:

$$8A_1 - 9A_2 - 10.5A_3 = 0$$

$$\frac{12R_A}{EI} \times \frac{12}{2} \times 8 - \frac{9000}{EI} \times \frac{9}{2} \times 9 - \frac{1}{3} \times \frac{9000}{EI} \times 6 \times 10.5 = 0$$

$$576R_A - 364,500 - 189,000 = 0$$

$$R_A = \frac{553,500}{596} = 960 \text{ lb}$$

$$R_B = 4000 - 960 = 3040 \text{ lb}$$

$$\Sigma M_B = 960 \times 12 - 9000 - 9000 + M_B = 0$$

$$M_B = -6480 \text{ ft-lb}$$

Note: This illustrative problem could have been solved by using the technique recommended before, i.e., by drawing the simple beam and restraining moment diagrams separately. In that case, the number of areas included in the separated moment diagram would have been increased by one (taking moments to left). The student is urged to make this further analysis.

PROBLEMS

9-10. A 2 by 8-in. Douglas fir beam (8 in. side vertical) 12 ft long and fixed at both ends is loaded uniformly with 500 lb per ft from its left reaction to a point 4 ft from the right reaction. Using $E = 2,000,000$ psi and the dressed-size dimensions, find the deflection at the center. *Answer:* 0.413 in.

9-11. Find the deflection and slope of the loaded quarter point of the beam of Problem 9-10. *Answers:* 0.00823 radians, 0.218 in.

9-12. Draw the shear and moment curve for the beam of Problem 9-10 if the right end is simply supported.

9-13. Find the deflection at the right end of the uniform load placed on the beam of Problem 9-10 if the left end is simply supported.

9-14. An 8-in. I 18.4-lb steel beam ($I_{x-x} = 64.2$ in.[4]) is fixed at both ends and loaded over the center half of its 16-ft length with a uniform load of 2000 lb per ft. Draw its shear and moment curves. *Answer:* $M_1 = 29,300$ ft-lb.

9-15. Determine the maximum deflection of the beam of Problem 9-14. *Answer:* 0.248 in.

9-16. Determine the slope and deflection of the beam of Problem 9-14 at one of its quarter points.

9-17. If one end of the beam in Problem 9-14 was simply supported, draw its shear- and bending-moment diagram.

9-18. Calculate the position of the points of inflection of a uniformly loaded beam of length l fixed at both ends. *Answer:* 0.2113l.

9-10. *Partially restrained beams*

When the restraint at the end of a beam is such as to be incapable of maintaining a horizontal slope, the beam is said to be *partially restrained*. The effect of relaxing a complete restraint is, among other things, to decrease the negative moment applied to the beam at that point. When a single span beam is relieved of all its end restraint, negative moment no longer exists.

For illustration, let us consider the fixed-ended uniformly loaded beam of Fig. 9-19(a). With full restraint, the composite bending-moment diagram is as indicated in Fig. 9-19(b) with O-O as its base line. Suppose,

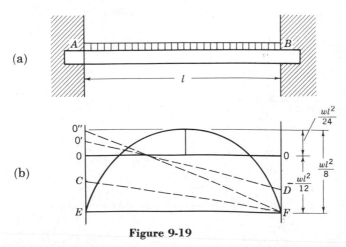

Figure 9-19

now, the restraint necessary to keep the tangent horizontal at point B were to slowly recede in intensity. At some intermediate stage, before complete elimination of the restraint, the zero line O-O would move to some new position O'-D. The slope at B would no longer be horizontal. Upon complete collapse of the end restraint, the zero line would move to O''-F. In each of these movements, the positive diagram would remain stationary.

Should the restraint at A also pass through a similar recession, the zero line would move through the position CF to its final position EF upon complete relaxation. With the complete relaxation of both ends, the beam becomes a simple beam, having a bending-moment diagram with line EF as a base.

Thus, as restraining moments are applied to the ends of a simple beam and later removed, the only change imparted to its bending-moment diagram is in the position of its zero axis. *The over-all height of the bending-moment diagram of any simple span simply supported or in any stage of fixity is equal to the maximum positive moment of the simply supported beam.*

Illustrative Problem 3. A beam 12 ft long, loaded with 1000 lb per ft, is supported and partially restrained at both ends (Fig. 9-20a). If the

Figure 9-20

restraint at the left end is $-\frac{1}{24}wl^2$ and that at the right end is $-\frac{1}{16}wl^2$, what is the maximum fiber unit stress if the cross section is 6 in. wide and 12 in. deep?

SOLUTION. Since the maximum bending moment that produces the maximum bending stress is not located at the center of the beam because of unsymmetrical restraints, it is necessary to locate the point of zero shear from the shear diagram. We shall, therefore, proceed with the determination of the moment and shear diagrams.

$$M_1 = -\tfrac{1}{24}wl^2 = \tfrac{1}{24} \times 1000 \times 144 = -6000 \text{ ft-lb}$$
$$M_2 = -\tfrac{1}{16}wl^2 = \tfrac{1}{16} \times 1000 \times 144 = -9000 \text{ ft-lb}$$
$$M_c = \tfrac{1}{8}wl^2 = \tfrac{1}{8} \times 1000 \times 144 = +18,000 \text{ ft-lb}$$

The negative signs given to the restraining moments M_1 and M_2 reveal that they impart tensile stresses to the upper fibers of the beam. M_1 must, therefore, act counterclockwise and M_2, clockwise.

Let us now calculate R_1 by taking moments about R_2.

$$\Sigma M_{R_2} = -6000 + 12R_1 - 1000 \times 12 \times \tfrac{12}{2} + 9000 = 0$$
$$12R_1 = 69,000, \qquad R_1 = 5750 \text{ lb}$$

Reaction R_2 can be found by taking moments about R_1 or by balancing the vertical forces.

$$\Sigma V = 5750 - 1000 \times 12 + R_2 = 0$$
$$R_2 = 6250 \text{ lb}$$

The shear diagram may now be drawn, since all the vertical forces have been evaluated.

The point of zero shear may easily be determined by the use of similar triangles.

$$\frac{5750}{6250} = \frac{x}{12 - x}, \qquad x = 5.75 \text{ ft}$$

Taking the moments to the left of the zero shear point gives the maximum positive bending moment $M_{\text{max.+}}$

$$M_{\text{max.+}} = 5750 \times 5.75 - \frac{1000 \times 5.75^2}{2} - 6000 = 10,540 \text{ ft-lb}$$

Comparing the maximum positive and negative moments on the bending-moment diagram reveals that the maximum positive moment is the largest. The maximum flexural stress is, therefore,

$$s = \frac{M_{\text{max.}}c}{I} = \frac{10,540 \times 12 \times 6}{\tfrac{1}{12} \times 6 \times 12^3} = 875 \text{ psi}$$

PROBLEMS

9-19. The ends of a uniformly loaded beam are attached to columns that bend sufficiently to make the moment at each end equal to $-wl^2/16$ when a load is applied. Calculate the moment at the middle of the beam and the position of the points of inflection. *Answer:* $wl^2/16$, $0.147l$, $0.853l$.

9-20. Draw the shear- and bending-moment diagram for the beam of Illustrative Problem 3, if the restraining moment M_1 were reversed in direction.

9-21. A careful dynamometer check of the reactions of a 30-ft steel bridge span reveals that when loaded with 6000 lb per linear ft, the reactions R_1 and R_2 are, respectively, 72,000 and 108,000 lb. If both end moments are negative, determine the difference between the two and indicate which of the two is the larger. *Answer:* M_2, 540,000 ft-lb.

9-22. The two bronze-pillow block bearings at each end of a 9-ft shaft 4 in. in diameter produce end restraints of $-\frac{1}{16}wl^2$ and $-\frac{1}{24}wl^2$ at the left and right ends, respectively. If 5000 and 3000-lb pulley loads act at the left and right third points, respectively, determine the maximum shear and flexure unit stresses produced in the shaft.

BEAMS ON THREE SUPPORTS

9-11. *Interior reactions obtained by balancing deflections*

When a simply supported beam is bolstered by an additional reaction placed under its mid-point, its center deflection may be reduced to zero. This fact is conveniently employed in the study of statically indeterminate beams and may be illustrated as follows.

In Fig. 9-21(a) is shown in uniformly loaded simple beam of length l. Its maximum deflection, which occurs at its mid-point, is

$$\Delta = \frac{5}{384}\frac{wl^4}{EI}$$

In Fig. 9-21(b) is shown acting upwards the same beam with a concentrated load R_2 at its mid-point. From § 8-10, such a load was shown to produce a maximum displacement of

$$\frac{1}{48}\frac{Pl^3}{EI} \quad \text{or, in our case,} \quad \frac{1}{48}\frac{R_2 l^3}{EI}$$

Now, if both loads are applied simultaneously the upward deflection caused by the unknown reaction R_2 can be made equal to the maximum downward deflection caused by the uniform load. This balanced condition will place R_2 at the same elevation as R_1 and R_3, fulfilling the usual requirement of a loaded beam placed on multiple supports. The resulting equation may, thereupon, be solved for the reaction R_2.

$$\frac{1}{48}\frac{R_2 l^3}{EI} = \frac{5}{384}\frac{wl^4}{EI}$$

$$R_2 = \tfrac{5}{8}wl \tag{9.20}$$

From an analysis of the vertical forces, knowing that $R_1 = R_3$, we obtain

$$2R_1 + \tfrac{5}{8}wl = wl$$

$$R_1 = \tfrac{3}{16}wl \tag{9.21}$$

$$R_3 = \tfrac{3}{16}wl \tag{9.22}$$

The resulting shear diagram is shown in Fig. 9-21(d).

(a)

(b)

(c)

(d)

(e)

Figure 9-21

9-12. *Negative moments at interior reactions*

The bending-moment diagram may now be drawn by adding algebraically the shear areas. Thus, the maximum positive moment equals

$$M = \frac{1}{2} \times \frac{3}{16}wl \times \frac{3}{8} \times \frac{l}{2} = \frac{9}{512}wl^2 \tag{9.23}$$

Further consideration of the shear area reveals that the next shear area to be considered is negative and much larger than the positive area just computed. Its area

$$A_2 = -\tfrac{1}{2} \times \tfrac{5}{16}wl \times \tfrac{5}{16}l = -\tfrac{25}{512}wl^2$$

This, added algebraically to the positive area in A_1, gives

$$M_2 = \tfrac{9}{512}wl^2 - \tfrac{25}{512}wl^2 = -\tfrac{16}{512}wl^2 \tag{9.24}$$

Thus, we note for the first time the presence of a negative moment over the interior reaction. This should not come as a complete surprise, however, since the interior reaction, in assuming the same elevation as R_1 and R_3, caused the center of the beam to convex upward, thereby placing the upper fibers in tension. Since, in the analysis of most beams of two or more spans, the supports are considered on the same elevation, we may ordinarily expect that a negative moment exists over each interior reaction when each span is loaded.

9-13. Moment-area method of finding bending moments at interior reactions

It would be amiss to assume that the method used in the foregoing analysis would be as easy to use for all beams placed on three supports. Not all interior reactions are located midway between the two outside reactions. Neither are the loads uniformly distributed or the end moments equal to zero. These complications make advisable another more convenient method of determining interior bending moments and reactions. Such a method is developed from the basic principles of moment area.

In the beam of Fig. 9-22, let it be required to obtain the bending moment over reaction R_2 as well as the magnitude of the three reactions R_1, R_2, and R_3.

To commence our discussion, let us draw a free body of each span length by passing a section through the beam along the action line of R_2. Immediately after being cut, the restraining moment at R_2 is reduced to zero and each span becomes a simple beam. The positive bending-moment diagram (divided by EI to obtain M/EI diagram) for the beam in this separated condition with no restraining moment acting is shown in Fig. 9-22(d). If, now, the restraining moments M_2 are restored to the severed ends of the beam in order to obtain the same elastic curve as existed prior to cutting, the additional bending-moment diagrams would be triangular and are placed below the axis for convenience until substantiated by subsequent computation.

Figure 9-22

Having completed the bending-moment diagram as far as presently possible, let us now turn our attention to the elastic curve of the beam. Assuming the elastic curve at R_2 to be pitched downward to the left, let us draw a tangent at this point extended to cross the action lines of R_1 and R_3 forming similar triangles MNL and RSN. From these triangles, we may write the following proportion:

$$\frac{t_{MN}}{20} = -\frac{t_{SN}}{18} \qquad (9.25)\,*$$

This is a very important relationship, because it and others similar to it provide a means for equating the unknowns of two adjacent spans. The value of t_{MN} and t_{SN} may now be found, to be later substituted into Eq. 9.25, M_2 being assumed positive.

* See § 8-8 for discussion of signs of tangential deviations.

$$t_{MN} = \frac{160,000}{EI} \times 10 \times 10 + \frac{M_2}{EI} \times 10 \times \frac{40}{3} \qquad (9.26)$$

$$t_{SN} = \frac{133,300}{EI} \times 4 \times \frac{16}{3} + \frac{133,300}{EI} \times 5 \times \frac{34}{3} + \frac{M_2}{EI} \times 9 \times 12 \quad (9.27)$$

Substituting t_{MN} and t_{SN} in Eq. 9.25, we obtain

$$\frac{16,000,000}{EI} + \frac{400}{3}\frac{M_2}{EI} = -\frac{20}{18}\left(\frac{10,390,000}{EI} + \frac{108M_2}{EI}\right)$$

$$253.3M_2 = -27,520,000$$

$$M_2 = -108,800 \text{ ft-lb}$$

Proceeding now to the determination of the exterior reactions R_1 and R_3, let us fix our attention upon the two free-body diagrams of Fig. 9-22(c). By taking the moments about R_2 of the forces to the left of the cut section, we obtain

$$\Sigma M'_{R_2} = 20R_1 - 32,000 \times 10 + 108,800 = 0$$

$$R_1 = \frac{211,200}{20} = 10,560 \text{ lb}$$

Taking moments to the right of R''_2, there results

$$\Sigma M''_{R_2} = 18R_3 - 30,000 \times 10 + 108,800 = 0$$

$$R_3 = \frac{191,200}{18} = 10,610 \text{ lb}$$

In the determination of R_2, it must be remembered that its magnitude is contributed by the weight applied to both spans. Any attempt to obtain its value by moments should take this fact into consideration. Taking moments about R_1 and R_3 to determine R'_2 and R''_2, results in the following:

$$\Sigma M_{R1} = 20R'_2 - 32,000 \times 10 - 108,800 \qquad (9.28)$$

$$R'_2 = \frac{428,800}{20} = 21,440 \text{ lb}$$

$$\Sigma M_{R_3} = 18R''_2 - 30,000 \times 8 - 108,800 \qquad (9.29)$$

$$R''_2 = \frac{348,800}{18} = 19,390 \text{ lb}$$

$$R_2 = R'_2 + R''_2 = 21,440 + 19,390 = 40,830 \text{ lb} \qquad (9.30)$$

Check on vertical forces.

$$\Sigma V = R_1 + R_2 + R_3 - 32,000 - 30,000 = 0$$

$$10,560 + 40,830 + 10,610 - 62,000 = 0 \qquad (9.31)$$

$$0 = 0$$

9-14. Résumé for solving beams on three supports

The solution of all statically indeterminate beams resting on three supports follows the general outline given below.

(1) Consider each span to be simply supported—that is, remove temporarily all restraining moments over the supports.

(2) Draw the bending-moment diagrams for these simple beams acted upon by the applied loads only.

(3) Remove the external loads temporarily. Restore the restraining moments. Although these restraining moments will be indeterminate in magnitude and direction, we may assume that one always occurs over the interior support as well as over each exterior support if rigidly fixed.

(4) Draw the bending-moment diagrams for the restraining moments as they act on each span. Where a restraining moment occurs at each end of a beam, the bending-moment diagram will be a trapezoid. If a restraining moment occurs at but one end, the bending-moment diagram is a triangle. The relative magnitude of the controlling ordinates in the restraining-moment diagrams is unnecessary for a correct solution. All restraining-moment diagrams are drawn below the zero axis for convenience until their location is finally substantiated.

(5) Draw an assumed elastic curve of the beam, considering both the applied loads and restraining moments acting.

(6) If the beam has no fixed reaction, draw a tangent to the elastic curve at the center support and obtain a relationship of the tangential deviations occurring at the outer supports from the similar triangles constructed by the tangent.

(7) Find the tangential deviation at the outer supports, and substitute them in the tangential deviation relationship found in step (6).

(8) More convenient moment-area relationships may be found if the beam has fixed ends. These may be found from a known change in slope or a known tangential deviation.

(9) The solution of the necessary simultaneous equations will yield the magnitude and direction of each restraining moment.

Illustrative Problem 4. Draw the shear- and bending-moment diagram for the beam shown in Fig. 9-23. Calculate the necessary I beam to take the load, the deflection at the center of the left span, and the slope over the middle reaction. The beam is supported laterally over its full length.

SOLUTION. After removing all restraints from the beam, the bending-moment diagrams for each span are drawn as shown in Fig. 9-23(d). Then, considering the restraints alone, their bending-moment diagrams are drawn below the axis, also shown in Fig. 9-23(d). All that is known at this stage concerning the restraining-moment diagrams is that they are trape-

Figure 9-23

zoidal by virtue of the unknown restraining moment at each end of both beams, and that they have the same moment ordinate at R_2. The bending moment over an interior reaction must be the same for the adjacent spans, since they have a common radius of curvature at this point (Eq. 8.2).

The restraining moments. Having completed the temporary layout of the bending-moment diagram, let us now turn our attention to obtaining moment-area relationships that will provide a solution for the unknown restraining moments. One of the first that might be selected is based on the zero tangential deviation at B between A and B. Expressed in equation form, we have

$$\Sigma M_B \text{ (to left)}^* = 12{,}000 \times \tfrac{4}{2} \times \tfrac{2}{3} \times 4 + 12{,}000 \times \tfrac{8}{2} \times (4 + \tfrac{8}{3})$$
$$+ M_1 \times \tfrac{12}{2} \times \tfrac{2}{3} \times 12 + M_2 \times \tfrac{12}{2} \times \tfrac{1}{3} \times 12 = 0$$

* The value of EI was purposely omitted from these equations for convenience.

or, $$2M_1 + M_2 = -16,000 \qquad (9.32)$$

A similar relationship may be found between C and B:

$$\Sigma\, M_B \text{ (to right)}^* = 8430 \times 15 \times \tfrac{2}{3} \times \tfrac{15}{2} + M_3 \times \tfrac{15}{2} \times 10 \\ + M_2 \times \tfrac{15}{2} \times \tfrac{15}{3} = 0$$

from which $$2M_3 + M_2 = -16,900 \qquad (9.33)$$

Since Eqs. 9.32 and 9.33 include three unknown moments, another equation must be found. Noting that a zero slope exists at both A and C, there is no change in slope between these two points. Therefore, the algebraic sum of the M/EI areas between these two points must equal zero.

$$\sum_A^C A^* = 12,000 \times 6 + \tfrac{2}{3} \times 15 \times 8430 + \tfrac{1}{2} \times 12(M_1 + M_2)$$
$$+ \tfrac{1}{2} \times 15(M_2 + M_3) = 0$$
$$6M_1 + 13.5M_2 + 7.5M_3 = -156,300 \qquad (9.34)$$

A simultaneous solution of Eqs. 9.32, 9.33, and 9.34 yields the following answers:

$$M_1 = -4675 \text{ ft-lb}, \qquad M_2 = -6650 \text{ ft-lb}, \qquad M_3 = -5125 \text{ ft-lb}$$

The reactions. Referring to the free-body diagrams of Fig. 9-23b, we may obtain the reactions by writing simple equilibrium equations. Thus, R_1 may be obtained by taking moments about point B to the left.

$$\Sigma\, M_B \text{ (left)} = 12R_1 - 4675 - 4500 \times 4 + 6650 = 0 \qquad (9.35)$$
$$R_1 = 1335 \text{ lb}$$

Reaction R_3 is obtained by taking moments about the same point to the right.

$$\Sigma\, M_B \text{ (right)} = 15R_3 - 5125 - 300 \times 15 \times \tfrac{15}{2} + 6650 = 0 \quad (9.36)$$
$$R_3 = 2150 \text{ lb}$$

An algebraic sum of all the vertical forces produces R_2,

$$\Sigma\, V = 1335 + R_2 + 2150 = 9000$$
$$R_2 = 5515 \text{ lb}$$

The value of R_2 may be checked by finding the sum of R'_2 and R''_2 from moment equations of the two free bodies taken about points A and C, respectively.

The shear- and composite bending-moment diagrams are shown in Fig. 9-24.

I beam required. A glance at the shear- and bending-moment diagrams reveals that the critical shear and moment values are, respec-

Figure 9-24

tively, 3165 lb and 6650 ft-lb. To meet the flexural requirements, the
section modulus must be

$$\frac{I}{C} = \frac{M}{S} = \frac{6650 \times 12}{20,000} = 3.99$$

Use 5-in. I 10-lb beam; $I/c = 4.8$ in.^{3}; web thickness = 0.210 in.; and
$I = 12.1$ in.^{4}

Although this beam has a more than sufficient section modulus, its
weight is less than any other capable of taking the load.

A check on the shear strength reveals the stress to be

$$s_s = \frac{V}{td} = \frac{3165}{0.210 \times 5 \text{ in.}} = 3010 \text{ psi}$$

which is much less than the allowable stress of 13,000 psi.

Deflection at mid-point of span AB. Inasmuch as the deflection at
any point on span AB is also a tangential deviation between A and the

desired point, its value may be computed directly from the separated M/EI diagrams of Fig. 9-23(d). Thus

$$y'_6 = t'_6 = \frac{9000}{EI} \times \frac{6}{2} \times 2 - \frac{4675}{EI} \times \frac{6}{2} \times 4 - \frac{5660}{EI} \times \frac{6}{2} \times 2 \quad (9.37)$$

$$y'_6 = \frac{36,060}{EI} = \frac{36,060 \times 1728}{30 \times 10^6 \times 12.1} = 0.172 \text{ in.}$$

The slope over the middle reaction. The slope at point B is equal to the algebraic sum of the M/EI areas between A and B, since the slope at A is horizontal.

$$\theta_B = \frac{12,000}{EI} \times \frac{12}{2} - \frac{4675}{EI} \times \frac{12}{2} - \frac{6650}{EI} \times \frac{12}{2}$$

$$= + \frac{4000}{EI} = + \frac{4000 \times 144}{30 \times 10^6 \times 12.1} = 0.00159 \text{ radian} \quad (9.38)$$

PROBLEMS

9-23a, b, c, d, e, f, g, h, j, k. Draw the shear- and bending-moment diagrams for the beams designated in Fig. 9-25. Determine the most economical I beam to withstand the load. Use 20,000 and 13,000 psi as allowable flexure and shear stresses, respectively. Assume beams to be laterally supported. *Answers:*
(a) $R_1 = 0.63$ kips, $M_2 = -4.5$ ft-kips; (c) $R_1 = 4.33$ kips, $M_2 = -20.1$ ft-kips;
(e) $R_1 = 0.89$ kips, $M_2 = -3.86$ ft-kips; (g) $R_1 = 1.75$ kips, $M_2 = -9.50$ ft-kips;
(j) $R_1 = 6.00$ kips, $M_2 = -12.00$ ft-kips.

9-24. Calculate the position of the points of inflection of the beam of Illustrative Problem 3. *Answer:* 1.15 ft, 10.35 ft.

9-25. Calculate the position of the points of inflection of the beam shown in Fig. 9-22.

9-26. By the method of balancing deflections, find the magnitude of the roller reaction acting on a uniformly loaded beam fixed at one end and freely supported at the other. *Answer:* $\frac{3}{8} wl$.

THE SOLUTION OF CONTINUOUS
BEAMS OF MORE THAN TWO SPANS

9-15. General procedure

The procedure used in solving continuous beams of more than two spans is identical to that used in the previous article on two-span beams. The difficulty will, however, generally increase as the number of spans increases.

In Fig. 9-26(a) is shown a continuous beam of three spans. If we separate the three spans at the reactions, we may indicate each as a free

Figure 9-25

body (Fig. 9-26b). Considering, temporarily, only the active forces P_1 and P_3, positive triangular bending-moment diagrams are developed on the outer spans, as shown in Fig. 9-26(d). Since no active force acts on the middle span, there is no positive bending-moment diagram developed.

If, now, the active forces are removed and only the restraining moments considered, the negative bending-moment diagrams of Fig. 9-26(d) are obtained.

Considering now the beam and its deflected elastic curve (Fig. 9-26c), tangents drawn to the elastic curve at the reactions form similar triangles

Figure 9-26

from which restraining-moment relationships may be obtained. Thus

$$\frac{t_{AB}}{l_1} = -\frac{t_{CB}}{l_2} \quad \text{and} \quad -\frac{t_{BC}}{l_2} = \frac{t_{DC}}{l_3} \qquad (9.39, 9.40)$$

When the tangential deviations are replaced by their equivalent in terms of the restraining moments M_1 and M_2, simultaneous equations are obtained that provide an easy solution of these same moments. Assuming M_1 and M_2 to be positive, we obtain

$$t_{AB} = \frac{P_1 l_1}{4} \times \frac{l_1}{2} \times \frac{l_1}{2} + \frac{M_1 l_1}{2} \times \frac{2}{3} l_1 = \frac{P_1 l_1^3}{16} + \frac{M_1 l_1^2}{3}$$

$$t_{CB} = \frac{M_2 l_2}{2} \times \frac{l_2}{3} + \frac{M_1 l_2}{2} \times \frac{2}{3} l_2 = \frac{M_2 l_2^2}{6} + \frac{M_1 l_2^2}{3}$$

Inserting the value of t_{AB} and t_{CB} in Eq. 9.39 gives

$$-\frac{P_1 l_1^2}{16} - \frac{M_1 l_1}{3} = \frac{M_2 l_2}{6} + \frac{M_1 l_2}{3} \qquad (9.41)$$

The second required equation is produced by the substitution of t_{BC} and t_{DC} in Eq. 9.40.

$$t_{BC} = \frac{M_1 l_2}{2} \times \frac{1}{3} l_2 + \frac{M_2 l_2}{2} \times \frac{2}{3} l_2 = \frac{M_1 l_2^2}{6} + \frac{M_2 l_2^2}{3}$$

$$t_{DC} = \frac{P_3 l_3}{4} \times \frac{l_3}{2} \times \frac{l_3}{2} + \frac{M_2 l_3}{2} \times \frac{2}{3} l_3 = \frac{P_3 l_3^3}{16} + \frac{M_2 l_3^2}{3}$$

$$\frac{M_1 l_2}{6} + \frac{M_2 l_2}{3} = -\frac{P_3 l_3^2}{16} - \frac{M_2 l_3}{3} \qquad (9.42)$$

The simultaneous solution of Eqs. 9.41 and 9.42 provides the values of M_1 and M_2. Further investigations of reactions, deflections, slopes, and inflection points may be made using the same procedures as developed in previous articles. The following illustrative problem will show in detail the solution of an actual case.

Illustrative Problem 5. Draw the shear- and bending-moment diagram for the continuous beam shown in Fig. 9-27.

SOLUTION. Since no completely fixed ends are present on this continuous beam, it is necessary to solve this problem by drawing tangents to the beam at the two interior reactions and obtaining from the resultant similar triangles the following expressions:

$$-\frac{t_{AB}}{15} = \frac{t_{CB}}{20}, \qquad -\frac{t_{DC}}{9} = \frac{t_{BC}}{20} \qquad (9.43, 9.44)$$

The tangential deviations necessary for substitution in Eqs. 9.43 and 9.44 are as follows:

$$t_{AB} = \frac{6670}{EI} \times \frac{5}{2} \times \frac{10}{3} + \frac{6670}{EI} \times \frac{10}{2} \times \frac{25}{3} + \frac{M_2}{EI} \times \frac{15}{2} \times 10 \qquad (9.45)$$

$$t_{CB} = \frac{2}{3} \times \frac{15,000}{EI} \times 20 \times 10 + \frac{M_2}{EI} \times \frac{20}{2} \times \frac{40}{3} + \frac{M_3}{EI} \times \frac{20}{2} \times \frac{20}{3} \qquad (9.46)$$

$$t_{BC} = \frac{2}{3} \times \frac{15,000}{EI} \times 20 \times 10 + \frac{M_2}{EI} \times \frac{20}{2} \times \frac{20}{3} + \frac{M_3}{EI} \times \frac{20}{2} \times \frac{40}{3} \qquad (9.47)$$

$$t_{DC} = \frac{2000}{EI} \times \frac{3}{2} \times 2 + \frac{2000}{EI} \times \frac{6}{2} \times 5 + M_3 \times \frac{9}{2} \times 6 \qquad (9.48)$$

After substitution and simplification, the following simultaneous equations are obtained:

$$10M_2 + 29M_3 = -312,000 \qquad (9.49)$$

$$35M_2 + 10M_3 = -366,200 \qquad (9.50)$$

Figure 9-27

Solving these equations, we obtain

$$M_2 = -8220 \text{ ft-lb}$$
$$M_3 = -7920 \text{ ft-lb}$$

The negative sign indicates that the assumption of positive-restraining moments was incorrect. The restraining bending-moment diagrams are shown correctly in Fig. 9-27(c).

Having determined all of the restraining moments, we next proceed to the calculation of the reactions and the determination of the shear diagram.

To get R_1. Use the first span as a free body (Fig. 9-28).

$$\Sigma M_{R_2} = R_1 \times 15 - 2000 \times 10 + 8220 = 0 \qquad (9.51)$$

Figure 9-28. The solution indicates that upper fibers are in tension.

The signs obtained from the moment criteria are used only in obtaining the *direction* of the couples. Once the direction is known, the laws of equilibrium are used to obtain other unknown reactions and couples — that is, $M_2 = -8220$ ft-lb is plus in Eq. 9.51, acting the same way as R_1.

$$15R_1 = 20,000 - 8220$$

$$R_1 = \frac{11,740}{15} = 785 \text{ lb}$$

To get R_2. Use the first two spans as a free body (Fig. 9-29).

Figure 9-29

$$\Sigma M_{R_3} = 785 \times 35 - 2000 \times 30 + R_2 \times 20 - 6000 \times 10$$
$$+ 7920 = 0 \quad (9.52)$$

$$27,500 - 60,000 + 20R_2 - 60,000 + 7920 = 0$$
$$20R_2 = 84,580, \qquad R_2 = 4230 \text{ lb}$$

To get R_4. Use the last span as a free body (Fig. 9-30).

Figure 9-30. The solution indicates that R_4 should act downward.

$$\Sigma M_{R_3} = R_4 \times 9 - 1000 \times 6 + 7920 = 0 \quad (9.53)$$

$$R_4 = \frac{6000 - 7920}{9} = -\frac{1920}{9} = -215 \text{ lb}$$

which means that the R_4 reaction is acting down instead of as shown in Fig. 9-30.

To get R_3. Use the last two spans as a free body (Fig. 9-31).

Figure 9-31

$$\Sigma \, M_{R_2} = (-215) \times 29 + R_3 \times 20 - 1000 \times 26 - 6000$$
$$\times 10 + 8220 = 0 \quad (9.54)$$
$$20R_3 = 6230 + 26{,}000 + 60{,}000 - 8220$$
$$R_3 = \frac{84{,}010}{20} = 4200 \text{ lb}$$

Check $\Sigma \, V = 0$.

Reactions	Loads
785.0	2000
4230.0	1000
4200.0	6000
9215.0	9000 lb
− 215.0	
9000.0	

PROBLEMS

9-27a, b, c, d, e, f, g, h. Draw the shear- and bending-moment diagram for the beams designated in Fig. 9-32, p. 302. Determine the most economical steel, I-beam section to withstand the load. Use 20,000 and 13,000 psi as maximum allowable flexure and shear stresses, respectively. Assume beams to be laterally supported.

Answers: (a) $R_0 = 8.98$ kips, $R_3 = 13.78$ kips, $M_{max.} = 47.9$ ft-kips;
      (c) $R_0 = 7.06$ kips, $R_3 = 10.70$ kips, $M_{max.} = -64.4$ ft-kips;
      (e) $R_0 = 4.00$ kips, $R_3 = 0.38$ kips, $M_{max.} = 40.0$ ft-kips;
      (g) $R_0 = 6.13$ kips, $R_3 = 3.86$ kips, $M_0 = M_{max.} = -32.5$ ft-kips.

9-28. Calculate the position of the inflection points for the beam of Illustrative Problem 4.

9-29. Calculate the slope at the center of the first span of the beam of Illustrative Problem 4 in terms of E and I. *Hint.* Use separated moment diagrams. *Answer:* 576,000/EI radians.

Figure 9-32

9-30. Calculate the deflection at the center of span BC of the beam of Illustrative Problem 4 in terms of E and I. *Answer:* $86,700/EI$.

9-31. Find the slope of the beam of Problem 9-27g, immediately above reaction R_2 in terms of E and I.

9-16. The three-moment equations

Because of the frequency with which continuous beams laden with uniform load occur, the relationship of the internal-resisting moments at any three successive reactions and the load applied to the intervening spans is given by the *three-moment equation for uniformly distributed load*. It is expressed as follows:

$$M_1l_1 + 2M_2(l_1 + l_2) + M_3l_2 = -\frac{w_1l_1^3}{4} - \frac{w_2l_2^3}{4} \tag{9.55}$$

where M_1, M_2, and M_3 are the restraining moments at any three consecutive reactions; l_1 and l_2 are the lengths of the two adjacent intervening spans; and w_1 and w_2 are the loads on spans l_1 and l_2, respectively. The beam must be of constant cross section.

The three-moment equation for concentrated loads

$$M_1l_1 + 2M_2(l_1 + l_2) + M_3l_2 = -\sum \frac{P_1a_1}{l_1}(l_1^2 - a_1^2)$$
$$-\sum \frac{P_2b_2}{l_2}(l_2^2 - b_2^2) \tag{9.56}$$

bears a great deal of similarity to that for uniform loads. The expression included within the first summation sign is determined for every one of the concentrated loads acting on the left span. P_1 is the general term applied to any one of the concentrated loads acting on this span, and a_1 is the distance of such a load from the No. 1 support.

The second expression is similarly written for every load on the right-hand span, b_2 being the distance of each such load from the No. 3 support. M_1, M_2, and M_3 are, as before, the restraining moments on any three consecutive reactions. Lengths l_1 and l_2 represent the included adjacent span lengths.

Assuming a five-span beam having four intermediate supports, with an unknown restraining moment above each one, four applications of the three-moment equation must be made — that is, for spans 1 and 2, 2 and 3, 3 and 4, and 4 and 5. If the restraining moments at the end supports are equal to zero, the above four equations are sufficient to obtain the four unknown interior restraining moments. The application of any three moment equations may be made to any two adjacent spans by using the proper subscripts.

Each of the foregoing equations is easily derived by the use of the moment-area method. If used consistently, it may be advisable to memorize them. However, emphasis cannot be too strongly made to study the method by which they are derived. For in so doing, all problems of continuous beams are solved with the same approach and require no memorized formula.

MOMENT DISTRIBUTION

9-17. Introduction

The moment distribution method of determining restraining moments in beams and structural framework was developed by Hardy Cross in 1932. Its speed and simplicity of application have made it one of the best, if not the best, methods of beam and structural analysis available. In the development of its basic principles, all clockwise moments and the angular displacements they produce are considered positive. When incorporated into moment diagrams, however, restraining moments computed by moment distribution must be made to agree in sign with the conventional bending moment criterion.

9-18. Discussion of basic principles of moment distribution

In Fig. 9-33(b) are drawn the bending moment diagrams of the two spans of a continuous beam, assuming the beam to be *artificially locked in a*

Figure 9-33. Dashed line indicates final moment diagram for balanced beam.

horizontal position over support B. It is noted that over this support, beam BA requires a clockwise restraining moment of 30 ft-kips to maintain its horizontal position while BC requires an 18 ft-kip counterclockwise moment.

Actually, there is no outside or artificial restraint holding the beam in that position. The two beams, integrally connected, must provide the restraining moment for each other. If the artificial restraint is removed, joint B must rotate because beam BC cannot provide the 30 ft-kip moment to keep beam BA horizontal at B. Conversely, beam BA has more than enough moment resistance to keep beam BC horizontal at B. Equilibrium, therefore, can be attained only by rotating joint B in the direction of the unbalanced moment (counterclockwise). In so doing, beam BA reduces its required resisting moment M_{FBA} (see § 9-10) and beam BC increases its moment M_{FBA} until they are both equal to each other. The beam is then in equilibrium. By this method of reasoning, the restraining moment over support B should have a value between 18 and 30 ft-kips. The amount of rotation (i.e., the corrective moments) required to bring the beam to its equilibrium position is obtained by the principles of moment distribution.

9-19. Development of basic principles of moment distribution

When a beam fixed at one end and freely supported at the other is depressed an angle θ_a at its freely supported end (Fig. 9-34) by a moment

$$\frac{M_{ab}}{EI} \times l \times \frac{l}{2} - \frac{R_1 l}{EI} \times \frac{l}{2} \times \frac{2}{3} l = 0$$

$$M_{ab} = \tfrac{2}{3} R_1 l$$

$$M_{ba} = \tfrac{1}{2} M_a$$

$$\frac{R_1 l}{EI} = \frac{3 M_{ab}}{2 EI}$$

also

$$\frac{M_{ab} l}{EI} - \frac{3 M_{ab}}{2 EI} \times \frac{l}{2} = \theta_a$$

$$\frac{M_{ab} l}{4 EI} = \theta_a$$

$$M_{ab} = \frac{4 EI \theta_a}{l}$$

Figure 9-34

M_{ab}, the value of M_{ab} obtained by moment-area principles is equal to $4EI\theta_a/l$. Closer observation reveals that just half the value of the applied moment or $2EI\theta_a/l$ is transmitted with the same algebraic sign to the fixed end. The coefficient of one half is termed *the carry-over factor*.

If the end opposite the applied moment is hinged ($M_{ba} = 0$), the applied moment is equal to $3EI\theta_a/l$. This can be obtained from the moment-area principles or by the method of superposition as shown in Fig. 9-35. The carry-over factor from the left to right end is, of course, equal to zero and no amount of rotation at the applied moment end will cause a moment at the hinge.

Figure 9-35

In the typical continuous beam shown in Fig. 9-36, let us consider the beam to be locked in a horizontal position over each support with the exception of E, which is hinged. In this locked, hypothetical condition, assume the fixed-end moments to be computed and the bending-moment diagrams drawn (Fig. 9-36b). If joint C is unlocked now it will rotate

Figure 9-36

clockwise into equilibrium. The moments created by rotation will be *superimposed* on the fixed end moments present before rotation, making the moments on each side of the joint equal. Stating this equality in general terms

$$M_{CB} + M_{CD} = 0 \tag{9.57}$$

$$M_{FCB} + \frac{4EI_2\theta_C}{l_2} + M_{FCD} + \frac{4E_3I\theta_C}{l_3} = 0$$

from which

$$E\theta_C = -\frac{M_{FCB} + M_{FCD}}{4K_2 + 4K_3} = -\frac{\Sigma\ M_{Fc}}{\Sigma\ (CK)_C} \tag{9.58}$$

where

$$K_2 = I_2/l_2 \quad \text{and} \quad K_3 = I_3/l_3. \tag{9.59}$$

The value of θ_C is the angle of rotation required to bring the joint into equilibrium. Inserting this value in the moment M_{CB} and M_{CD}, we obtain

$$M_{CB} = M_{FCB} + \frac{4EI_2\theta_C}{l_2} = M_{FCB} - \frac{4K_2}{\Sigma\ CK_C}(\Sigma\ M_{Fc})$$

$$= M_{FCB} - r_{CB}(\Sigma\ M_{Fc}) \tag{9.60}$$

and $\qquad M_{CD} = M_{FCD} + \dfrac{4EI_3\theta_C}{l_3} = M_{FCD} - \dfrac{4K_3}{\Sigma\, CK_C}(\Sigma\, M_{Fc})$

$$= M_{FCD} - r_{CD}(\Sigma\, M_{Fc}) \qquad\qquad (9.61)$$

These are the moments occurring in the beam at joint C upon the removal of the artificial locking restraint, assuming the joints at B and D are to remain locked. Simultaneous modifications of moment will occur in M_{BC} and M_{DC} equal to one-half the balancing moments introduced at joint C.

Before operations are moved to the other joints, joint C is locked. Rotation is then permitted at another joint, using similar correction moments, generally stated as $\dfrac{-C_x K_x}{\Sigma\,(CK)_x}(\Sigma\, M_x)$, where C_x is either 3 or 4 depending on whether the opposite joint is hinged or fixed, respectively. Rotating this joint to a balanced condition may throw the first joint out of equilibrium. Successive balancing and rebalancing will, however, produce a state of equilibrium over the entire beam and permit the removal of all artificial locks.

Let us apply the theory to the beam previously presented in Fig. 9-33. Because the *moment distribution criterion assumes all clockwise restraining moments are positive*, the moments M_{FBA} and M_{FBC} are $+30$ and -18 ft-kips, respectively. Their algebraic sum ($\Sigma\, M_{FB}$) of $+12$ ft-kips represents an unavailable clockwise moment demand or a counterclockwise unbalance.

The distribution factors, allocating this unbalance to the two members AB and BC framing into joint B is obtained from the following calculation.

MEMBER	C	K	CK	$\dfrac{CK}{\Sigma\, CK} = r$	$-r(\Sigma\, M_{FB})$
BA	4	$\dfrac{240}{16} = 15$	60	0.667	-8.0
BC	3	$\dfrac{120}{12} = 10$	30	0.333	-4.0
			$\Sigma\, CK = \overline{90}$	$\overline{1.000}$	$\overline{-12.0}$

If now, the excess moment of 12 ft-kips is distributed -8.0 ft-kips to BA and -4.0 ft-kips to BC, joint B will be in balance with 22.0 ft-kips on each entering member. Because joint B rotated and added a negative moment of -8.0 ft-kips to BA, one half of that amount of moment, with the same algebraic sign, was induced at joint A. A fixed joint such as A is able to take as much moment as can be imposed upon it. There being no other joints requiring adjustment to equilibrium, the beam is in equilibrium. The restraining moments over the supports are determined by the algebraic addition of the moments at the end of each span.

Illustrative Problem 6. Determine the restraining moment over each support for the continuous beam shown in Fig. 9-37 by moment distribution ($I =$ constant).

SOLUTION

Figure 9-37

CALCULATION OF DISTRIBUTION FACTORS

| | Joint B | | | | | Joint C | | | |
MEMBER	C	K	CK	r	MEMBER	C	K	CK	r
BA	3	$\frac{I}{20}$	$\frac{3I}{20}$	0.530	CB	4	$\frac{I}{30}$	$\frac{4I}{30}$	0.40
BC	4	$\frac{I}{30}$	$\frac{4I}{30}$	0.470	CD	4	$\frac{I}{20}$	$\frac{4I}{20}$	0.60
				1.000					1.000

Note: Single underscoring lines indicate joint is temporarily balanced; double lines indicate final balance.

PROBLEMS

9-32a, b, c, d, e, f, g, h, j, k. Determine the restraining moments over the supports of those beams shown in Fig. 9-25 by moment distribution.

9-33a, b, c, d, e, f, g, h. Determine the restraining moments over the supports of those beams shown in Fig. 9-32 by moment distribution.

PLASTIC ANALYSIS AND DESIGN OF STATICALLY INDETERMINATE BEAMS

9-20. Introduction

The major limiting factor in every elastic design problem is the allowable working stress. Not only does it dictate the most economical section required but it also provides an ample margin of strength for contingencies. An unnecessarily low allowable stress results in an inexcusable waste of material, while an excessively high stress produces a false and possibly dangerous economy.

The theory of plastic analysis proposes an economical and justifiable procedure to permit the development of the reserve strength in structural materials. This new concept would base analysis and design on the plastic strength rather than on the attainment of the yield point.

9-21. Basic features of plastic analysis and design

The increase in allowable load permitted by plastic design is derived from a new understanding of *limiting usefulness.* Heretofore, when applied to a beam this term meant that it lost its usefulness upon the attainment of the yield stress on any one of its sections. The allowable stress was based on this yield stress. It is important to note, however that, even after the stress on a section attains the yield point, a considerable amount of elastic strength still remains in the interior fibers (Fig. 9-38); see also § 7-12. One of the features of plastic design is the use of this reserve strength in the determination of the allowable load.

The second feature of plastic design applied to indeterminate beams pertains to the use of redistributed moments developed through the formation of *plastic hinges.* These plastic hinges develop at points of maximum moment and when fully formed produce a reasonably constant rotational resistance called the *plastic moment.* Because a plastic moment cannot increase in magnitude and the section on which it operates acts as a hinge, any

Figure 9-38

additional load applied to the beam must be resisted by other portions which have retained some of their elastic restraint. This shifting of resistance under perfectly stable conditions levels off the magnitudes of the maximum moments occurring on an indeterminate beam and permits a new evaluation of its limit of maximum usefulness.

These two features of plastic analysis and design will now be presented in the following illustrative problems.

Illustrative Problem 7. Compare the maximum uniform loads permitted on a low-carbon structural steel beam 6 ft long, and fixed at each end by the elastic and plastic analysis methods, if its cross section is 4 in. wide by 6 in. deep (Fig. 9-39). Use a factor of safety of 2.0 based on a yield point of 30,000 psi. Section modulus equals 24 in.[3] Assume elastic limit stress to be equal to yield stress (see Fig. 9-38).

SOLUTION. *Elastic design:* From § 9-8 the end and center moments of a uniformly loaded beam fixed at each end were shown to be $wl^2/12$ and

Figure 9-39

$wl^2/24$, respectively. Using the greater of these two moments in the flexure formula, the maximum uniform load the beam can carry is computed as

$$w = \frac{12 \times 30,000 \times 24}{36 \times 12} = 20,000 \text{ lb per ft}$$

Its safe load using the factor of safety of 2.0 is equal to 10,000 lb per ft.

Plastic design: The restraining moments at the ends of the beam at the time the load of 20,000 lb per ft is acting are equal to $M_y = wl^2/12$, or 60,000 ft-lb. Suppose now the load were to increase. Immediately the outside fibers of the end sections would yield, and the transformation process from elastic to plastic resistance at that section would start (see Fig. 9-38). This process takes place gradually as more load is applied, and it terminates when the resisting moment attains the value of the constant plastic moment M_p. This, for our rectangular section, is equal to $1.5M_y$, or 90,000 ft-lb (§ 7-12). Upon the attainment of this moment, each end section rotates as a plastic hinge shifting the points of inflection closer to the ends. Since the moment at these hinges cannot increase, the beam becomes only partially restrained. With the ordinates to the moment diagram increasing with increased load, the moment at the center section must necessarily increase until it, too, attains the value of the plastic moment. At this point the beam will have lost its stability and will have arrived at its maximum useful limit (Fig. 9-39(h).

At the time the beam loses stability, the load acting on it computed from the free body of one-half of the beam, is equal to

$$\frac{wl}{2} \times \frac{l}{4} = 2 \times 90,000$$

$$w = 40,000 \text{ lb per ft}$$

or twice the critical load computed by the elastic analysis.

It should be noted that at no time between the initial yielding at the end sections and the formation of the center hinge was the beam on the verge of collapse. Moreover, the beam deflected less than a corresponding simple beam because of its end restraining moments M_p.

The allowable load permitted on the beam using the plastic analysis with a factor of safety of 2.0 is, therefore, equal to 20,000 lb per ft. This load will just develop yielding at the end sections. The beam, however, will function as safely as any other.

9-22. Comments on plastic design

Plastic design should not be considered as a replacement for elastic design. Actually, only a limited number of structures can be analyzed by this method, although the quantity of materials affected may be large.

Obviously, any design calling for exact deflection calculations, or including the effects of fatigue, buckling, brittle fracture, etc., cannot be analyzed by plastic analysis.

Illustrative Problem 8. In the beam of Fig. 9-40 determine the magnitude of P for both elastic and plastic design. Use a factor of safety of 2.0, based on a yield strength of 30,000 psi. Shape factor = 1.14, and I/C = 20 in.[3] Use the stress-strain diagram given in Fig. 9-38.

SOLUTION. *Elastic analysis:* The elastic analysis of this beam limits the load to 13,300 lb, based on the maximum moment on the beam of $\frac{6}{32}PL$.

ELASTIC ANALYSIS	PLASTIC ANALYSIS

(a)   Plastic hinges at B, D and E
(d)

Moment diagram, elastic loading at yield point
(b)

Moment diagram, plastic loading
(e)

Computations

$$M_y = \tfrac{6}{32}P_yL = \frac{s_yI}{C} = \frac{30,000 \times 20}{12} = 50,000 \text{ ft-lb}$$

$$P_y = \frac{30,000 \times 20 \times 32}{6 \times 10 \times 12}$$

$$P_y = 26,670 \text{ lb}$$

$$P = \frac{26,670}{2} = 13,330 \text{ lb}$$

Computations

$$M_p = 50,000 \times 1.14 = 57,000 \text{ ft-lb}$$

$$(R_A)_p = (R_C)_p = \frac{57,000}{5} = 11,400 \text{ lb}$$

$$\Sigma M_{R_2} = 11,400 \times 10 - 5P_p + 57,000 = 0$$

$$P_p = \frac{114,000 + 57,000}{5} = 34,200 \text{ lb}$$

$$P = \frac{34,200}{2} = 17,100 \text{ lb}$$

$R_1 = 4150 \text{ lb}$ $R_2 = 18,300 \text{ lb}$ $R_3 = 4150 \text{ lb}$
Actual loading, elastic analysis
(c)

$R_1 = 5700 \text{ lb}$ $R_2 = 22,800 \text{ lb}$ $R_3 = 5700 \text{ lb}$
Actual loading, plastic analysis
(f)

Figure 9-40

Plastic analysis: Following a procedure similar to that used for the previous illustrative problem, the loads P are increased until the moments over support R_B, and those under each load P attain a value of the plastic moment M_p. The value of P at the occurrence of plastic moments at B, D, and E is determined by a free-body analysis.

Illustrative Problem 9. Calculate the WF section required for the continuous beam of Illustrative Problem 8, using the elastic and plastic design methods, if P equals 17,100 lb. Use a factor of safety of 2.0, based on a yield strength of 30,000 psi. Steel has a stress-strain diagram given in Fig. 9-38. Shape factor equals 1.14. Disregard shear or lateral buckling.

SOLUTION. Note that plastic design required here is the reverse of the plastic analysis presented in Illustrative Problem 8. The steps comparing the two designs are shown in Fig. 9-41.

ELASTIC DESIGN	*PLASTIC DESIGN*
Step 1: Calculate the bending moment diagrams, using shear area:	*Step* 1: Anticipate the location of plastic hinges

Step 2: Calculate the allowable stress:

$$s = \frac{30,000}{2.0} = 15,000 \text{ psi}$$

Step 3: Calculate $\frac{I}{C}$ required:

$$\frac{I}{C} = \frac{32,100 \times 12}{15,000} = 25.7 \text{ in.}^3$$

Step 4: Select WF beam required:
10″ WF 25 lb

Step 2: Calculate M_p, using moment equation for point D. Apply factor of safety to load:

$$M_D = \left(17,100 - \frac{M_p}{10}\right) 5 = M_p$$
$$1.5 \ M_p = 17,100 \times 5$$
$$M_p = 57,000 \text{ ft-lb}$$

Step 3: Obtain M_y; calculate $\frac{I}{C}$ required:

$$M_y = \frac{57,000}{1.14} = 50,000 \text{ ft-lb}$$
$$\frac{I}{C} = \frac{50,000 \times 12}{30,000} = 20.0 \text{ in.}^3$$

Step 4: Select WF beam required:
10″ WF 21 lb

Figure 9-41

PROBLEMS

Note: Use the stress-strain diagram of Fig. 9-38 in the solution of the following problems. Let yield stress equal 30,000 psi.

9-34. Compare the maximum concentrated load that may be placed at the midpoint of a fixed ended steel beam, 12 ft long, by the elastic and plastic analysis method, if its cross section is 4 in. wide and 6 in. deep. Use a factor of safety of 2.0, based on the yield stress. *Answers:* 20 kips, 30 kips.

9-35. Do Problem 9-34, using equal concentrated loads at the third points.

9-36. Compare the values of the maximum concentrated loads which act at the centers of a two-span 10-in. *WF* 49-lb continuous beam (each span equals 20 ft) by the elastic and plastic analysis methods. Use a factor of safety of 2.0, based on the yield stress. Shape factor equals 1.14. *Answers:* 18.2 kips, 23.4 kips.

9-37. Compare, by the elastic and plastic analysis methods, the maximum uniform load that may be applied to a 10 in. *WF* 49-lb continuous beam of 3 20-ft spans and fixed at each end. Use a factor of safety of 1.5, based on the yield stress. Shape factor equals 1.14.

9-38. Design a fixed-ended *WF* beam 12 ft long, uniformly loaded with 4,000 lb per ft, by the elastic and plastic design methods. Use a factor of safety of 1.5, based on the yield stress. *Answers:* Elastic $I/c = 28.8$ in.^{3}, plastic $I/c = 18.95$ in.^{3}

Note: Many previous problems given in this chapter may be assigned for solution by the method of plastic analysis.

Chapter Ten

STRESSES DUE TO ECCENTRICALLY APPLIED LOADS

10-1. *A fundamental relationship*

Whenever an axial load is moved to a position parallel to the longitudinal axis of the member upon which it acts, the cross sections perpendicular to that axis are subjected to a combination of both axial and bending stresses. The reason for the occurrence of this combination of stresses may best be ascertained by a quick review of a fundamental relationship established in the study of elementary mechanics. The illustration concerns the resolution of a force into a force and a couple. A discussion of this relationship follows.

10-2. *Resolution of a force into a force and a couple*

If bar AB of Fig. 10-1 were acted upon by force P, its tendency to turn about point A would be measured by the moment of P about A, or Pa. If two opposing forces, P' and P'', equal and parallel to P were now to be added to the same bar, the moment of the force system and its turning effect about point A would still be Pa, because the moments of the two added forces would cancel each other. The summation of the verti-

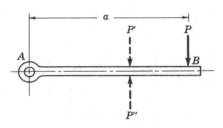

Figure 10-1

cal forces would also remain the same. Since this resolution allows forces P'' and P to be considered as a couple, and P' as a single force, we may conclude that the *external* effect of a force may be made equal to a force and a couple by adding two forces which are equal, opposite, and parallel to the given force. Although the point at which the two opposing forces are added is optional, the opportunity of using the remaining single force P' for a specific purpose, such as is indicated in the next paragraph, should not be overlooked. It should be remembered that in this resolution all the forces are externally applied.

10-3. *The action of an eccentric load on a short compression member*

Consider a vertical force P acting in a plane of symmetry of the block shown in Fig. 10-2. It will be noted that the block is subjected to a combination of both compressive and bending strains. Let us now add on the center line of the block two additional *external* forces, P' and P'', that are equal and parallel to P and opposite to each other. The addition of these forces to the block will not, of course, alter its equilibrium condition, since they cancel each other. The three forces comprising couple PP'' and force P' will, therefore, have the same effect as would force P acting alone.

Figure 10-2

$$\frac{4\,0}{\underline{4\,0}}$$
$$1\,6\,0\,0$$

But from Chapter 2 we learned that an axial load, such as P', produces only direct (in this case compressive) stress on cross sections perpendicular to its action line. It was also indicated in Chapter 7 that a couple can produce only pure bending stress. Thus, we may further conclude that the addition of forces P' and P'' on the perpendicular passing through the centroid of the area upon which the stress is desired produces the same effect as force P would acting alone and affords a means of separating the direct from the bending stress.

To illustrate, suppose the block of Fig. 10-2 to have a cross section of 12 by 12 in. If force P equals 14,400 lb and has an eccentricity of 3 in., the moment of couple PP'' will be

$$M_{pp''} = Pe = 3 \times 14{,}400 = 43{,}200 \text{ in.-lb}$$

The maximum bending unit stress produced by this bending moment will, therefore, be

$$s = \frac{Mc}{I} = \frac{Pec}{I} = \frac{43{,}200 \times 6}{\frac{1}{12} \times 12 \times 12^3} = 150.0 \text{ psi}$$

The compressive stress due to force P' will be

$$s_c = \frac{P'}{A} = \frac{14{,}400}{144} = 100 \text{ psi}$$

These two stresses, which act simultaneously, may be algebraically added in accordance with the principle of superposition if their total does not exceed the proportional limit of the material of which the member is made. The maximum and minimum stresses found on the cross section at points A and B, respectively, may be expressed algebraically as follows, using the plus sign to indicate tension and the minus sign to indicate compression,

$$s_A = -\frac{P'}{A} - \frac{Mc}{I} = -\frac{P}{A} - \frac{Pec}{I} \tag{10.1}$$

$$= -\frac{14,400}{144} - \frac{43,200 \times 6}{\frac{1}{12} \times 12 \times 12^3}$$

$$= -100 - 150 = -250 \text{ psi (compression)}$$

$$s_B = -\frac{P'}{A} + \frac{Mc}{I} = -\frac{P}{A} + \frac{Pec}{I} \tag{10.2}$$

$$= -\frac{14,400}{144} + \frac{43,200 \times 6}{\frac{1}{12} \times 12 \times 12^3}$$

$$= -100 + 150 = 50 \text{ psi (tension)}$$

The stress distribution on the cross section is represented graphically in Fig. 10-3.

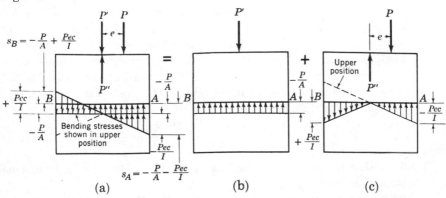

Figure 10-3

Effect of varying the eccentricity. As the value of the eccentricity e (Fig. 10-3) is reduced, the magnitude of the couple PP'' and its accompanying bending unit stress are also reduced. The compressive unit stress P'/A remains the same, however, since the magnitude and location of force P' does not change.

The condition that exists at point B when the direct compression unit stress P'/A equals the tensile bending unit stress Pec/I is of considerable engineering importance because it determines the limiting position of P necessary to retain a compressive unit stress over the entire cross-sectional area. Any further increase in the value of e would enable the maximum tensile flexural stress at B to exceed the counteracting compressive unit stress, as shown in the problem of the preceding paragraph.

This limiting position of force P is obtained by setting the two stresses at B equal to each other.

$$\frac{P'}{A} = \frac{Pec}{I}$$

Since $P' = P$ and $I = Ar^2$, where r is the radius of gyration of the section about the bending axis, we may write

$$\frac{P}{A} = \frac{Pec}{Ar^2}$$

from which

$$e = \frac{r^2}{c} \tag{10.3}$$

The above equation is general in that it applies to all cross sections. For rectangular sections as used above, the value of e will be

$$e = \frac{1}{c} \times \frac{I}{A} = \frac{1}{c} \times \frac{bd^3}{12} \times \frac{1}{bd} = \frac{d^2}{12c}$$

But $c = d/2$, making $e = \dfrac{d^2}{12 \times d/2} = \dfrac{d}{6}$ $\tag{10.4}$

Thus, we are assured that no tensile stress will occur on a cross section of a rectangular block as long as the eccentric load located on an axis of symmetry acts within a distance of $d/6$ to either side of the center. Interpreted in a slightly different way, this statement sometimes reads "Keep the load in the middle third to prevent tension on the outer fibers."

To ascertain the limiting value of eccentricity for a vertical cylinder, one needs only substitute the proper values of I, A, and c in Eq. 10.3.

$$e = \frac{1}{c} \times \frac{I}{A} = \frac{1}{d/2} \times \frac{\pi d^4/64}{\pi d^2/4} = \frac{d}{8} \tag{10.5}$$

It follows that to prevent tension in a vertical cylinder, the load must be kept within the *middle fourth*.

The equations for limiting eccentricities find their greatest use in the design of members made of materials that have relatively little strength in tension. Such materials are concrete, brick, cast iron, plaster of Paris, and so forth. In the design of a plain concrete dam, for instance, the resultant force at any rectangular cross section must be kept within the *middle third* to prevent tension.

PROBLEMS

10-1. A short compression member, Fig. 10-4, 12 by 12-in. in cross section has a load of 50,000 lb applied on one axis of symmetry, 1 in. from the center of the cross section. Determine the stresses on section A-A. Show suitable sketches.

10-2. In the preceding problem, how great an eccentricity should force P have to obtain a tensile unit stress of 200 psi on cross section A-A? Show sketch of stress distribution. *Answer:* 3.15 in.

Figure 10-4   Figure 10-5

10-3. If in Problem 10-1 it is desired to maintain only compressive stress on section A-A, what limiting value may the eccentricity have? Show sketch of stress distribution.

10-4. A rectangular concrete footing 5 ft wide by 6 ft long supports an eccentric load of 200,000 lb (Fig. 10-5) which acts on the longer axis of symmetry but 6 in. off the shorter axis. Determine the stress distribution at the base of footing due to this applied load. *Answer:* Maximum stress is 10,000 lb per sq ft.

10-5. Four bolts, arranged in a rectangular pattern, hold the offset fixture of Fig. 10-6. Determine the unit stress on the net area of the bolts if the offset plate, which is acted upon by the eccentric load as shown, is located mid-way between pairs of resisting bolts. Total bolt area = 1.00 sq in.

Figure 10-6   Figure 10-7

10-6. A wooden beam is 12 ft long, 6 in. wide, and 15 in. deep. The beam is hinged at the left end and is simply supported at the right end. There is a uniform load of 1000 lb per ft over the entire length of the beam and a compressive load of 9000 lb applied at the centroid of the right end. Determine the maximum tensile and compressive unit-stresses in the beam. Disregard the deflection of the beam. Hinge is located on center line of beam. *Answers:* s_c = 1057 psi, s_t = 857 psi.

10-7. A C frame (cross section 1 in. by 3 in.) with pin supports at A and B, is subjected to loads as shown in Fig. 10-7. (a) Determine the maximum fiber stress and state where it occurs. (b) What is the maximum fiber stress acting on the vertical section Y-Y? The 1 in. dimension is perpendicular to the plane of the paper. *Answer:* (a) 12,800 psi. (b) 8800 psi.

10-8. A compression block, whose cross-section measures 6 in. by 12 in., carries two eccentric loads as shown in Fig. 10-8. Find stress at edge ab and at edge cd of the right section $abcd$.

Figure 10-8

10-4. When an eccentric load on a short compression member does not lie in a plane of symmetry

The more general case of eccentrically applied loads on short compression members occurs when the applied load P does not fall within a plane of symmetry (Fig. 10-9). To determine the stresses imposed on cross section $ABCD$, place two equal, opposite, and parallel forces P_1 and P_2 on the axis line passing through the center of its cross section. The force P_1 will produce direct compression unit stress and the couple PP_2 bending stress. The plane of the couple is not, however, in either of the two principal bending planes. This difficulty can be overcome by adding two more equal, opposite, and parallel forces P_3 and P_4, placed on axis 1-1 at the foot of a perpendicular dropped from the point of action of force P. The five forces now acting on our member provide the following stresses.

(1) Force P_1. A uniformly distributed compression unit stress.
(2) Couple PP_4. A bending unit stress about axis 1-1.
(3) Couple P_2P_3. A bending unit stress about axis 2-2.

When placed in equation form, the stresses at the corners of cross section $ABCD$ are as follows:

$$s_A = -\frac{P}{A} + \frac{Pa \sin \theta}{I_{1-1}} \times \frac{b}{2} + \frac{Pa \cos \theta}{I_{2-2}} \times \frac{d}{2} \tag{10.6}$$

$$s_B = -\frac{P}{A} + \frac{Pa \sin \theta}{I_{1-1}} \times \frac{b}{2} - \frac{Pa \cos \theta}{I_{2-2}} \times \frac{d}{2} \tag{10.7}$$

$$s_C = -\frac{P}{A} - \frac{Pa \sin \theta}{I_{1-1}} \times \frac{b}{2} - \frac{Pa \cos \theta}{I_{2-2}} \times \frac{d}{2} \tag{10.8}$$

Figure 10-9

$$s_D = -\frac{P}{A} - \frac{Pa\sin\theta}{I_{1-1}} \times \frac{b}{2} + \frac{Pa\cos\theta}{I_{2-2}} \times \frac{d}{2} \qquad (10.9)$$

From a perusal of the above formulas, it is evident that s_C is the maximum compressive stress, and s_A is the maximum tensile stress produced on cross section $ABCD$. To obtain the limiting position of P that will mark the beginning of tensile stress at A, the equation of stresses occurring at A must be made equal to zero. When a line is drawn through the locus of points on the cross section, marking the beginning of tensile stress anywhere on the cross section, the area enclosed by this line is known as the *kern*. It is shown as the shaded area in Fig. 10-10.

Figure 10-10

Illustrative Problem 1. If in Fig. 10-9 the load $P = 96$ kips, $b = 8$ in., $d = 12$ in., and the eccentricity with respect to both axes is 2 in., determine the stresses at the corners of the plane $ABCD$.

SOLUTION.

$$s_A = s_c + s'_t + s''_t$$

$$s_A = -\frac{96}{96} + \frac{96 \times 2 \times 4}{\frac{1}{12} \times 12 \times 8^3} + \frac{96 \times 2 \times 6}{\frac{1}{12} \times 8 \times 12^3}$$

$$= -1.0 + 1.5 + 1.0 = +1.5 \text{ kips per sq in.} \tag{10.10}$$

$$s_B = -1.0 + 1.5 - 1.0 = -0.5 \text{ kips per sq in.} \tag{10.11}$$

$$s_C = -1.0 - 1.5 - 1.0 = -3.5 \text{ kips per sq in.} \tag{10.12}$$

$$s_D = -1.0 - 1.5 + 1.0 = -1.5 \text{ kips per sq in.} \tag{10.13}$$

These stresses are plotted as ordinates to plane $ABCD$ (Fig. 10-11a). Because each of the three component stress patterns varies linearly from point

(a)   (b)

Figure 10-11

to point, their combined stress pattern must also vary linearly. Note from Fig. 10-11(b) that the neutral axis, drawn between the points of zero stress on the periphery, is not at right angles to the plane of the couple PP_2. *This is of great significance.* Only if the load acts on one of the principal axes of a section will the plane of bending coincide with the plane of the couple producing the bending. See assumptions of flexure formula, Chapter 7.

PROBLEMS

10-9. Determine the stresses at the corners of cross section $ABCD$ of the compression member in Fig. 10-9, if load P of 100,000 lb acts 2 in. off each axis of symmetry. Cross section equals 12 by 12 in. Show sketch of stress distribution. *Answer:* $s_A = 693$ psi, $s_B = -693$ psi, $s_C = -2080$ psi, $s_D = -693$ psi.

10-10. What would be the theoretical stress distribution on cross section $ABCD$ of Fig. 10-9, if load P of 100,000 lb acted through one of the corners of the cross section? Cross section equals 12 by 12 in. Show sketch of stress distribution.

10-11. If a short compression member has a cross section of 12 by 18 in. and a load of 150,000 lb is placed 2 in. off each axis of symmetry, what stress distribution would be obtained on a cross section perpendicular to its longitudinal axis? The load is parallel to the longitudinal axis of the member. *Answer:* $s_{max.} = -1848$ psi.

10-5. When an eccentric load is applied to a non-symmetrical cross-section

When an eccentric load is applied to a non-symmetrical cross section, the load is resolved, as previously suggested, into a force and a couple, the resolution taking place at the centroid of the cross section. Should the plane of the couple not coincide with a principal axis, the procedure explained in § 7-8 should be followed to obtain the flexural stresses. These, combined algebraically with the direct stresses produced by the central force, will give the total stresses acting on the section.

PROBLEMS

10-12. If a couple of 200,000 in.-lb is applied on axis y-y of the section shown in Fig. 10-12, causing compression on the upper fibers, (a) locate the position of the neutral axis; (b) what will the stresses be at the six corners shown on the cross section? *Answers:* (a) $\theta = 12°55'$ (b) $s_A = -2660$ psi, $s_B = -990$ psi, $s_F = 2040$ psi.

10-13. If a load of 20 kips were applied at point B perpendicular to the cross section shown in Fig. 10-12, locate the position of the neutral axis and determine the stresses at points B and F. *Answers:* $s_B = -2210$ psi, $s_F = +1300$ psi.

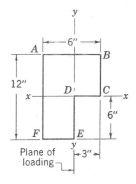

Figure 10-12

10-6. Critical stress in C frames

The supporting member or frame for many pieces of industrial equipment is made in the form of a C. Punch and drill presses, riveting and welding machines, cranes, off-center supports are only some of the more important apparatus that are built with a resemblance to this shape. In each instance, forces act on the ends of the C to either spread or compress the opening. Being farthest from the applied loads, those sections opposite the opening generally develop the maximum stresses.

Let us investigate the stresses due to an applied load of 12,000 lb on section A-A of Fig. 10-13. To clarify this problem, that portion of the C frame above section A-A is removed and shown in Fig. 10-14. The addition of the two equal, opposite, and parallel forces necessary in the resolution

Figure 10-13

(a)

(b)

Figure 10-14

of force P requires the location of the center of gravity of section A-A. Its computation follows, the moments being taken about the inside edge of the section.

	AREA (sq in.)	x	Ax
I	12	5	60
II	12	1	12
	$\Sigma A = 24$		$\Sigma Ax = 72$

$$\bar{x} = \frac{\Sigma Ax}{\Sigma A} = \frac{72}{24} = 3 \text{ in.}$$

It is now possible to resolve force P into a force and a couple by adding the two 12,000-lb forces at the center of gravity of the section. Bearing in mind that each of these three forces is an external force, there are now acting on the free body an external couple PP_1 and a single external force P_2. Although it is not difficult to visualize that the couple produces tensile stress at B and compression stress at C, some difficulty may be experienced in determining the character of the stress produced by force P_2. This difficulty may be easily overcome, however, by recalling the fact that P_2, as an upward-acting external force, requires a downward-acting internal-resistance stress on section A-A to hold it in equilibrium. Since this stress acts away from section A-A of the free body (Fig. 10-14), it must be a tensile stress.

Written in equation form, the stresses at B and C are

$$s_B = + \frac{P}{A} + \frac{Pec}{I} \qquad (10.14)$$

$$s_C = + \frac{P}{A} - \frac{Pec}{I} \qquad (10.15)$$

Section A-A

Figure 10-15

Before the numerical value of these stresses may be computed, however, the value of I must be obtained about the center-of-gravity axis for the whole section (Fig. 10-15). The required computation follows:

$$
\begin{array}{llll}
 & I_{\text{c.g.}} & Ad^2 & I_{\text{c.g.}} + Ad^2 \\
\text{I}\ldots\ldots\ldots & \tfrac{1}{12} \times 2 \times 6^3 = 36.0 & 12 \times \overline{2}^2 = 48.0 & 84.0 \\
\text{II}\ldots\ldots\ldots & \tfrac{1}{12} \times 6 \times 2^3 = 4.0 & 12 \times \overline{2}^2 = 48.0 & 52.0 \\
 & & \Sigma\,(I_{\text{c.g.}} + Ad^2) = & \overline{136 \text{ in.}^4}
\end{array}
$$

The numerical values of s_B and s_C may now be computed, bearing in mind that one is located 3 in., the other, 5 in. away from the neutral axis.

$$s_B = + \frac{12{,}000}{24} + \frac{12{,}000 \times 18 \times 3}{136} = 500 + 4760 = +5260 \text{ psi}$$

$$s_C = + \frac{12{,}000}{24} - \frac{12{,}000 \times 18 \times 5}{136} = +500 - 7940 = -7440 \text{ psi}$$

PROBLEMS

10-14. The offset bracket shown in Fig. 10-16 is acted upon by a force of 2500 lb. Find the maximum normal stress acting on section A-A if its cross section measures $\frac{1}{2}$ in. thick by 3 in. deep.

10-15. If, in Problem 10-14, the force of 2500 lb were rotated downward through an angle of 45°, what would be the maximum normal stress acting on section A-A located 8 in. away from the center of the hole? *Answer:* 16,450 psi.

Figure 10-16

Figure 10-17

Figure 10-18

10-16. In Fig. 10-17 is shown a test specimen for testing the shear strength of glued joints. Assuming no distortion of the joint and a load of 2000 lb, determine the theoretical bending stress imposed on the glued surface under this arrangement. What is the stress distribution on cross section *ABCD*? What arrangement could be more satisfactorily employed in obtaining the shear strength of glued surfaces?

10-17. A metal-shaping machine has a frame as shown in Fig. 10-18. If load *P* has a maximum value of 8000 lb, find the maximum normal stresses developed on cross section *A-A*. *Answer:* 1595 psi, 2210 psi.

10-18. Revise the length of the stem in the *T* section of Fig. 10-18 to make the maximum tensile stress on section *A-A* equal to 3000 psi.

10-19. A life-boat stanchion (Fig. 10-19) is made from a steel pipe having a 3-in. outside diameter and a $\frac{1}{4}$-in. wall thickness. What load may be applied to the stanchion through an eccentricity of 36 in. if the maximum allowable normal stress is 20,000 psi? *Answer:* 752 lb.

10-20. A tension member has a 2-in. offset forged into its length. If a cross-section at the offset is as indicated in Fig. 10-20, determine the stress distribution acting upon this section if the load is 60,000 lb.

10-7. Eccentrically loaded riveted joints

Whenever a riveted joint is subjected to an eccentric load, the method used for the determination of the imposed stresses is once again based upon the resolution of the applied force into another force and a couple. Let us

Figure 10-19   Figure 10-20

illustrate by considering the joint of Fig. 10-21. Here the loads imposed upon a crane runway girder are carried by two gusset plates placed on either ride of a main column. It is desired to find the shearing stresses in the sivets if the load placed on each plate is 10,000 lb and each rivet has a diameter of $\frac{7}{8}$ in.

From our previous discussions, it is evident that the 10,000-lb loads will tend to twist as well as push downward the plate on which each is acting. To separate these two effects, such that the single force resulting from the resolution will produce a direct shearing stress $= P/A$, two equal, opposite, and parallel loads need to be added on the vertical center line of each rivet system. Since each plate represents a similar loading condition, let us consider the left plate only.

Determination of direct-shear stress. Because load P_1 passes through the centroid of the rivet group, it produces a resisting shear of equal magnitude acting upward on each rivet.

$$(s_s)_D = \frac{P}{A} = \frac{10,000}{6 \times \frac{\pi}{4}\left(\frac{7}{8}\right)^2} = 2780 \text{ psi}$$

Determination of rotational-shear stress. Couple PP_2, as is true of every couple, can only produce rotation, which will always take place about the center of resistance of a rivet group that is assumed to coincide with its centroid. The centroid of the rivet group of Fig. 10-22 is, by virtue of its symmetry, located at point O.

The determination of the rotational shearing stresses may now proceed by one of two methods:

Figure 10-21

Method 1. This method is based on two assumptions:

(1) The shearing stress on a body subjected to the action of couples varies with the distance from the center of rotation.

(2) That the moment of the applied couple PP_2 is equal to the sum of the moments of the rivet forces acting about point O.

Thus, rivets A, B, C, and D have the same rotational shearing unit stress $(s_s)_R$, since each is located 5 in. away from the center of rotation O. Rivets E and F, located only 3 in. from O, are acted upon only by $\frac{3}{5}(s_s)_R$. These stresses acting on cross-sectional areas of $\frac{7}{8}$-in.-diameter rivets produce forces whose moments equal the moment of the couple PP_2. Thus, we may write

$$4 \times (s_s)_R \times 0.60 \times 5 + 2 \times \tfrac{3}{5}(s_s)_R \times 0.60 \times 3 = 10{,}000 \times 10$$
$$12(s_s)_R + 2.16(s_s)_R = 100{,}000$$

$$(s_s)_R = \frac{100{,}000}{14.16} = 7060 \text{ psi (rivets } A, B, C, \text{ and } D)$$

$$\tfrac{3}{5}(s_s)_R = 4240 \text{ psi (rivets } E \text{ and } F)$$

Method 2. This method is based upon the application of the torsion formula, its moment of inertia being placed equal to the polar moment of inertia of the rivet group taken about the center of rotation O. Thus,

$$J = \Sigma \left(J_{\text{c.g.}} + Ad^2\right)$$

Since, however, the value of the polar moment of each rivet about its own centroidal axis is usually insignificant in contrast to the Ad^2 term, we may write the value of the polar moment equal to

$$J = \Sigma\ Ad^2$$

Thus

$$J = 4 \times 0.60 \times 5^2 = 60.0 \text{ in.}^4$$

$$2 \times 0.60 \times 3^2 = \underline{10.8}$$

$$70.8 \text{ in.}^4$$

Inserting this value in the torsion formula, using the distance to the outermost rivet equal to c, we obtain

$$(s_s)_R = \frac{Pec}{J} = \frac{10{,}000 \times 10 \times 5}{70.8}$$

$$= \cdot 7060 \text{ psi (rivets } A, B, C, \text{ and } D)$$

$$\tfrac{3}{5}(s_s)_R = 4240 \text{ psi (rivets } E \text{ and } F)$$

Note. No variation of stress is considered across the cross-sectional area of a resisting rivet.

A comparison of both methods reveals that either may be used to produce the same result.

Obtaining the resultant stress. In the derivation of the torsion formula, the direction of stress at any point was found to be tangent to the circle drawn through that point having its center at the center of rotation of the resisting area. As applied to the present problem, this statement indicates that the torsional stress on the various rivet areas acts tangential to the concentric circle passing through them (Fig. 10-22). To combine these stresses with the upward-acting direct shearing stress, we must obtain their vector sum. In other words,

$$s_s = (s_s)_D \nrightarrow (s_s)_R \tag{10.16}$$

where the sign $\rightarrow$ infers vector addition.

Thus, the resultant shearing stresses as obtained from the vector diagrams of Fig. 10-22 are as follows:

For Rivets A and D:
$$s_s = 2780 \nrightarrow 7060 = 7280 \text{ psi}$$

For Rivets B and C:
$$s_s = 2780 \nrightarrow 7060 = 9000 \text{ psi}$$

For Rivet E:
$$s_s = 4240 - 2780 = 1460 \text{ psi}$$

For Rivet F:
$$s_s = 4240 + 2780 = 7020 \text{ psi}$$

Figure 10-22

PROBLEMS

10-21. Find the shearing unit stress developed in each of the rivets of the horizontal chord member shown in Fig. 10-23. Rivet diameter is $\frac{7}{8}$ in. *Answer:* $(s_s)_A = 13,880$ psi.

10-22. Find the maximum force P that can be permitted on the bracket shown in Fig. 10-24 if the maximum allowable shearing stress on the rivets is 10,000 psi. Rivet diameter is $\frac{7}{8}$ in. Disregard the strength of the angle.

Figure 10-23

Figure 10-24

10-23. Find the maximum shearing unit stress in the rivets of Fig.10-25. Rivet diameter is $\frac{7}{8}$ in. *Answer:* $(s_s)_{AB} = 10{,}610$ psi.

10-24. Find the maximum force P permitted on the joint of Fig. 10-26 if the maximum allowable shearing stress on the rivets is 10,000 psi and the rivets are $\frac{7}{8}$ in. in diameter.

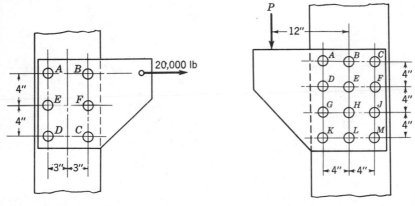

Figure 10-25   Figure 10-26

10-25. Find the maximum shearing unit stress in the rivets of Fig. 10-27. Rivet diameter is $\frac{7}{8}$ in. *Answer:* $s_A = 11{,}380$ psi, $s_B = 10{,}280$ psi, $s_C = 7650$ psi, $s_D = 5900$ psi, $s_E = 9900$ psi, $s_F = 8630$ psi.

Figure 10-27

10-8. *Eccentrically loaded welded joints*

The analysis of eccentrically loaded welded joints is similar to the analysis of eccentrically loaded riveted joints. Consider the joint shown in

Figure 10-28

Fig. 10-28. In order to separate the direct and rotational shearing effects, the applied load of 20 kips is resolved into a force and a couple by adding the forces P_1 and P_2 to the joint on a line passing through the centroid of the resisting welds. Thus the direct stress due to P_1 is equal to

$$(s_s)_D = \frac{20,000}{\frac{1}{2} \text{ in.} \times 0.707 \times 20 \text{ in.}} = 2830 \text{ psi}$$

The rotational shearing stress due to the couple PP_2 will be maximum at points A, B, C, and D, and is found by modifying the torsion formula, J being equal to the sum of I_{x-x} and I_{y-y} of the throat areas.

$$I_{x-x} = \Sigma \, Ad^2$$
$$= (10 \times \tfrac{1}{2} \times 0.707 \times 5^2)2 = 176.5 \text{ in.}^4$$
$$I_{y-y} = (\tfrac{1}{12} \times \tfrac{1}{2} \times 0.707 \times 10^3)2 = \underline{\quad 58.9 \quad}$$
$$235.4 \text{ in.}^4$$

$$\text{Max } (s_s)_R = \frac{T_R r}{J} = \frac{20,000 \times 12 \times 7.07}{235.4} = 7210 \text{ psi}$$

The maximum shear stress at any point is found by taking the vector sum of its direct and rotational shearing stresses. Thus at points B and C (Fig. 10-28b) where the critical stress occurs, the maximum shear stress equals 9430 psi.

Other more involved eccentrically loaded welded joints, acted upon by a couple lying in the plane of the welds, are solved in the same manner shown above. In such problems, it is imperative that the center of gravity of the resisting welds is determined first by considering each straight length of weld as a rectangle, having an area equal to its length times its throat distance. The two added forces P_1 and P_2 required for the resolution into a force and a couple are always added on a line passing through the centroid. To calculate the polar moment of inertia pass x and y axes through the centroid of the resisting welds and compute the I_{x-x} and I_{y-y} of the rectangular areas previously mentioned. The sum of I_{x-x} and I_{y-y} will give the required value of J.

If the load applied to an eccentrically loaded welded joint produces flexural stresses on the weld accompanied by a direct shear (Fig. 10-29), the

| Figure 10-29 | Figure 10-30 |

resultant stress at a point can not be found by vectorial addition. Reference should be made to the chapter on Combined Stress for the solution to such problems. If, however, the flexural stresses produced by the moment occur with direct tensile or compressive stresses acting in the same direction such as in Fig. 10-30, a simple algebraic addition provides the total stress at any point.

PROBLEMS

Use A.I.S.C. maximum allowable shearing stress of 13,600 psi on the throat of fillet welds in solving the following problems.

10-26. If in Fig. 10-28, the top and bottom fillet welds are 8 in. long and have a leg equal to $\frac{5}{16}$ in., what load having an eccentricity of 15 in. can be sustained? *Answer:* 12,400 lb.

10-27. Determine the minimum size of fillet weld required for the weld arrangement shown in Fig. 10-28 if the load is 15 kips and acts with an eccentricity of 12 in.

10-28. In the joint of Fig. 10-31, compute the maximum safe load P that can be applied. *Answer:* 10,200 lb.

10-29. What would be the maximum stress in the weld of Fig. 10-31 if the eccentricity is reduced to 8 in. and the load P is 12 kips?

10-30. What maximum safe load P can the joint of Fig. 10-31 sustain if an additional fillet weld of $\frac{5}{16}$ in. leg is placed from A to D (on opposite side of plate)? $e = 9$ in. *Answer:* 18,500 lb.

Figure 10-31

10-31. If the weld BC in Fig. 10-31 were placed from A to D, what load P could be safely sustained if its location were not changed? $e = 8$ in. *Answer:* 15,600 lb.

10-9. *Stresses in close-coiled helical springs*

The analysis of the resisting stresses of a close-coiled helical spring originates with the resolution of its applied force into a force and couple as it acts on a free body of that spring. Let us consider the free body of the spring in Fig. 10-32(b). As the tension in this free body was released by

Figure 10-32

cutting the spring at section A, the adjoining surfaces must inevitably have slid by each other, indicating the relapse of direct shearing stresses. Then, because the distance between the coils of this spring decreased, there must have been a release of an internal-resisting couple. For illustration, let us consider Fig. 10-32(c), a single coil from the same spring. If this coil were now cut at its mid-point by a radial section and pinned together with a dowel placed along the axis of the spring, any movement of one half section relative to the other would cause rotation of the surfaces at B. Referring again to our free body, Fig. 10-32(b), it must now be evident that as the distance between the coils decreased, internal resistance couples that produce rotation must have been released on every section with, of course, their accompanying torsional shear stress. Having thus established the two basic types of stress in a spring, let us determine their magnitude.

Add two forces at the centroid of section A, equal and parallel to P, and opposite to each other. Forces P and P_2 constitute an external couple that twists section A. Opposing this action must be a counter couple T_R acting on the same section, whose action is somewhat similar to the resisting torque developed in a straight cylindrical shaft. This stress will be recalled as being

$$s_s = \frac{T_R c}{J}, \quad \text{or} \quad \frac{Pec}{J}$$

where c has been made equal to the radius, i.e., the distance from the center of rotation to the outermost fiber.

Torsional resisting stress
(a)

Direct shear stress
(b)

Combined torsional and direct shear stress
(c)

Figure 10-33

In order that this internal couple T_R oppose the couple Pe in Fig. 10-22(b), it must act counterclockwise. The resisting torsional shearing unit stress on section A is represented in Fig. 10-33(a).

The direct stress produced by the upward force P_1 causes the resisting stress to act downward. Its magnitude, equal to $s_s = P/A$ is portrayed in Fig. 10-33(b). When combined, the direct and torsional stresses present a picture somewhat as shown in Fig. 10-33(c).

Under the action of tensile load P_1, the spring is seen to have its maximum shearing unit stress developed on its inner wall. The same would be true if the load were compressive instead of tensile. Regardless, therefore, of the character of the axial load, the inner wall of the spring is its most critically stressed portion.

Adding the direct and torsional shearing unit stresses vectorally, the maximum shearing unit stress as shown in Fig. 10-33(c) is obtained:

$$s_s = \frac{P}{A} + \frac{Pec}{J}$$

$$s_s = \frac{P}{A} + \frac{Pec}{Ar^2} = \frac{P}{A}\left(1 + \frac{ec}{r^2}\right) \tag{10.17}$$

The effect of assuming the torsional stress on the cross section of a spring to be identical to that found on the cross section of a straight cylinder is to render the above equation less accurate as the curvature of the spring is increased. To compensate for this difference, a multiplication factor, known as the *Wahl's correction factor*, is inserted in the above equation to produce the theoretical maximum shearing stress. A table showing the variation of the Wahl's correction factor with the spring index, which is a ratio of the mean coil diameter D to the wire diameter d, is now presented.

TABLE 6

WAHL'S CORRECTION VALUES*

D/d	k_1	D/d	k_1	D/d	k_1
2.00	2.06	4.25	1.37	8.00	1.18
2.25	1.87	4.50	1.35	9.00	1.16
2.50	1.75	4.75	1.33	10.00	1.14
2.75	1.65	5.00	1.31	11.00	1.13
3.00	1.58	5.50	1.28	12.00	1.12
3.25	1.52	6.00	1.25	13.00	1.11
3.50	1.48	6.50	1.23	14.00	1.10
3.75	1.44	7.00	1.21	15.00	1.10
4.00	1.40	7.50	1.20	16.00	1.09

* Derived by A. M. Wahl of Westinghouse Electric and Manufacturing Co., Pittsburgh, Pa.

Where theoretical

$$s = k_1 \frac{Pec}{J}$$

$$m = \frac{D}{d} = \text{spring index} = \frac{\text{mean diameter of coil}}{\text{diameter of wire}}$$

and

$$k_1 = \frac{4m-1}{4m-4} + \frac{0.615}{m} \tag{10.18}$$

10-10. *The work principle*

When a *constant* force P is moved a distance Δ in the direction of the force, *the work performed by the force* is $P\Delta$. Suppose, now, that the force started at zero pounds and gradually increased to its full value P after moving through the distance Δ. If the increase in P were uniform, the work performed would only be $\frac{1}{2}P\Delta$.

These introductory remarks also apply to the deformation of any body under the action of a gradually applied load. The amount of external work performed on such a body is also equal to $\frac{1}{2}P\Delta$, where P is the value of the load after producing its maximum deflection.

As this gradually applied force P deforms the body and performs external work equal to $\frac{1}{2}P\Delta$, the resistance forces scattered through the body perform an identical amount of internal work in passing through their respective strains. This balance of external and internal work allows the presentation of the following verbal equation:

work performed by external forces in contact with body =
internal work caused by resistance forces*

10-11. *Application of work principle to deflection of springs*

If an axial load P were to be gradually applied to a spring until its maximum axial-deformation value of Δ had been attained, the work performed on the spring would be $\frac{1}{2}P\Delta$. Resisting this deformation are a couple T_R and direct shear force P_R acting on every vertical cross section of the spring. Disregarding the effect of the direct shear force, which is ordinarily very small, the internal work performed on the spring by the couple T_R,† twisting the entire length of the spring through an angle θ, is approximately equal to $\frac{1}{2}T_R\theta$. Thus we may write the equation:

$$\tfrac{1}{2}P\Delta = \tfrac{1}{2}T_R\theta = \tfrac{1}{2}Pe\theta$$

from which
$$\Delta = e\theta \qquad (10.19)$$

Substituting in this equation the value of

$$\theta = \frac{Pel}{GJ}$$

(derived in § 5-8) and letting $l = 2\pi en$, where n is the number of turns of a close-coiled spring, there results

$$\Delta = \frac{2\pi Pe^3 n}{GJ} \qquad (10.20)$$

If the polar moment of inertia $J = \pi d^4/32$ were now to be inserted in the above expression, the equation would read

---

* A more detailed account of external and internal energy is presented in Chapter 14.

† From the study of mechanics, the work produced by a couple T_R rotating through an angle θ, expressed in radians, is $T_R\theta$. In this case, the couple is constant throughout the rotation.

$$\Delta = \frac{64Pe^3n}{Gd^4} \tag{10.21}$$

which appears as the deflection formula for closely coiled springs in many of our mechanical-engineering handbooks. The interpretation of each of the items of the above equation, including the units in which each is most frequently used, is as follows:

Δ = spring deflection, in in.

P = axial load on spring, in lb.

e = eccentricity of load: the distance from the action line of the load to the center of the cross-sectional area where stress is desired; mean radius in in.

n = number of active coils participating in the deflection.

G = shear modulus of elasticity, in lb per sq in.

d = diameter of wire, in in.

Illustrative Problem 2. A helical, steel compression spring is to be designed to resist a deflection of 2 in. when subjected to an axial load of 300 lb. If the diameter of the wire is $\frac{1}{4}$ in., and the mean diameter of the coil is $1\frac{1}{4}$ in., find the number of coils required. Allowable shearing unit stress is 80,000 psi.

SOLUTION.

$$\Delta = \frac{64Pe^3n}{Gd^4}$$

$$2 = \frac{64 \times 300 \times \overline{0.625}^3 \times n}{12 \times 10^6 \times (0.25)^4}$$

$$n = \frac{2 \times 12 \times 10^6 \times (0.25)^4}{64 \times 300 \times (0.625)^3} = 20$$

Such a computation should not be considered complete until the stress is checked. Only if the stress is below the allowable should the previous computation be allowed.

Check on stress.

$$s_s = \frac{P}{A}\left(1 + \frac{ec}{r^2}\right) = \frac{300}{\frac{\pi}{4}\left(\frac{1}{4}\right)^2}\left(1 + \frac{0.625 \times 0.125}{\left(\frac{1}{4}\right)^2 \frac{1}{8}}\right) = 67{,}400 \text{ psi}$$
$$\text{(approximate)}$$

From Table 6, the Wahl correction factor for a spring having a spring index of 8 is equal to 1.18. The more accurate stress is therefore

$$1.18 \times 67{,}400 = 79{,}600 \text{ psi}$$

PROBLEMS

10-32. A helical tension spring made of steel wire 0.080 in. in diameter has an outside diameter of 0.55 in. Determine the extension of the spring upon the application of an axial load of 40 lb. $n = 10$ coils. *Answer: 0.677 in.*

10-33. Determine the load that must be applied to a compression spring to produce a deflection of 3 in. if the wire diameter is 0.192 in.; the outside diameter, 1 in.; and the number of coils, 36.6. $G = 12 \times 10^6$ psi.

10-34. A phosphor-bronze tension spring having a 0.625 in. outside diameter is to be made from 0.080-in. wire. If the deflection desired is 2 in., how many coils will be necessary if the load applied is 40 lb? $G = 5 \times 10^6$ psi. *Answer: 7.93.*

10-35. A helical, steel tension spring is to be stressed to a maximum value of 100,000 psi with a load of 200 lb. If the diameter of the wire is 0.192 in.; the outside diameter, $1\frac{1}{2}$ in.; and the deflection at full load, 3 in., find the number of coils necessary.

10-36. A cantilever beam (Fig. 10-34) is built into a vertical wall at its left end. Under its right end is fitted a steel spring having a spring constant of 9000 lb per in. Calculate the force exerted by the beam upon the spring due to the application of the load P of 3200 lb. Disregard the weight of the beam. I of beam $= 100$ in.^{4} $E = 30 \times 10^6$ psi. *Answer: 2.37 kips.*

Figure 10-34

10-12. *Discussion of deflection formula for springs*

The previous deflection formula is approximate for the following reasons:

(1) The effect of the deflection due to the direct shear force was not taken into account. Although of little effect for most springs, this feature assumes increased importance as the ratio of wire diameter d to eccentricity e increases. Its omission underestimates the magnitude of the deflection.

(2) The length of the spring is not exactly $2\pi en$, but slightly greater, dependent on the over-all height of the spring and the number of coils involved.

(3) The use of formula $\theta = Pel/GJ$ applies only to cylindrical shafts subjected to twisting couples. Its use for springs having small radii would result in a smaller computed deflection value than that actually obtained.

(4) As the pitch between the coils changes, the value of e also changes.

(5) The minimum cross section of the wire is not in the same plane as the axis of the spring. The value of J used in the derivation is slightly smaller than actually exists.

(6) The wire diameter may vary slightly from the ordered diameter by the amount of the manufacturer's tolerance. Since the deflection varies with the fourth power of the diameter, any variation in diameter may have an appreciable effect on the deflection.

10-13. *Exact spring evaluation and design*

Although these discrepancies make the above equation incapable of being used for accurate deflection computations, a fair estimate of its value may be obtained. For a more accurate evaluation of the action of a spring that has already been made, or when required to design a spring to meet certain exacting conditions, it would be well to refer to the various design charts made available by several, large, spring manufacturers.

Chapter Eleven

COLUMNS

11-1. *The problem of column design*

The design of columns presents a problem less possible of exact solution than any other thus far presented. Some of the reasons are:

(1) There is no definite demarcation point between a column that is relatively short and a compression block that is relatively tall. In some fields of column design, the distinction between the two is arbitrarily assumed with the help of experimental data.

(2) Although a column is, for all practical purposes, a straight, homogeneous compression member, it is never made theoretically perfect. Any deviation in its alignment, lack of homogeneity, or presence of internal stresses will act as a source of bending and possible ultimate collapse. Although these defects are of only secondary importance in the design of beams or tension members, they are of primary importance in determining the resistance of a column.

(3) The inability to apply a perfectly axial load causes slight eccentricities to be imposed upon the column that may contribute markedly to its bending tendency and possible ultimate collapse.

(4) The character and magnitude of the end restraint of ordinary columns may vary greatly. Since the type of end connection and the relative stiffness of the connected members both contribute to the magnitude of the restraint, it is not difficult to realize the complexity of this phase of the problem alone.

Since an exact quantitative measure of each of these four items would be difficult, if not impossible, of practical attainment, the study of column action and design has resulted, for the most part, in the application of irrational column formulas to existing experimental and theoretical data, notably those obtained from Euler's equation.

11-2. The slenderness ratio

Figure 11-1

An item that appears in nearly every column formula is the *slenderness ratio*, which is the ratio of the unsupported length of a column to its least radius of gyration. To evaluate the strength of any column, the l/r ratio should be its maximum value. Should lateral support be offered to one of the principal axes of a column cross section, as for instance, axis y-y of Fig. 11-1, its effect could not be considered in determining the slenderness ratio about the other principal axis x-x. Radii of gyration of all standard sections are found in handbooks under the section entitled *Elements of Sections*. A selected list of standard sections with their common properties, including the radii of gyration, will be found at the back of this book.

Illustrative Problem 1. Determine the slenderness ratio of a 12-in. *WF* 65.0-lb section, 20 ft long.

SOLUTION. $l = 240$ in., $r_{x\text{-}x} = 5.28$ in., and $r_{y\text{-}y} = 3.02$ in.

$$\text{slenderness ratio} \left(\frac{l}{r}\right)_{y\text{-}y} = \frac{240}{3.02} = 79.4$$

Illustrative Problem 2. If, in the previous problem, lateral support is given to the y-y axis of the I beam at its mid-point, determine the new slenderness ratio of the column.

SOLUTION. $l_{x\text{-}x} = 240$ in., $l_{y\text{-}y} = 120$ in., $r_{x\text{-}x} = 5.28$ in., and $r_{y\text{-}y} = 3.02$ in.

$$\left(\frac{l}{r}\right)_{x\text{-}x} = \frac{240}{5.28} = 45.4, \qquad \left(\frac{l}{r}\right)_{y\text{-}y} = \frac{120}{3.02} = 39.7$$

The critical slenderness ratio, which previously was about axis y-y, has now changed to axis x-x and is equal to 45.4.

Illustrative Problem 3. Determine the slenderness ratio of a 4 in. by 4 in. by $\frac{1}{4}$ in. angle, 10 ft long.

Figure 11-2

SOLUTION. An angle section has a minimum radius of gyration z-z that should be carefully noted (Fig. 11-2). $l = 120$ ft, $r_{z\text{-}z} = 0.80$ in., $r_{x\text{-}x} = 1.25$ in., and $r_{y\text{-}y} = 1.25$ in.

$$\left(\frac{l}{r}\right)_{z\text{-}z} = \frac{120}{0.80} = 150$$

PROBLEMS

11-1. Calculate the slenderness ratios of the following sections: (1) An 8-in. I 18.4-lb beam 14 ft long. (2) A 4 by 6-in. timber 8 ft long. (3) A 5 by 3 by $\frac{1}{2}$-in. angle 10 ft long.

11-2. The symmetrical axes of two 9-in. 13.4-lb channels are placed on the same horizontal axis. What should be the distance between the webs in order to have the radii of gyration the same about the two principal axes? The flanges extend outwards. *Answer:* 5.62 in.

11-3. Compare the least radii of gyration of the following steel sections: (1) A 4 by 4 by $\frac{3}{8}$-in. angle. (2) A solid rectangular section 1.7 by 1.7 in. (3) A hollow circular section 4 in. in outside diameter and 3.52 in. in inside diameter. (4) A 5-in. I 10.0-lb column. In each case, the area is approximately the same. Which of these sections should make the strongest column?

11-3. The importance of radius of gyration in column design

Radii of gyration of column sections bear an important part in the design of columns and serve as measures of their lateral stability. Since the radii of gyration are direct functions of a column cross section, it is through their judicious manipulation that the final column selection is made. Unless a column must meet certain space or directional strength requirements, the radii of gyration about the two principal axes are made as nearly alike as possible. In so doing, the column will not carry an unnecessary and uneconomical amount of material, and it will be equally strong in either direction.

11-4. Experimental column curves

When a series of medium carbon-steel columns having hinged ends and varying slenderness ratios are placed under increasing axial compression loads to failure, and the values of l/r and P/A at failure are plotted for each column, an average curve similar to that shown in Fig. 11-3(a) is obtained.

If still another plot is made, using the failure data from a series of aluminum-alloy columns having hinged ends and similar slenderness ratios, it would appear as shown in Fig. 11-3(b).

From observation of these two failure curves for columns, it is appar-

$\frac{l}{r}$ = slenderness ratio

Figure 11-3

ent that for the lower values of l/r, the compressive unit stress at failure is fairly constant. This is as we might expect, since the strength of short, stubby compression blocks is not materially affected by even substantial changes in their lengths. For all practical purposes, this limiting value of P/A is the compressive yield strength of the material, the aluminum alloy in this illustration having a lower yield strength than the medium carbon steel. It is interesting to note at this point that in all previous problems concerning stresses in compression members, those members were referred to as *compression blocks*. Their stubbiness prevented any *column action* from interfering with the development and computation of resistance stresses. Column action is indicated by the reduction of the value of P/A (Fig. 11-3) as the value of l/r is increased.

Of significance in Fig. 11-3 is the fact that the curve for the aluminum-alloy 2017-T3 is below that for medium-carbon steel. This is primarily due to the lower stiffness of the aluminum alloy. The modulus of elasticity for 2017-T3 alloy is approximately 10,000,000 psi, whereas that for steel is approximately 30,000,000 psi. Although the effect of the modulus of elasticity decreases as the length decreases, its tendency to depress the curve in proportion to the moduli at high values of l/r causes the entire 2017-T3 curve to fall below that of the steel.

Another point of significance revealed by Fig. 11-3 is the comparative length of the constant P/A portions of both curves. The curve with the greater stiffness (namely, steel) terminates its horizontal portion of the curve at approximately $l/r = 60$. That for the aluminum is terminated at approximately $l/r = 30$. We may expect this variation to persist as materials with varying moduli of elasticity are studied. Wood, as an added example, has a modulus of elasticity of approximately 2,000,000 psi, and has a limiting value of constant P/A of approximately $l/r = 10$. A continued attempt to correlate compression test data will be made after an analysis is made of Euler's formula for tall, slender columns.

COLUMNS WITH HIGH SLENDERNESS RATIOS

11-5. Euler's formula — a general discussion

Having concerned ourselves to this point primarily with the left-hand portion (low l/r values) of the experimental curves of Fig. 11-3, let us now consider those portions pertaining to columns having high values of l/r. These columns will be referred to as *tall, slender* columns.

A *theoretically perfect* column having an indefinitely high slenderness ratio and loaded with a perfectly axial compressive load will not bend no matter how great the load becomes. It will crush instead. If, however, such a column is purposely bent and is subjected to a compressive load to maintain the deflection, its bending characteristics can be effectively studied in obtaining its buckling load.

Suppose the load maintaining the deflection is gradually decreased. A point is soon attained in the load-removal process when the column becomes perfectly straight. The load still applied to the column upon the attainment of perfect straightness is known as *Euler's critical load*. This load is also that limiting load which the column can carry under practical conditions without buckling. Let us proceed with its derivation.

Derivation. Consider a theoretically perfect column (Fig. 11-4) whose ends are free to rotate about hinges which remain in perfect vertical alignment as load is applied. If the column is now purposely bent and a vertical load P applied to maintain this deflected position, the general elastic curve equation is assumed to be similar to that derived for a simple beam (Eq. 8.6):

$$EI \frac{d^2y}{dx^2} = M$$

Choosing the positive directions of the x and y axes as downwards and to the right respectfully as indicated on Fig. 11-4, the above equation may be written more specifically as

$$EI \frac{d^2y}{dx^2} = -Py$$

The negative sign results from the fact that the slope dy/dx changes from a positive value at the origin to a negative value at $x = l$, thus making the

Figure 11-4. The increment
$$\frac{d}{dx}\left(\frac{dy}{dx}\right)$$
must be negative to change
the positive slope at A to the
negative slope at B.

change of slope d^2y/dx^2 a negative value. Were this equation now to be expanded and multiplied by $2dy$, it would appear as

$$EI\left(2\frac{dy}{dx}\,d\frac{dy}{dx}\right) = -2Py\,dy$$

This expression may then be integrated to give

$$EI\left(\frac{dy}{dx}\right)^2 = -Py^2 + C_1$$

By substituting the value of $dy/dx = 0$ when $y = \Delta$, C_1 becomes $P\Delta^2$, making the equation read

$$EI\left(\frac{dy}{dx}\right)^2 = P(\Delta^2 - y^2) \quad \text{or} \quad \frac{dy}{dx} = \sqrt{\frac{P}{EI}}\,\sqrt{\Delta^2 - y^2}$$

By separating the variables, the equation may be written

$$\frac{dy}{\sqrt{\Delta^2 - y^2}} = \sqrt{\frac{P}{EI}}\,dx$$

which when integrated gives

$$\sin^{-1}\frac{y}{\Delta} = \sqrt{\frac{P}{EI}}\,x + C_2$$

But $x = 0$ when $y = 0$, making $C_2 = 0$. Thus

$$\frac{y}{\Delta} = \sin\sqrt{\frac{P}{EI}}\,x \qquad (11.1)$$

The equation above defines the elastic curve of the column as a continuous sine wave whose amplitude equals the maximum deflection Δ. The greatest importance of the equation lies not, however, in defining the deflection curve but in permitting the determination of the critical load.

In determining this load, it is first necessary to note that the projected length of the deflected column is not exactly equal to its total length l. In fact; not until the load is reduced to a value that will just make the column straight will the projected length equal the actual length. The value of the load sustained by the column as it becomes straight is the *Euler critical load*.

In order to obtain the Euler critical load, the column curvature is reduced to the point where Δ is infinitesimally small and the column is just about straight. Under this condition, the left-hand portion of Eq. 11.1 still remains zero and the value of x is for all intents and purposes equal to l. Thus, Eq. 11.1 becomes

$$\frac{y}{\Delta} = 0 = \sin\sqrt{\frac{P}{EI}}\,l$$

The angle $l\sqrt{P/EI}$ whose sine equals zero must therefore equal π or some multiple of π, depending upon the number of half-sine waves that are included in the column length. It follows that the minimum or critical value of P for a column whose length equals one half of a sine wave, i.e., for a column with a bend on one side of the axis and hinged at each end is found by equating

$$\sqrt{\frac{P}{EI}}\,l = \pi \quad \text{or} \quad P = \frac{\pi^2 EI}{l^2} \qquad (11.2)$$

This is known as *Euler's column formula* for tall, slender columns, the variables of which are defined as E = modulus of elasticity of the column material in psi, I = minimum moment of inertia of cross section, in in.⁴, l = unsupported length in inches.

It is important to associate the formula above with a column which when loaded will bend into the shape of one half of a sine wave. Should the column have a reverse bend and have a shape consisting of two half-sine waves or one complete sine wave, the equation would be modified by setting

$$\sqrt{\frac{P}{EI}}\,l = 2\pi \quad \text{or} \quad P = \frac{4\pi^2 EI}{l^2} \qquad (11.2a)$$

In other words, the strength of a tall, slender column hinged at each end increases by the square of the number of half-sine waves included in its length.

Figure 11-5

An important assumption. An important assumption made in the derivation of this formula is that the theoretical column under consideration is so slender that the resistance offered by the direct compressive stresses is negligible when compared to the bending stresses. This assumption would, therefore, permit the application of the formula only to columns having high slenderness ratios. Fortunately, the agreement of experimental data and the values obtained from the formula for high values of l/r is relatively good. As the slenderness ratios decrease, however, the formula and experimental values diverge (Fig. 11-5).

11-6. The effect of variables on Euler's formula

The location of the point of tangency of the Euler and experimental curves is again a function of the relative stiffness of the columns (points S and T, Fig. 11-5). As the modulus of elasticity of the column material decreases, the point of tangency moves toward the vertical axis. In fact, Euler's curves move progressively into the corner formed by the P/A and l/r axes as the values of E become smaller and smaller.

11-7. The buckling action of a tall, slender column

To bring Euler's formula for tall, slender columns into a more practical realm, let us investigate a tall, slender column of ordinary straightness and uniformity similar in size and shape to that previously used in the theoreti-

Figure 11-6. Effect of initial eccentricities. A = small initial eccentricity; B = large initial eccentricity.

cal discussion. After carefully placing the column in a vertical position, let us apply an increasing axial load. Immediately upon the application of the load, the column will start to bend (Fig. 11-6, curve A). Although the amount of bend is very small, the effect of the initial eccentricities and residual stresses is in evidence from the very start. As loading continues, deflection will generally increase at a slightly faster rate.

With the approach of Euler's critical load, however, the deflection becomes greater and greater until at the very moment of its attainment, practically all of the bending resistance is gone. The addition of a very small load will at this point cause an excessively large deflection or a possible collapse. Curve B has been drawn on the same diagram to indicate the effect of an increased initial eccentricity of the column or the load on the magnitude of the deflection.

11-8. *Euler's design formula*

Since the exact magnitude of the eccentricity existing in a column is never known, it is essential that the applied load be kept considerably lower than the theoretical Euler load. The general form of Euler's equation used for design purposes is

$$\frac{P}{A} = \frac{\pi^2 E}{f\left(\dfrac{l}{r}\right)^2} \tag{11.3}$$

where I was substituted by its equal Ar^2 and f is a factor of safety.

It is apparent from the above formula that every material having a different modulus of elasticity will have a different Euler's design formula.

Also, as was intimated in a previous paragraph, the lower limit of l/r, at the point of tangency of Euler's and experimental curves, will also change. For instance, the lower limit of l/r for Euler's equation is approximately 150 for low-carbon steel and 83 for 2017-T3 aluminum alloy. Euler's equation will hold for all higher values of l/r.

Useful from a viewpoint of economy is the fact that low-cost, low-carbon steel will prove as acceptable as high-cost, high-carbon steel for tall, slender columns. This is true because all steel, regardless of its cost, has substantially the same modulus of elasticity.

Illustrative Problem 4. Determine the axial compressive load a 2 by 2 by $\frac{1}{4}$-in. angle made of 2017-T3 structural aluminum can carry if its length is 6 ft.

Euler's equation must be used if the slenderness ratio exceeds 83. Use a factor of safety of 2.25. $A = 0.94$ sq in., $r_{x\text{-}x}$ or $r_{y\text{-}y} = 0.60$ in., $r_{z\text{-}z} = 0.39$ in., and $E = 10,300,000$ psi.

SOLUTION. In order to determine whether the Euler formula will apply to this column, the value of l/r must first be obtained:

$$\frac{l}{r} = \frac{72}{0.39} = 185$$

Euler's equation does apply. Substituting the proper values, we obtain

$$\frac{P}{0.94} = \frac{9.85 \times 10,300,000}{2.25 \times (185)^2}$$

$$P = 1240 \text{ lb}$$

Illustrative Problem 5. Select the most economical structural-steel I section 20 ft long to carry an axial compressive load of 50,000 lb with a factor of safety of 2.5. Assume the column to have hinged ends.

SOLUTION. Without the knowledge of a cross-sectional area, the value of the minimum radius of gyration cannot be computed. It also follows that without an l/r ratio, the immediate selection of the proper column formula is impossible. We are, therefore, forced to use the following trial procedure.

Since most of the steel sections designed on the basis of Euler's formula have P/A values of 7500 psi or less, the area of the final section should be approximately seven or more square inches. In the steel handbook table of I beams the minimum radius of gyration for such beams having from seven to ten square inches of area, is about 1.0 in. Dividing this value into 240 in. of length gives an approximate value of l/r equal to 240, which is well within the limits applicable to Euler's formula. Although for checking purposes, the exact l/r value must be determined at the conclusion of this problem, this method may save considerable time in determining a tentative justification for the use of Euler's formula.

Substituting in Euler's equation

$$P = \frac{\pi^2 EI}{l^2}$$

presents only one unknown, the moment of inertia I, from which a suitable section may be found.

$$2.5 \times 50,000 = \frac{9.85 \times 30,000,000 \times I}{(240)^2}$$

$$I = 24.4 \text{ in.}^4$$

This value of I represents the minimum value the column must have to withstand the load. For an I beam with no lateral supports, this minimum value always occurs about the y-y axis. Looking at Table 15 for American Standard I beams reveals that a 15-in. 60.8-lb I beam ($I = 26.0$ in.⁴) is the lightest I beam that will provide a minimum moment of inertia greater than the 24.4 in.⁴ required.

The value of l/r of this column is $240/1.21 = 198$, which is well above the lower limit of 150 generally used for steel columns in the Euler class.

PROBLEMS

11-4. Determine the axial compressive load a 6-ft length of streamlined, aircraft steel tubing can hold if its structural characteristics are as follows: area = 0.2161 sq in., $I_{x-x} = 0.0376$ in.⁴, $I_{y-y} = 0.1494$ in.⁴, $r_{x-x} = 0.4170$ in., and $r_{y-y} = 0.8313$ in. Use factor of safety of 2.5.

11-5. A $2\frac{1}{2}$ by $2\frac{1}{2}$ by $\frac{1}{4}$-in. angle 10 ft long is to be subjected to an axial compressive load. If made of steel, how much may the angle carry, assuming a factor of safety of 2.5? *Answer:* 2340 lb.

11-6. A steel compression strut 10 ft long is to be made from an equal-leg angle. If the load to be carried is 5000 lb, what most economical angle section should be used, using a factor of safety of 3? *Answer:* $3\frac{1}{2}$ in. $\times$ $3\frac{1}{2}$ in. $\times$ $\frac{1}{4}$ in.

11-7. A certain safety device for a dam supported by two steel angles is designed to collapse at a total specific load of 20,000 lb. If the length of each angle is 12 ft, what angle sections should be used? Keep back to back distance less than $\frac{3}{4}$ in.

11-8. Determine the cross-sectional dimensions of a square timber column, 20 ft long, to take an axial compressive load of 20,000 lb. Use $E = 2,000,000$ lb per sq in. and a safety factor of 3. The lower limit of l/r for a Euler curve for wood of the above modulus is about 50.

11-9. A 2024-T3 aluminum-alloy bar having a 1 by 2-in. cross section is to be axially compressed. Determine the critical length at which buckling will take place if $E = 10,300,000$ psi, and the stress at the beginning of buckling action is 3440 psi. Determine the magnitude of critical stress if the length is 6 ft. *Answer:* 49.6 in., 1640 psi.

11-9. Effect of end conditions

In the previous analysis of Euler's equation, each column was assumed to have pivoted ends. This assumption is a rather important one, since a change of end conditions imposed upon such a column may have a marked effect upon its load-carrying capacity. The following table indicates the effect of several changes of end condition on the load-carrying capacity of a tall, slender column.

TABLE 7
EFFECT OF VARIOUS END CONDITIONS
ON TALL, SLENDER COLUMNS

General Formula: $\dfrac{P}{A} = \dfrac{\pi^2 E}{\left(\dfrac{kl}{r}\right)^2}$		
End Condition	k	No. Times Stronger than Pivot-Ended Column
(a) Both ends fixed..............................	0.5	4
(b) One end fixed, the other pivoted................	0.7	2
(c) Both ends pivoted.............................	1.0	1
(d) One end fixed, the other free...................	2.0	$\frac{1}{4}$

In the foregoing table and in Figs. 11-7 and 11-8, it is revealed that the load-carrying capacity of a tall, slender column is increased or decreased by a change in end conditions insofar as that change increases or decreases the distance between its hinges or inflection points. As an inflection

Figure 11-7

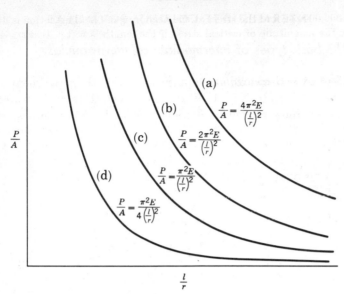

Figure 11-8

point is developed and made to travel away from its support toward the mid-point of the column, the load-carrying capacity of the column increases in inverse proportion to the square of the distance between the hinges or inflection points.

Since the column in type (d) would have to be rotated its full length about its base to make a column similar in shape to the type (c) column, its equivalent length is equal to $2l$, and the load reduction to the square of the coefficient of l. Because column strength at low values of l/r is unaffected by the fixity of the ends and is instead dictated by the yield strength of the material, the point of tangency between the experimental and Euler curves moves toward the right with increased fixity.

PROBLEMS

The following problems are to be solved with the use of modified Euler formulas, assuming that they will satisfy the l/r limitations of the imposed end conditions.

11-10. Determine the allowable compressive load on the column of Problem 11-4, assuming both ends fixed.

11-11. Determine the allowable compressive load on the column of Problem 11-5, assuming one end fixed and the other pivoted. *Answer:* 4680 lb.

11-12. What angle section should be used for Problem 11-6 if both ends are fixed?

11-13. If one end of each of the angles in Problem 11-7 is fixed and the other free to move, what angle sections must be used to withstand the load most economically? *Answer:* Two 4 by $3\frac{1}{2}$ by $\frac{1}{4}$-in. angles.

INTERMEDIATE COLUMN FORMULAS

11-10. *The basic types of intermediate column formulas*

In an endeavor to provide an equation to cover the experimental points on the P/A, l/r diagram (Fig. 11-9) lying between the $s = P/A$ and Euler equations, numerous intermediate column formulas have been suggested.

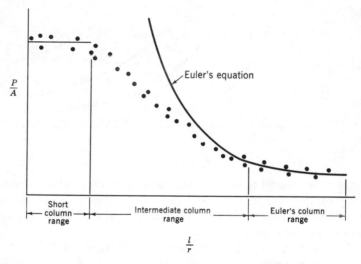

Figure 11-9

Because the experimental points are usually scattered, some difficulty has been encountered in providing formulas meeting with universal approval. Investigators of the past have disagreed as to the correct trend of these experimental points. At present, failure formulas for columns may generally be grouped into four different basic types, namely:

(1) The straight-line equation:

$$\frac{P}{A} = s_y - C_v \frac{l}{r} \tag{11.4}$$

(2) The parabolic equation:

$$\frac{P}{A} = s_y - k\left(\frac{l}{r}\right)^2 \tag{11.5}$$

(3) The Gordon-Rankine equation:

$$\frac{P}{A} = \frac{s_y}{1 + \phi\,(l/r)^2} \tag{11.6}$$

(4) The secant equation:

$$\frac{P}{A} = \frac{s_y}{1 + \dfrac{ec}{r^2} \sec \dfrac{l}{2r}\sqrt{\dfrac{P}{AE}}} \tag{11.7}$$

The last equation is not as much a type equation as are the first three, since it is used as a separate equation under that name. Its complexity and the difficulty accompanying its use has caused it to be employed sparingly in practice. However, it is considered to be the most refined column formula that will ever be obtained.

11-11. Intermediate column buckling formulas

Attempts have been made in times past to provide an entirely rational intermediate column formula. None has as yet been forthcoming. The difficulty of anticipating the effect of initial eccentricities seems beyond pure mathematical reasoning. Consequently, the ultimate strength formulas for axially loaded intermediate columns are based almost entirely on experimental data, modified upon occasion by individual and collective opinion.

Several such formulas for common engineering materials are:

Straight-line:

1. STRUCTURAL LOW-CARBON STEEL

$$\frac{P}{A} = 37,500 - 125\,\frac{l}{r} \tag{11.8}$$

Compressive yield strength = 30,000 psi

$$\text{Upper } \frac{l}{r} = 150$$

2. DURALUMIN (2017-T3)

$$\frac{P}{A} = 43,800 - 350\,\frac{l}{r} \tag{11.9}$$

Compressive yield strength = 37,000 psi

$$\text{Upper } \frac{l}{r} = 83$$

3. DURALUMIN (2024-T3)

$$\frac{P}{A} = 56,600 - 510\,\frac{l}{r} \tag{11.10}$$

Compressive yield strength = 46,000 psi

$$\text{Upper } \frac{l}{r} = 73$$

4. Cast Iron

$$\frac{P}{A} = 34,000 - 88\,\frac{l}{r}$$ (11.11)

Compressive yield strength = 28,300 psi

$$\text{Upper } \frac{l}{r} = 100$$

5. Oak

$$\frac{P}{A} = 5400 - 28\,\frac{l}{r}$$ (11.12)

$$\text{Upper } \frac{l}{r} = 64$$

Parabolic:

6. Low-Carbon, Structural Steel

$$\frac{P}{A} = 40,000 - 1.35\left(\frac{l}{r}\right)^2$$ (11.13)

$$\text{Upper } \frac{l}{r} = 120$$

Gordon-Rankine:

7. Low-Carbon Structural Steel

$$\frac{P}{A} = \frac{50,000}{1 + \dfrac{1}{18,000}\left(\dfrac{l}{r}\right)^2}$$ (11.14)

8. Magnesium, AM-C58S Extruded

$$\frac{P}{A} = \frac{46,000}{1 + 0.00071\left(\dfrac{l}{r}\right)^2}$$ (11.15)

Of the foregoing column equations, those pertaining to low-carbon structural steel are plotted on Fig. 11-10. It is evident that the spread between these graphs is an indication of the scatter of the experimental data and the degree of conservatism used to record their variation in equation form. The equation

$$\frac{P}{A} = \frac{40,000}{1 + \dfrac{1}{18,000}\left(\dfrac{l}{r}\right)^2}$$

has been added to serve as contrast to the straight-line equation as well as the other equation of the Gordon-Rankine type.

Figure 11-10. Plots of ultimate strength equations for axially loaded low-carbon structural steel columns.

11-12. *The limitations of intermediate column buckling formulas*

It is apparent from Fig. 11-10 that intermediate column formulas may have upper limits of l/r. Some may even have a lower limit given by a minimum l/r or the compressive yield strength of the material. Before using an intermediate column formula, it is essential that the limitations imposed upon it are completely understood.

11-13. *The effect of fixing the ends of an intermediate column*

Should it be possible to fix the ends of an intermediate column, its strength would be increased. The added strength given to the column would vary from zero, for those approaching a compression block, to the maximum values already developed for tall, slender columns. The greatest strength that could accrue to an intermediate column completely fixed at its ends would therefore be computed using its l/r value multiplied by a factor k between 0.5 and 1.0.

But the vast majority of intermediate columns in modern framed steel structures do not have ends which are fixed, but ends which are only *partially fixed*. Therefore the constant k, which is used to determine the effective l/r, is closer to the value 1.0 than to 0.5. Unless the magnitude of the end restraint can be clearly established, no end restraint is considered to act and the value of k is taken as 1.0.

Illustrative Problem 6. (a) What axial load can a standard 8-in. *I* beam 4 ft long, made of 2024-T3 aluminum alloy, carry before it collapses? $I_{x-x} = 57.55$ in.^{4}, $I_{y-y} = 3.73$ in.^{4}, and $A = 5.40$ sq in.

(b) If its length were increased to 6 ft, what load could it hold? $E = 10.2 \times 10^6$ psi.

(c) If the column in part (a) had partially fixed ends ($k = 0.75$), what load could it hold?

SOLUTION. (a) The slenderness ratio of the column to be investigated is computed as follows:

$$\frac{l}{r} = \frac{48}{\sqrt{3.73/5.40}} = \frac{48}{0.83} = 57.8$$

Since this slenderness ratio lies between the limits set for the 2024-T3, straight-line, intermediate column formula given on page 355, its use is justified.

$$\frac{P}{A} = 56,600 - 510\,\frac{l}{r}$$
$$P = 5.40(56,600 - 510 \times 57.8) = 146,200 \text{ lb}$$

(b) If its length were increased to 6 ft, its slenderness ratio would be

$$\frac{l}{r} = \frac{72}{0.83} = 86.8$$

This value is above the upper limit for the intermediate column formula. The Euler's equation must, therefore, be used.

$$\frac{P}{A} = \frac{\pi^2 \times E}{(l/r)^2}, \qquad P = \frac{5.40 \times 9.86 \times 10.2 \times 10^6}{86.8^2} = 72,400 \text{ lb}$$

(c) The load that could be applied to the column in part (a) if its ends were partially fixed is

$$\frac{P}{A} = 56,600 - 510 \times 0.75 \times \frac{l}{r}$$
$$P = 5.40(56,600 - 510 \times 0.75 \times 57.8) = 186,000 \text{ lb}$$

PROBLEMS

All columns referred to in these problems have hinged ends unless specified otherwise.

11-14. What maximum axial load can a 10-in. *I* 25.4-lb steel column 8 ft long withstand? Use the straignt-line formula. *Answer:* 185,400 lb.

11-15. If the above column were partially fixed at each end, what maximum load could be applied? Use the straight-line formula. $k = 0.75$.

11-16. What diameter would be required for a steel rod 5 ft long if an axial load

of 90,000 lb would cause its collapse? Use parabolic formula if it is applicable.
Answer: 2.18 in.

11-17. Determine the critical length of a 4 by 4 by $\frac{3}{8}$-in. steel angle that would fail under a load of 70,000 lb. Use the Gordon-Rankine formula.

11-18. Solve Problem 11-16, assuming the rod to be made of 2017-T3 aluminum alloy. Use the straight-line formula. *Answer:* 2.84 in.

11-19. Solve Problem 11-17, assuming the angle to be made of AM-C58S extruded magnesium. Use Gordon-Rankine-type formula.

11-14. *Intermediate column formulas for design of compression members*

In the practical design of columns for structural frameworks and machines, a factor of safety must be applied to the ultimate-strength equations given in § 11-11. The magnitude of the factor of safety employed usually varies from 2 to 3.5, depending on the possible variation in magnitude and axial application of load P, the possible crookedness of the column, and the effects of possible column failure.

In the design of columns, the cross-sectional area, and also to a large extent the radius of gyration, vary with the magnitude of the load applied. Resulting values of l/r may, therefore, vary considerably. To maintain the same factor of safety for all the l/r values encountered will cause the various intermediate design equations to assume curves similar in shape to those obtained for the ultimate-strength relationships. It also follows that the intermediate column formulas having an upper limit of l/r will become tangent or produce an acute angle to a Euler's design equation at this limiting l/r value. Similarly, those intermediate column formulas that have a lower limit of l/r will have their corresponding values in close agreement with the corresponding allowable compressive strength of the column material.

The design of an axially loaded column seldom includes, in practice, the effect of end restraints. Even though the base and top of a column may be securely riveted, a sufficient amount of movement is generally possible to warrant the consideration of hinged ends. Although welded column connections seem to provide greater justification for including the effect of fixed ends, it is the exception rather than the rule that they are so treated. The A.I.S.C. code provides for the possibility of semirigid and rigid types of construction however they may be obtained.

All the intermediate column formulas presented in this article are in common use. They have been culled from the many such formulas that have appeared in technical literature. Because of the frequency with which the three types of equations are currently used, those formulas appearing in bold type in this chapter, as well as their limitations and their supporting equations, should be committed to memory.

11-15. Straight-line design formula

The most simple intermediate column formula is the straight-line formula represented in general form by the equation

$$\frac{P}{A} = s - C\frac{l}{r} \tag{11.16}$$

The values of s and C are equal to the values of s_y and C_y appearing in Eq. 11.4, divided by the factor of safety. The value of s is the intercept on the P/A axis, and C represents the slope of the line. An upper and lower limit of l/r are generally used to confine the formula's working range.

One of the most familiar straight-line formulas for designing axially loaded columns with hinged ends is obtained by applying a factor of safety of 2.5 to the ultimate-strength Eq. 11.8. Its final form is

$$\boxed{\frac{P}{A} = 15{,}000 - 50\frac{l}{r}} \tag{11.17}$$

with the l/r range between 50 and 150.

To permit the design of those columns having lower or higher values of l/r than indicated above, two supplementary adjoining equations are always used for this type of intermediate formula.

Columns having l/r ratios below 50 are designed in a manner similar to that of a compression block, using

$$\boxed{\frac{P}{A} = 12{,}500 \text{ psi}} \tag{11.18}$$

When the l/r ratio exceeds 150, the Euler-type design formula

$$\boxed{\frac{P}{A} = \frac{6.4E}{(l/r)^2}} \tag{11.19}$$

is to be used. This latter formula would appear at first to have a factor of safety below the 2.5 required. It has, however, been experimentally determined that the equation most closely following the failure values for columns in the 150- to 200-l/r range is

$$\frac{P}{A} = \frac{16E}{(l/r)^2} \tag{11.20}$$

rather than the theoretical Euler equation. This is undoubtedly due to the failure to include the effects of the compressive strength in the development of the Euler formula. Applying the factor of safety of 2.5 to the foregoing formula results in Eq. 11.19.

Figure 11-11 records the plots of each of these three equations. Together they constitute a series of equations, hereafter to be called the *straight-line series*, that record the maximum allowable stress for each l/r ratio. *It is a very conservative series of column formulas*, as is shown by contrasting the series with the other design equations shown in Fig. 11-11. Since both the straight-line and Euler formulas produce almost

Figure 11-11. Graphs of equations used for designing axially loaded hinge-ended columns of structural steel.

identical allowable stresses in the l/r range between 150 and 220, both could be used without noticeable design differences. It is usual, however, to limit the l/r ratio of main compression members to 120 for safety reasons.

Another straight-line formula often used in the design of axially loaded, pin-ended, structural-steel columns is the Chicago Building Code formula:

$$\frac{P}{A} = 16{,}000 - 70\,\frac{l}{r} \tag{11.21}$$

Its limits for the design of main structural members are 30 and 120, and for secondary members, such as lateral bracing, the upper limit is extended to 150.

Straight-line formulas used in the design of axially loaded, pin-ended columns of various other materials are as follows:

CAST IRON

$$\frac{P}{A} = 9000 - 40\,\frac{l}{r} \tag{11.22}$$

used between $l/r = 0$ and $l/r = 70$.

ALUMINUM ALLOY — 2017-T3

$$\frac{P}{A} = 19{,}500 - 155\,\frac{l}{r}$$

$$\text{Upper } \frac{l}{r}\text{ limit} = 83 \tag{11.23}$$

Maximum allowable compressive stress = 16,500 psi. For above $\frac{l}{r} = 83$, use $\frac{P}{A} = \frac{22{,}000{,}000}{(l/r)^2}$.

STRUCTURAL TIMBER

$$\frac{P}{A} = 1000 - 6\,\frac{l}{r} \tag{11.24}$$

$$\text{Upper } \frac{l}{r}\text{ limit} = 100$$

11-16. Straight-line equations for alloyed materials

The two numerical components of a straight-line equation record the P/A axis intercept and the slope of the line. The intercept value agrees closely with the allowable compressive strength of the column material. The slope value C depends on two items (a) the P/A axis intercept, or the allowable compressive strength and (b) the position of the Euler design equation corresponding to the modulus of the elasticity of the column material and modified with the same factor of safety as used for the straight-line equation.

If, therefore, the straight-line design formulas for a series of steel columns of varying alloy content were investigated (Fig. 11-12) their P/A intercepts would increase with an increase in allowable compressive strength while the position of the lower extremity of each line would remain relatively fixed, since the modulus of elasticity of all steel alloys is practically the same.

We should expect, for example, the straight-line design equations for steel to have (a) an increased value of the P/A intercept s, (b) an increased slope C, and (c) a decreased upper limit of l/r as the percentage of carbon is increased to approximately 1 per cent, and as other alloying materials are added. The lower l/r limit may also possibly decrease to provide a consistent factor of safety. A perusal of Fig. 11-12 will show how these design formulas vary. Column equation $P/A = 37{,}500 - 200l/r$ would pertain to a steel having a carbon content of about 0.8 per cent, whereas the equation $P/A = 15{,}000 - 50l/r$ refers to a low-carbon steel containing about 0.2 per cent carbon.

Figure 11-12. Graph showing effect of increased allowable compressive strength and constant modulus of elasticity on straight-line design formulas.

11-17. *Straight-line formulas for columns having various end rigidities*

The effect of changing the rigidity of the ends of a column on its column formula for pin ends is shown in Fig. 11-13. Because the rigidity

Figure 11-13

of the ends has no effect on short compression members and an increasing effect as the l/r ratio increases, the straight-line formula may be thought to rotate about its y-axis intersection until it again becomes tangent to the proper Euler curve. As the ends approach a fixed position, therefore, the slope of the straight-line equation decreases and the upper limit increases. If one end is free to sway and the other end is fixed, the slope of the equation is increased, and the upper l/r limit is decreased.

Another point of interest to remember in the study of columns is that with decreasing moduli of elasticity, the corresponding Euler curve is placed closer to the origin of the P/A, l/r diagram. Drawing a tangent to such a Euler curve will reveal a smaller range of usefulness for the straight-line equation and a decreased upper l/r limit.

Illustrative Problem 7.   Select the most economical wide-flange (WF) pin-ended steel column, 18 ft long, to sustain an axial load of 200,000 lb. Use the straight-line series of equations.

SOLUTION. If the column to be designed were to have a round or square section whose minimum radius of gyration could be determined in terms of the area A, the solution would be comparatively simple, entailing but one unknown. Since the difficulty of obtaining r in terms of A for a WF section involves considerable time, the determination of a most economical column section is best done by trial.

An assumption is first made of the stress P/A placed on the column. Since P/A cannot exceed 12,500 psi and cannot be lower than 7500 psi ($l/r = 150$), let us choose the mid-way stress of 10,000 psi as our assumed stress.

The area corresponding to this assumed stress will then be

$$A = \frac{P}{s} = \frac{200,000}{10,000} = 20 \text{ sq in.}$$

A trial WF section must now be found (Table 16) that has approximately this area. To be economical, this trial column should also have a minimum cross-sectional area, or weight per foot, with a maximum value of rigidity expressed by the value of $I_{\min}$ or $r_{\min}$. Obviously, therefore, a WF column with a square cross section will be more economical than one with a great depth and a narrow flange, since its moments of inertia will be more nearly alike.

Let our first selection be a 12 by 12-in. WF 72-lb column (area = 21.16 sq in. and $r_{\min} = 3.04$ in.). This is a trial section and must now be verified or rejected on the basis of its allowable load and economy.

The slenderness ratio of this column, which shall dictate the proper design formula to be used and the allowable stress to be placed on the column, is

$$\frac{l}{r} = \frac{18 \times 12}{3.04} = 71.0$$

The intermediate column formula $P/A = 15{,}000 - 50 \; l/r$ may, therefore, be used to obtain the maximum allowable compressive stress. Substituting the value of the l/r found for this trial section, we obtain

$$\frac{P}{A} = 15{,}000 - 50 \times 71 = 11{,}450 \text{ psi}$$

This stress is the maximum allowable stress that may be placed on a column having an l/r of 71. The minimum area required to withstand the load of 200,000 lb, using this stress is

$$A = \frac{P}{s} = \frac{200{,}000}{11{,}450} = 17.45 \text{ sq in.}$$

We have thus shown that the column selected, having an area of 21.16 sq in., has an l/r such that only 17.45 sq in. are required to sustain the load. It is obvious that the trial column is too large. We must now make another selection whose area will be closer to that required without excessively reducing the value of the minimum r.

Proceeding slowly, let us take as our second selection a 12 by 12-in. 65-lb column ($A = 19.11$ sq in. and $r_{\text{min.}} = 3.02$ in.). Its value of l/r is

$$\frac{l}{r} = \frac{18 \times 12}{3.02} = 71.5$$

The maximum allowable compressive stress corresponding to this value of l/r is

$$\frac{P}{A} = 15{,}000 - 50 \times 71.5 = 11{,}430 \text{ psi}$$

The minimum area required to withstand the load using this allowable stress is

$$A = \frac{P}{s} = \frac{200{,}000}{11{,}430} = 17.5 \text{ sq in.}$$

With an l/r almost exactly the same as that for the first column, the value of the maximum allowable stress and the required area was bound to be very close to that already found.

Our next step is to further close, if possible, the gap between the available and required areas. Excess area means wasted material and unnecessary cost. Still working with square sections, our attention is drawn to the columns of the 10 by 10-in. WF class. The only column of interest would be the 10 by 10-in. WF 60-lb column (area $= 17.66$ sq in.). But owing to its very much smaller $r_{\text{min.}}$ of 2.57, it is reasonable to believe that the allowable stress will be so much lower than that previously

found as to require an area in excess of 17.66 sq in. Calculations prove
this belief to be correct, 18.60 sq in. being required.

Our only further avenue of calculation now lies with the use of *WF*
columns of rectangular cross section. The one column that has less weight
than the 56-lb column previously found acceptable is the 12 by 10-in. *WF*
58-lb column ($a = 17.06$ sq in. and $r_{min.} = 2.51$ in.). It is obvious, however, that this section will be inadequate in view of our previous $r_{min.}$ of 3.02
having required a minimum area of 17.5 sq in.

Because the A.I.S.C. handbook reveals *no other column of lesser weight
having a greater minimum radius of gyration, the 12 by 12-in. WF 65-lb
column is the most economical column available to support the load.*

Ordinarily, an axially loaded column will be one whose radii of gyration about its principal axes will have as little variance as possible — making necessary the selection of a more or less square column. It is because of
space limitations and eccentric loadings that rectangular columns find a
great deal of use.

If rolled *WF* sections do not provide sufficient capacity, or if their
resistance about their principal axes is unsuitable for the loading conditions imposed, columns may be fabricated from several smaller sections,
such as angles, channels, plates, *I* beams, and *WF* columns. When columns
are fabricated their values of *I*, *r*, and *c* must be determined.

11-18. *The parabolic design formula*

The parabolic formula proposed by J. B. Johnson for the design of
axially loaded columns has become increasingly popular in recent years.
Since this formula provides allowable compressive stresses for short as well
as intermediate columns, it eliminates the use of a lower l/r limit and the
short column formula. Its convenience and relative accuracy in furnishing
compressive stresses for l/r ratios from zero through the intermediate
column range have led to its adoption by the American Institute of Steel
Construction. The formula included in their present specification is

$$\frac{P}{A} = 17{,}000 - 0.485 \left(\frac{l}{r}\right)^2 \qquad (11.25)$$

which is used for pin-ended steel columns with values of l/r not greater
than 120 (Fig. 11-11). Above the value of $l/r = 120$, a Gordon-Rankine-
type formula,

$$\frac{P}{A} = \frac{18{,}000}{1 + \dfrac{1}{18{,}000}(l/r)^2} \qquad (11.26)$$

is used. A discussion of this formula will follow in the next article.

Illustrative Problem 8.   Select the most economical wide-flange (*WF*) pin-ended steel column, 18 ft long, to sustain a load of 200,000 lb. Use formula 11.25.

Note. The requirements of this problem are exactly the same as those for Illustrative Problem 7, where the straight-line formula was used.

SOLUTION.   Commencing with the assumed stress and area as in Illustrative Problem 7, let us again choose the 12-in. *WF* 72-lb section (area = 21.16 in.² and $r_{min.}$ = 3.04 in.) as our first choice. The *l/r* for this section will be 71, the same as previously computed.

The allowable compressive stress furnished by the parabolic formula for this slenderness ratio is

$$\frac{P}{A} = 17{,}000 - 0.485 \times \overline{71}^2 = 14{,}560 \text{ psi}$$

Dividing the stress into the load, we obtain as our required minimum area,

$$A = \frac{P}{s} = \frac{200{,}000}{14{,}560} = 13.65 \text{ sq in.}$$

This first choice might have been made more skillfully with a smaller discrepancy occurring between the selected and required areas, since the parabolic formula is more liberal in allowing greater stresses on column cross sections. It was purposely done, however, to show that regardless of the initial stress assumption, the final selection will be the same.

Obviously, the first selection is much too heavy for the area required. Let us try the 10 by 10-in. sections. It is well to remember when selecting a column from a lighter series that the value of the minimum radius of gyration usually decreases. This will decrease the allowable stress and increase the area required. The 10-in. *WF* 49-lb (area = 14.4 sq in. and $r_{min.}$ = 2.54 in.) column will be investigated.

The value of *l/r* is

$$\frac{l}{r} = \frac{18 \times 12}{2.54} = 85$$

The maximum allowable stress corresponding to this slenderness ratio is

$$\frac{P}{A} = 17{,}000 - 0.485 \times \overline{85}^2 = 13{,}500 \text{ psi}$$

The area required is

$$A = \frac{P}{s} = \frac{200{,}000}{13{,}500} = 14.8 \text{ sq in.}$$

Because the area required is greater than that available, a larger column must be selected.

It might seem to be satisfactory at first sight to select the next larger column in the 10-in. series as being the most economical column. However, it will be noted that a 12 by 10-in. *WF* 53-lb (area = 15.59 sq in. and $r_{min.}$ = 2.48 in.) column is available that is slightly lighter and has approximately the same minimum radius of gyration.

An investigation reveals that

$$\frac{l}{r} = \frac{18 \times 12}{2.48} = 87$$

$$\frac{P}{A} = 17,000 - 0.485 \times \overline{87}^2 = 13,320 \text{ psi}$$

Area required is

$$A = \frac{P}{s} = \frac{200,000}{13,320} = 15.00 \text{ sq in.}$$

Although this selection is the most economical column that can be obtained on a weight basis, other practical considerations may dictate selection of the 10 by 10-in. *WF* 54-lb column.

A comparison of Illustrative Problems 7 and 8 reveals that the use of the more liberal parabolic formula saved 11 lb per linear ft of column.

11-19. *Gordon-Rankine design formula*

A formula that has enjoyed widespread use in the design of steel columns is the Gordon-Rankine formula

$$\frac{P}{A} = \frac{18,000}{1 + \dfrac{1}{18,000}\,(l/r)^2} \tag{11.26}$$

applicable to axially loaded pin-ended columns (Fig. 11-11). This formula is usually specified for use within a lower limit of $l/r = 60$ and an upper limit of 120 when dealing with main compression members. For bracing and other secondary members, the upper limit is increased to 200.

The formula above with its stated limits has been, and continues to be, included in many municipal and private specifications. A few years ago the American Institute of Steel Construction changed the conditions under which the above formula was being used in its specifications. The present stipulation permits its use for only secondary compression members having l/r values between 120 and 200. For main compression members up to $l/r = 120$, the parabolic formula given in the previous article has been substituted.

To obtain a Gordon-Rankine column-design formula from an ultimate-strength formula of the same type, the numerator of the ultimate formula is divided by the factor of safety desired. For example, the design formula for pin-ended columns of type AM-C58S magnesium alloy arranged for a factor of safety of 2.5 is obtained by dividing that value into the ultimate-strength formula given on page 356.

$$\frac{P}{A} = \frac{18,400}{1 + 0.00071\left(\frac{l}{r}\right)^2} \tag{11.27}$$

Maximum P/A stress = 8620 psi.

Illustrative Problem 9.   Select the most economical wide-flange pin-ended steel column 18 ft long to sustain a load of 200,000 lb. Use the Gordon-Rankine formula.

Note. The requirements for this problem are exactly the same as given in Illustrative Problems 7 and 8.

SOLUTION. Assuming a stress of 12,000 psi, the trial area is equal to

$$A = \frac{P}{s} = \frac{200,000}{12,000} = 16.67 \text{ sq in.}$$

This assumption merely assists in securing a trial column and bears no part in the ensuing portion of the problem.

Assuming no prior benefit from the column selections of Illustrative Problems 7 and 8, the 10-in. WF 60-lb ($a = 17.66$ sq in. and $r_{min.} = 2.57$ in.) column seems a logical choice. Its slenderness ratio is

$$\frac{l}{r} = \frac{18 \times 12}{2.57} = 84$$

The maximum allowable stress for an l/r ratio of 84 is

$$\frac{P}{A} = \frac{18,000}{1 + \dfrac{1}{18,000}\,(84)^2} = 12,920 \text{ psi}$$

The required area is, therefore,

$$A = \frac{P}{s} = \frac{200,000}{12,920} = 15.47 \text{ sq in.}$$

Since the discrepancy between the available and required areas is over 2 sq in., a possibility exists for a better selection. Such is the case because the 10-in. WF 54-lb column has a slightly greater area than that required for a column with an almost identical minimum radius of gyration.

Checking the selection reveals the l/r ratio as 84.3 and the maximum allowable stress as 12,900 psi. The area required is, then, 15.50 sq in. Because the 10-in. WF 54-lb beam is the lightest column that will sustain the applied load, it is the most economical column for the stated conditions.

11-20. *Use of handbook in designing columns*

In the A.I.S.C. handbook, there has been tabulated the maximum allowable axial loads for pin-ended steel columns using the column formulas proposed by that agency. Since the use of the A.I.S.C. formulas is widespread, the tables can be used very effectively. Other handbooks are available having tables compiled for other design formulas.

In Fig. 11-14 are shown portions of the page from which the column of Illustrative Problem 8 may have been selected. To find the most economical 18-ft column for the 200,000-lb applied load, it is merely necessary to run through the tables of safe loads on the horizontal line marked *18 ft* for loads which will be slightly above the 200,000-lb value. Each such load is further investigated by noting the weight per foot of the column, which is found at the top of the same vertical column. The column with the smallest weight per foot that will sustain the applied load will be the most economical selection.

Un-braced Length (ft)	Nominal Depth and Width and Weight per Ft						
	12 by 10		12 by 8			10 by 10	
	58	53	50	45	40	112	100
6	283	258	240	216	192	548	490
17	235	214	173	154	137	466	416
18	229	208	163	145	129	455	406
19	222	201	*154*	*136*	*121*	443	395

Most economical column 12 by 10-in. *WF* 53 lb.

Figure 11-14

PROBLEMS

11-20. Determine the maximum allowable axial load that may be placed on a 10-in. *WF* 54-lb column, 16 ft long, using (a) the straight-line formula (Eq. 11.17), (b) the Chicago Building Code formula (Eq. 11.21), and (c) the present American Institute of Steel Construction formula.

11-21. Determine the maximum allowable axial load that may be placed on a 10-in. *I* 25.4-lb beam, 8 ft long, by the (a) A.I.S.C. formula, (b) the Gordon-Rankine design formula (Eq. 11.26), and (c) the straight-line formula (Eq. 11.17). *Answer:* (a) 90,500 lb, (b) 86,000 lb, (c) 74,200 lb.

11-22. If two 6 by 4 by $\frac{1}{2}$-in. angles, 10 ft long, were placed with their long sides back to back and separated by $\frac{1}{2}$ in., what maximum allowable axial load could be applied? Use A.I.S.C. specifications.

11-23. What equal-leg angle made of 2017-T3 aluminum alloy should be used to carry an axial load of 20,000 lb, if the length is 10 ft and the straight line-Euler series of formulas is prescribed? Assume aluminum sections to be similar to those made of steel. *Answer:* 8 by 8 by $\frac{1}{2}$ in.

11-24. What maximum allowable load may be applied to a structural column consisting of two 12 by $\frac{1}{2}$-in. plates and two 10-in. 20-lb channels, 25 ft long? The channels are placed back to back with the plates against the flanges. The tips of the opposing channels are 12 in. apart. Use A.I.S.C. specifications.

11-25. Determine the most economical *WF* column to carry an axial load of 150,000 lb, if the length is 12 ft and the A.I.S.C. specifications are prescribed.

11-26. Solve Problem 11-25, assuming the length of column to be 22 ft. *Answer:* 10 by 10 in. *WF* 49 lb.

11-27. Select the most economical *WF* column to carry an axial load of 150,000 lb, if the length is 14 ft and the Gordon-Rankine design formula is prescribed.

11-28. Solve Problem 11-27, using the straight-line formula (Eq. 11.17). *Answer:* 10 by 10 *WF* 49 lb.

11-29. Find the lightest structural-steel *I* beam, 14 ft long, that can be used as a column under an axial load of 60,000 lb. Use the A.I.S.C. specifications.

11-30. Compare the saving in weight, if any, that would accrue by substituting magnesium for structural steel in a round bar serving as a column to support a load of 2000 lb. $L = 3$ ft. Sp. Gr., magnesium $= 1.8$, steel $= 7.80$. Use Gordon-Rankine-type design formulas. *Answer:* 28.9 per cent.

11-21. Wood columns

Rectangular. The Forest Products Laboratory has developed a fourth-degree parabolic equation,

$$\frac{P}{A} = s\left[1 - \frac{1}{3}\left(\frac{l}{Kb}\right)^4\right] \tag{11.28}$$

for the design of pin-ended, rectangular wood columns in the intermediate column range — where the ratio of the unsupported length, l, to the least transverse dimensions, b, varies from 11 to such ratios of l/b that make $P/A = \frac{2}{3}s$, that is, where $l/b = K$. In this equation $s =$ the allowable compression stress parallel to the grain and $K = \frac{1}{2}\pi\sqrt{E/6s}$, where E is the flexure modulus of elasticity in bending.

For the design of short columns having an l/b ratio less than 11, the allowable compressive stress parallel to the grain, s, is the controlling factor.

From the point where $P/A = \frac{2}{3}s$, or where $l/b = K$ to the point where $l/b = 50$, Euler's equation with a factor of safety of 3 is used.

$$\frac{P}{A} = \frac{\pi^2 E}{36(l/b)^2} \tag{11.29}$$

In the table below are given the values of s, K, and E for common structural grades of timber.

TABLE 8

CHARACTERISTICS OF COLUMNS MADE FROM COMMON STRUCTURAL
GRADES OF TIMBER, KEPT CONTINUOUSLY DRY
(Compression, psi)

Species	s	E	K
Red cedar.....................................	560	1.0×10^6	27.1
Douglas fir....................................	880	1.6×10^6	27.3
Western hemlock.............................	720	1.4×10^6	28.3
White oak.....................................	880	1.2×10^6	27.8
Long leaf pine................................	1025	1.6×10^6	25.3
Redwood......................................	800	1.2×10^6	24.8
Spruce..	640	1.2×10^6	27.8

Circular. The above formulas may be used for circular wood columns, provided that there be substituted for b the length of the side of the cross section of a square column that has the same radius of gyration as the cross section of the circular column. The side of this equivalent square column is computed to be 0.866 times the diameter of the round column — that is, $b = 0.866d$. The value of A used in computing the total load is, of course, equal to the cross-sectional area of the round column.

Illustrative Problem 10. Determine the maximum allowable axial load that may be placed on a pin-ended rectangular timber column of Douglas fir having a cross section of 6 by 8 in. and a length of 6 ft. The column will be kept continuously dry.

SOLUTION. The values of s, E, and K for the column are, respectively, 880 lb per sq in., 1.6×10^6 psi, and 27.3. The value of l/b is equal to $\frac{72}{6} = 12$. Substituting these values in Eq. 11.28 we obtain:

$$\frac{P}{A} = s \left[1 - \frac{1}{3} \left(\frac{l}{Kb} \right)^4 \right] = 880 \left[1 - \frac{1}{3} \left(\frac{12}{27.3} \right)^4 \right]$$

$$= 880 \left[1 - \frac{0.0374}{3} \right] = 868 \text{ psi}$$

Maximum allowable load $P = 868 \times 6 \times 8 = 41,700$ lb.

Illustrative Problem 11. Determine the diameter of a round Douglas fir column, 6 ft long, that will sustain the 41,700-lb load placed on the rectangular column of the previous problem.

SOLUTION.

$$\frac{P}{\pi d^2/4} = 880 \left[1 - \frac{1}{3} \left(\frac{72}{27.3 \times 0.866d} \right)^4 \right]$$

$$\frac{41,700}{0.7854d^2} = 880\left[1 - \frac{1}{3}\left(\frac{3.04}{d}\right)^4\right] = 880d^4 - 53,000d^2 - 25,200 = 0$$

$$d = 7.8 \text{ in.}$$

The value of l/b of the column is then equal to

$$\frac{l}{b} = \frac{l}{0.866d} = \frac{72}{0.866 \times 7.8} = 10.65$$

which is within the useful range of the formula used.

PROBLEMS

11-31. Using the Forest Products Laboratory specifications for timber columns, determine the axial load that may be placed on 4 by 4 in. by 6-ft column of spruce. The column is to be used in a continuously dry location.

11-32. Determine the cross-sectional dimensions of a square column, 9 ft long and made of Douglas fir, that will carry a load of 75,000 lb. Assume a continuous dry location. Use the Forest Products Laboratory specifications. *Answer:* 9.3 by 9.3 in.

11-33. What will be the cross-sectional dimensions if the length of the column in Problem 11-32 is 24 ft?

11-34. Find the diameter of the most economical circular timber column made of Douglas fir that could replace the square column of Problem 11-32. *Answer:* 10.48 in.

11-22. *Eccentrically loaded steel columns*

Eccentricity about one symmetrical axis. Of the several methods employed in designing eccentrically loaded columns, the one which seems most simple to apply is that included in the A.I.S.C. specifications. It is based on the theory given in § 10-3, in which the stress due to an eccentric load placed on a short column is equal to

$$s = \frac{P}{A} + \frac{Pec}{I}$$

The first term indicates the axial stress developed by the eccentric load and the second term, the magnitude of the bending stress.

In the design of short columns, the value of s is not allowed to exceed the maximum allowable compressive stress of the material. Long columns, however, are designed on the basis of a reduced working stress obtained from one of the column formulas. Thus, in its application to long columns, we may write the above formula as

$$A = \frac{P}{s_r} + \frac{Pec}{s_r r^2} \tag{11.30}$$

where s_r is the reduced working stress and $I = Ar^2$. The value of r is the magnitude of the radius of gyration about the bending axis, not necessarily the minimum value for the cross section.

Let us now consider the relative magnitude of the terms on the right hand side of the equation as the eccentricity of the applied load varies from zero to a maximum. When the eccentricity is infinitesimally small, the second term is also small and the first term is relatively large. The condition is one approaching axial loading. The stress appearing in the denominator of the first term should therefore approach the reduced stress $*s_c$ for an axially loaded column. At the same time, the stress appearing in the denominator of the second term could vary considerably from s_c without materially changing its effect on the total cross-sectional area required for this loading.

When the eccentricity is great, the column is under almost pure bending and the second term $Pec/s_r r^2$ is the much more significant term. The stress more nearly representing this condition is s_f, the allowable flexural stress in bending. If the first term were still to retain its s_c stress it would bear little influence on the area required to resist this loading condition.

In consideration of the stresses produced by the extremes of eccentricity, Equation 11.30 is rewritten to include the stresses s_c and s_f.

$$A = \frac{P}{s_c} + \frac{Pec}{s_f r^2}$$

This may now be rewritten in the form

$$\frac{P/A}{s_c} + \frac{Pec/Ar^2}{s_f} = 1 \qquad (11.31)$$

or in the more condensed form appearing in the A.I.S.C. specifications,

$$\frac{f_a}{F_a} + \frac{f_b}{F_b} = 1 \qquad (11.32)$$

which indicates that the sum of the two left-hand terms shall not exceed unity for safe design.

The definition of each value is as follows:

$f_a =$ the actual axial stress P/A.

$f_b =$ the actual bending stress Mc/I.

$F_a =$ the maximum allowable column stress, assuming that only axial stress exists.

$F_b =$ the maximum allowable bending unit stress, assuming that only bending stress exists.

* Use A.I.S.C. column formulae (Eqs. 11.25 and 11.26) with their limitations.

Whenever the eccentricity produces bending about the major axis, the maximum allowable bending unit stress F_b is reduced if the ld/bt of the section is greater than 600 (see § 7-9), l being the unsupported length, d the depth of the member, b the width and t the thickness of the compression flange; all in inches (Fig. 11-15). If the value of ld/bt exceeds 600, the allowable flexural stress of 20,000 psi is reduced to

$$\frac{12,000,000}{ld/bt}$$

No stress reduction is considered if bending is about the minor axis (Fig. 11-16).

Figure 11-15 (left)

Figure 11-16. No stress reduction imposed by ld/bt.

Illustrative Problem 12. Select the most economical *WF* column, 14 ft long, that will sustain an axial load of 200 kips and an eccentric load of 80 kips applied to the minor axis, located 12 in. from the major axis.

SOLUTION. In order to select a trial section reasonably close to that required, the use of the bending factors (B_x and B_y) found at the bottom of the load tables in the A.I.S.C. handbook is recommended. These factors provide a convenient method of converting bending moments into approximately equivalent direct loads. B_x and B_y are, respectively, equal to the column area divided by the x-x and y-y section modulus. Since bending in our case takes place about the major axis (x-x), we must use B_x. Its range in values for 8 to 12 in. *WF* columns is from 0.333 to 0.177, respectively. Considering our load to be relatively heavy as far as these columns go, let us choose a value of 0.2 as our value of B_x. Thus

$$\text{bending moment} = M = 80 \times 12 = 960 \text{ in.-lb}$$

$$\text{equivalent direct load} = MB_x = 960 \times 0.2 = 192 \text{ kips}$$

$$\text{approximate direct column load} = 200 + 80 + 192 = 472 \text{ kips}$$

The following table was computed from investigations made of several 14-ft columns which, from the load tables found in the A.I.S.C. handbook, were shown to be capable of approximately sustaining the above load.

TABLE 9

INVESTIGATION OF TRIAL COLUMNS
SUBJECTED TO ECCENTRIC LOADING

Section	Allowable Column Load (kips)	Allowable Stress		Actual Stress		$\dfrac{f_a}{F_a} + \dfrac{f_b}{F_b}$
		Axial	Bending	Axial	Bending	
		F_a	F_b	f_a	f_b	
14 by 14 in. WF 103 lb	485	16,015	20,000	9250	5860	0.870
14 by 14 in. WF 95 lb	447	16,010	20,000	10,010	6370	0.943*
14 by 14 in. WF 87 lb	409	16,005	20,000	10,950	6950	1.029
14 by 12 in. WF 84 lb	383	15,500	20,000	11,330	7330	1.099
14 by 12 in. WF 78 lb	355	15,490	20,000	12,200	7930	1.185

* Use this value.

Typical computation. Investigation of 14 by 14 in. WF 95-lb column:

$$F_a = 17,000 - 0.485 \left(\frac{14 \times 12}{3.71} \right)^2 = 16,010 \text{ psi}$$

$$\frac{ld}{bt} = \frac{14 \times 12 \times 14.12}{14.545 \times .748} = 218$$

$$\therefore \quad F_b = 20,000 \text{ psi, working stress}$$

$$f_a = \frac{200 + 80}{27.94} \times 1000 = 10,010 \text{ psi}$$

$$f_b = \frac{M}{S} = \frac{80 \times 12}{150.6} \times 1000 = 6370 \text{ psi}$$

$$\frac{f_a}{F_a} + \frac{f_b}{F_b} = \frac{10,010}{16,010} + \frac{6370}{20,000} = 0.625 + 0.318 = 0.943$$

Since this is the lightest column whose two variable ratios have the greatest numerical value below 1, it is the most economical.

Notes. (a) The value of l/r in the column equation used in obtaining F_a is always the maximum value. (b) The value of c used in the determination of the bending stress f_b is always taken as the distance to the extreme fiber stress in the direction of the eccentricity.

PROBLEMS

Use A.I.S.C. specifications in the following problems.

11-35. Determine the most economical *WF* column, 15 ft long, to sustain an axial load of 120,000 lb and an eccentric load of 50,000 lb acting on the major axis, located 6 in. from the minor axis. *Answer:* 12 by 12-in. *WF* 72 lb.

11-36. How much axial load can a 10-in. *WF* 54-lb column, 16 ft long, take if it is already withstanding an eccentric load of 40,000 lb, placed on the minor axis 10 in. away from the major axis?

11-37. An axial load of 120,000 lb is being restrained by a 10-in. *WF* 54-lb column 16 ft long. What maximum eccentricity may a 20,000-lb load have when placed on the minor axis, without overstressing the column? *Answer:* 23.1 in.

11-38. What change in column section would be required if the length of the column in Problem 11-35 were changed to 20 ft?

11-39. Find the greatest unbraced height at which a 10 in. *WF* 49 lb column will safely support a load, at its top, of 80 kips placed on the minor axis 5 in. eccentric to the major axis.

11-40. A 12 in. *WF* 53 lb column carries a top load of 79 kips located on the *y* axis and eccentric 6.02 in. to the *x* axis. The height of the column is 36 ft. It is unbraced with reference to the *x* axis but is braced at a point 12 ft above the base with reference of the *y* axis. How much additional load, concentrically applied, could the column safely carry if additional bracing with reference to the *y* axis is introduced at 12 ft below the top? *Answer:* 26,000 lb.

11-41. A 14 in. by 8 *WF* 53 lb column (main member) has an unbraced height of 24 ft. What load, applied on the *y-y* axis at the flange face, could the column carry in addition to a concentric load of 54.8 kips? *Answer:* 31.9 kips.

11-42. Find the lightest 12 in. *WF* column with an unbraced height of 28 ft to carry a load of 182 kips applied at the top on the minor axis, with an eccentricity of 4 in. with respect to the major axis.

Columns eccentrically loaded about both symmetrical axes. When a column is eccentrically loaded with respect to both the major and minor axes, the relationship between the sum of the ratios of the applied and allowable stresses includes two bending effects, one about each of the symmetrical axes.

$$\frac{f_a}{F_a} + \left(\frac{f_b}{F_b}\right)_{x\text{-}x} + \left(\frac{f_b}{F_b}\right)_{y\text{-}y} = 1 \tag{11.33}$$

As indicated previously, the value of $(F_b)_{y\text{-}y}$ is always taken as 20,000 lb per sq in. The value of $(F_b)_{x\text{-}x}$ is, on the other hand, subject to the customary review of the ld/bt ratio of the column.

Illustrative Problem 13. A 12 in. *WF* 72 lb column with an unbraced height of 25 ft carries a concentric load of 90 kips, applied at the top. What additional load (also at the top) could the column carry if applied at a point which is 3 in. from the major axis and 2 in. from the minor axis? A.I.S.C. specifications.

SOLUTION.

$$P_D = 90 \text{ kips}, \qquad P_E = \text{Eccentric Load}$$

Total axial load $= 90 + P_E, \qquad M_{x\text{-}x} = P_E \times 3, \qquad M_{y\text{-}y} = P_E \times 2.$

Characteristics of column sections:

$r_{\min.} = 3.04 \text{ in.}, \qquad A = 21.16 \text{ sq in.}, \qquad \text{depth} = 12.25 \text{ in.},$

Flange width $= 12.04$ in., flange thickness $= 0.671$ in.,

$S_{x\text{-}x} = 97.5 \text{ in.}^3, \qquad S_{y\text{-}y} = 32.4 \text{ in.}^3$

$$\frac{l}{r} = \frac{25 \times 12}{3.04} = 98.7$$

$$F_a = 17,000 - 0.485(98.7)^2 = 12,250 \text{ psi}$$

$$F_a = 12,250 \text{ psi}$$

$$f_a = \frac{90 + P_E}{21.16}$$

$$\frac{ld}{bt} = \frac{25 \times 12 \times 12.25}{12.04 \times .671} = 454 \quad \therefore \quad F_b = 20,000 \text{ psi about } x\text{-}x \text{ axis}$$

$$\frac{f_a}{F_b} = \left(\frac{f_b}{F_b}\right)_{x\text{-}x} + \left(\frac{f_b}{F_b}\right)_{y\text{-}y} = 1$$

$$\frac{\dfrac{90 + P_E}{21.16}}{12.25} + \frac{\dfrac{P_E \times 3}{97.5}}{20} + \frac{\dfrac{P_E \times 2}{32.4}}{20} = 1$$

$$2.075 P_E = 245 - 85.1$$

$$P_E = 77 \text{ kips} \quad \text{(Maximum eccentric load that can be applied)}$$

PROBLEMS

Use A.I.S.C. specifications in the following problems.

11-43. Determine the lightest 12 in. *WF* section which will be safe as a column having an unbraced height of 14 ft, and which must provide for a total load at the top of 380 kips, a moment of 128 kip-in. about the major axis, and a moment of 24 kip-in. about the minor axis. *Answer:* 12 in. *WF* 92 lb.

11-44. A 14 *WF* 136 has an unbraced length of 18'-0" and carries a concentric load of 300,000 lb. What additional load may be carried at a point 11 in. from the *x-x* axis and $3\frac{1}{2}$ in. from the *y-y* axis? *Answer:* 80,000 lb.

11-45. Figure 11-17 shows the cross section of a 14 in. *WF* 87 lb member used as a column 20 ft long. If there is a load of 50 kips applied at point *A*, what additional load can be applied at point *C*?

Figure 11-17

$$I_{x\text{-}x} = 966.9 \text{ in.}^4$$
$$r_{x\text{-}x} = 6.15 \text{ in.}$$
$$I_{y\text{-}y} = 349.7 \text{ in.}^4$$
$$r_{y\text{-}y} = 3.70 \text{ in.}$$
$$\text{Area} = 25.56 \text{ sq. in.}$$

11-46. A 14 *WF* 219 is used as a column with an unbraced length of 20 ft. The column is to carry a concentric load of 350,000 lb and another load of 150,000 lb located 10 in. from the $x\text{-}x$ axis. How far to the right or left of the $y\text{-}y$ axis (but still 10 in. from the $x\text{-}x$ axis) may the 150,000 lb load be moved and still comply with A.I.S.C. specifications? *Answer: 5.07 in.*

11-23. *Secant formula*

It has already been noted that column design is based mainly on irrational formula because certain factors, such as non-homogeneity, crookedness, and difficulties of axial loading, produce unavoidable eccentricities. An attempt to evaluate these eccentricities and to include them in a rational column equation has led to the development of the well-known *secant formula*. It is derived as follows: Consider a column with a predetermined unavoidable eccentricity e to be superimposed on the x and y axes as shown in Fig. 11-18. Assuming the column to bend as a beam under the action of load P, its elastic curve equation will be

$$-EI\frac{d^2y}{dx^2} = M = Py$$

Multiplying both sides of the equation by $2\,dy$ and simplifying, we obtain

$$2\frac{dy}{dx}\,d\left(\frac{dy}{dx}\right) = -\frac{2P}{EI}\,y\,dy$$

Figure 11-18

Then, integrating,

$$\left(\frac{dy}{dx}\right)^2 = -\frac{P}{EI}y^2 + C_1$$

The value of C_1, obtained by substituting the simultaneously occurring values of $dy/dx = 0$ when $y = \Delta$, equals $P\Delta^2/EI$ which, when substituted in the foregoing equation produces

$$\frac{dy}{dx} = \sqrt{\frac{P}{EI}}\sqrt{\Delta^2 - y^2}$$

Gathering like terms,

$$\frac{dy}{\sqrt{\Delta^2 - y^2}} = \sqrt{\frac{P}{EI}}\,dx$$

Integrating a second time gives

$$\sin^{-1}\frac{y}{\Delta} = \sqrt{\frac{P}{EI}}\,x + C_2$$

But when $x = 0$, $y = e$, making $C_2 = \sin^{-1}(e/\Delta)$. The equation above then reads

$$\sin^{-1}\frac{y}{\Delta} - \sin^{-1}\frac{e}{\Delta} = \sqrt{\frac{P}{EI}}\,x$$

But y is equal to Δ when $x = l/2$ and $\sin^{-1}y/\Delta$ at that point is equal to $\sin^{-1}1$ or $\pi/2$. Substituting these values makes

$$\frac{e}{\Delta} = \sin\left(\frac{\pi}{2} - \sqrt{\frac{P}{EI}}\frac{l}{2}\right) \quad \text{or} \quad \frac{e}{\Delta} = \cos\frac{l}{2}\sqrt{\frac{P}{EI}}$$

whence

$$e = \Delta \cos\frac{l}{2}\sqrt{\frac{P}{EI}} \quad \text{and} \quad \Delta = e\sec\frac{l}{2}\sqrt{\frac{P}{EI}} \tag{11.34}$$

The maximum bending moment acting on the column is therefore

$$M = P\Delta = Pe\sec\frac{l}{2}\sqrt{\frac{P}{EI}} \tag{11.35}$$

If it is now desired to determine the maximum stress resulting from the application of the load P and its accompanying maximum moment noted above, let us substitute in

$$s = \frac{P}{A} + \frac{Mc}{I}$$

The maximum fiber stress on the column resulting from the application of a load P will then be

$$s = \frac{P}{A} + \frac{Pec}{Ar^2} \sec \frac{l}{2}\sqrt{\frac{P}{EI}} = \frac{P}{A}\left(1 + \frac{ec}{r^2} \sec \frac{l}{2r}\sqrt{\frac{P}{AE}}\right) \quad (11.36)$$

and $$\frac{P}{A} = \frac{s}{1 + \frac{ec}{r^2} \sec \frac{l}{2r}\sqrt{\frac{P}{AE}}} \quad (11.37)$$

To correctly use the preceding equations for design, note that (1) the angle $\frac{l}{2r}\sqrt{\frac{P}{AE}}$ is expressed in radians; (2) the values of e, c, and r should be in similar linear units — usually inches; and (3) the value of s should not exceed the proportional limit of the material.

To use Eq. (11.37) above in the design of columns, the value of s is generally taken as the yield strength s_y of the material, and the value of P, which is the load required to produce the yield stress is replaced by kP_w, in which k is a factor of safety and P_w is the working load. Furthermore, because the elastic curve is modified by the end conditions applied to the column, the value of l is multiplied by a constant f to give its "effective length." The generalized working formula therefore appears as

$$k\frac{P_w}{A} = \frac{s_y}{1 + \frac{ec}{r^2} \sec \frac{fl}{2r}\sqrt{\frac{kP_w}{AE}}} \quad (11.38)$$

Substituting $s_y = 32,000$ psi, $E = 30 \times 10^6$ psi, $k = 1.6$, f for hinged ends $= \frac{7}{8}$ and f for riveted ends $= \frac{3}{4}$*, the following effective design formulas for structural steel columns are derived.

For hinged ends,

$$\frac{P_w}{A} = \frac{20,000}{1 + \frac{ec}{r^2} \sec 0.875 \frac{l}{2r}\sqrt{\frac{1.6P_w}{AE}}} \quad (11.39)$$

For riveted ends,

$$\frac{P_w}{A} = \frac{20,000}{1 + \frac{ec}{r^2} \sec 0.75 \frac{l}{2r}\sqrt{\frac{1.6P_w}{AE}}} \quad (11.40)$$

Graphs of the above equations are shown on Fig. 11-19 using values of $ec/r^2 = 0.25$ and 1.0. The recommended A.I.S.C. equations are also shown plotted (Eqs. 11.25 and 11.26). Note the close approximation between the A.I.S.C. equations and the secant formula for pin ends using $ec/r^2 = 0.25$. It will also be noted that no l/r limitations are required for the secant formula.

* Recommended by A.S.C.E.

Figure 11-19. Graphs of secant formulas used for designing steel columns.
For hinged ends:

$$\frac{P_w}{A} = \frac{20,000}{1 + \frac{ec}{r^2} \sec 0.875 \frac{l}{2r} \sqrt{\frac{1.6P_w}{A \times 30 \times 10^6}}}$$

For riveted ends:

$$\frac{P_w}{A} = \frac{20,000}{1 + \frac{ec}{r^2} \sec 0.75 \frac{l}{2r} \sqrt{\frac{1.6P_w}{A \times 30 \times 10^6}}}$$

Use of the preceding equations in designing columns is facilitated by first plotting a series of curves showing the variation of P_w/A from l/r for various values of ec/r^2 (Fig. 11-20). From such a family of curves, designs can be made not only for columns with inherent natural eccentricity but also for those with a greater imposed eccentricity.

In the ordinary axially loaded column problem, the value of ec/r^2 must be estimated, depending on its straightness. This is not a simple task and results in further irrationality in the equation. Its value, however, lies generally between 0.10 and 1.0 for axially loaded columns, with 0.25 as the mean.

Illustrative Problem 14. Design a WF column 18 ft long to take a load of 200,000 lb. Assume hinged ends with $ec/r^2 = 0.25$.

SOLUTION. Assume an allowable stress of 12,500 psi. The trial required area will then be

$$A = \frac{200,000}{12,500} = 16 \text{ sq in.}$$

Figure 11-20. Plots of

$$\frac{P_w}{A} = \frac{20,000}{1 + \dfrac{ec}{r^2} \sec 0.875 \dfrac{l}{2r} \sqrt{\dfrac{1.6P_w}{A \times 30 \times 10^6}}}$$

with varying ec/r^2 and l/r values.

Let us try a 10-in. WF 54-lb column: $A = 15.88$ sq in., $r_{min.} = 2.56$ in., and its $\dfrac{l}{r} = \dfrac{18 \times 12}{2.56} = 84.3.$

The maximum allowable stress for this value of l/r as given by the secant formula is 13,500 psi (Fig. 11-19). The area required is therefore

$$A = \frac{200,000}{13,500} = 14.8 \text{ sq in.}$$

This indicates that the section might be too large for economy.

As a second try, consider a 12 by 10-in. WF 53-lb column:

$$A = 15.59 \text{ sq in.,} \quad r_{min.} = 2.48$$
$$\text{allowable stress} = 13,400 \text{ psi}$$
$$\text{required area} = \frac{200,000}{13,400} = 14.9 \text{ sq in.}$$

This is the most economical section that can be obtained.

PROBLEMS

11-47. Change the length of the desired column of Illustrative Problem 14 to 14 ft and determine the most economical section required. *Answer:* 10 in. WF 49 lb.

11-48. If the ends of the column of Illustrative Problem 14 were riveted, what most economical section would be required?

11-49. What maximum axial load can be applied to a 12-in. *WF* 79-lb column, 20 ft long, if $ec/r^2 = 0.25$ and its ends are hinged? *Answer:* 321,000 lb.

11-50. Through what range of length would the 12 by 10-in. *WF* 53-lb column of Illustrative Problem 14 remain the most economical column? Use the same load and column characteristics.

11-51. A section of steel column 18 feet high consists of a web 14 in. $\times \frac{3}{8}$ in. and four angles 5 in. $\times 3\frac{1}{2}$ in. $\times \frac{1}{2}$ in. placed $14\frac{1}{2}$ in. back to back with long legs outstanding. Determine the maximum load it can carry using the secant formula for hinged ends and $ec/r^2 = 0.40$. *Answer:* 230,000 lb.

11-52. A top chord member of a truss is to be 30 ft long and have applied to it a load of 400,000 lb. What most economical *WF* section should be used if the ends are to be riveted and $ec/r^2 = 0.80$?

Chapter Twelve

COMBINED STRESSES AND STRAINS

COMBINED STRESSES

12-1. *Introduction*

In previous chapters, detailed studies were made of the separate actions of axial, bending, and twisting forces. The question that now arises is: What would happen if two or more of these separate actions were to be applied simultaneously? After all, is not a shaft frequently subjected to bending and twisting forces at the same time? And is not a beam frequently acted upon by a longitudinal compression force while being bent? The development of the fundamental equations involved in resolving the several stresses induced by two or more of these separate actions will be the object of our ensuing study of combined stresses.

12-2. *Finding stresses at a point in a body*

In a previous article, it was revealed that a unit stress was obtained by dividing a force by the area on which it acted. This is no less true in the study of combined stresses. But because of the large variations of stress generally encountered in a body subjected to combined stresses, the areas considered must necessarily be so small that the average stress for such an area will be, for all practical purposes, its actual stress. In fact, the determination of stresses is generally made *at a point* in a body, the area of which is made visible only by a considerable magnification.

Let us consider the boiler of Fig. 12-1(a), and more specifically point M, at which a detailed stress study is to be made. It can be thought of as a dot made by a pencil point that, when expanded, looks like the shaded area of Fig. 12-1(b). It is inside this expanded dot that cutting planes, here represented by straight lines, are used to provide a free body from

385

(a)

(b)

Figure 12-1

which desired stresses may be computed.* By the judicious employment of the cutting planes, it is generally sufficient to use a free body having only three exposed sides — two sides containing known stresses, such as computed from P/A, Mc/I, Tr/J, and so forth, and the third side, those unknown and perhaps critical stresses that are to be found. For example, the rectangular *free body* shown in Fig. 12-1(b), on which the stresses have been computed by the thin-cylinder equations (Eqs. 4.3 and 4.4) must be cut still further to provide a triangular segment *DEF* on which a study might be made of the unknown stresses on its diagonal plane *EF*.

The cutting and recutting of free bodies into smaller and smaller free bodies is justifiable on the basis of equilibrium. If the body from which they were taken was in equilibrium, every portion of that body, no matter how small, was also in equilibrium. The stresses determined from these free bodies through the use of $\Sigma V = 0$, $\Sigma H = 0$, and $\Sigma M = 0$, are therefore necessarily equal to those stresses which were, in effect, in the body before the free bodies were removed.

In the application of the three laws of equilibrium to *free bodies*, it is important to remember that they pertain to forces alone. If stresses are to be included in these equations, they must first be multiplied by the area on which they act.

12-3. Principal planes — principal stresses

In any stress analysis, a designer must concern himself primarily with the determination of two major items:

(1) The types of stresses involved.
(2) Their maximum intensity at all critical locations.

Of invaluable assistance to the designer in his analysis is the fact that there occurs, at every point in a solid body, three mutually perpendicular planes, called *principal planes*, on which there is no shearing stress. The normal stresses occurring on these planes are called *principal stresses* and

---

* The internal pressure force is not shown on the free body *ABCD*, since it is perpendicular to the shell and does not alter the stresses acting on the exposed surfaces.

include the maximum and minimum values of the normal stress at that point. The two latter stresses are generally called the *maximum and minimum principal stresses*, the third principal stress being identified as the *intermediate principal stress*, having a magnitude somewhere between the other two. To clarify this point further, it is important that the maximum principal stress be delegated to that principal stress having the greatest numerical value.

The minimum principal stress, however, should be chosen on an algebraic basis as that principal stress having the widest algebraic divergence from the maximum principal stress. For example, if the three principal stresses acting at a point in a body are −3000 psi, +2000 psi, and +1000 psi (the minus sign pertaining to compression and the plus sign, to tension), the maximum principal stress is −3000 psi, the minimum principal stress is +2000 psi, and the +1000 psi is the intermediate principal stress.

The orientation of principal planes may, and generally does vary from point to point. The relative positions of the planes with respect to each other, however, do not change.

12-4. The state of two-dimensional stress

When a flat plate is placed under stress by central forces acting on its edges and lying in a plane parallel to its flat surfaces, the plate is said to be subjected to a state of *two-dimensional stress*. Because of the non-existence of lateral pressures on either of the flat surfaces, they are without shear and must be principal planes on which there is zero principal stress. It follows that the other two principal stresses envolved in this action must be perpendicular to each other and lie in the plane of the applied forces.

According to the theory heretofore presented in this book*, any cubical free body subjected to three-dimensional stress may be solved as a two-dimensional stress problem by progressively projecting the free body with its forces on planes parallel to any two adjacent sides. Viewing the free body in each instance from a position perpendicular to the desired plane of projection, only those forces acting on the periphery of the projected cube are assumed to act. In other words, the forces included within the projected area do not affect the stresses on the other mutually perpendicular planes. All projections are assumed to have a unit width in order to make the formation of lateral areas possible. Should, then, the stresses acting on the diagonal plane *ABHG* (Fig. 12-2) be desired, that projection (II) located at the right of the free body would be used in the calculations. Stresses on other diagonal planes — for instance, *ADHE* —

---

* Maximum Normal Stress Theory (§ 12-14).

Figure 12-2

would be determined from that projection on whose enclosed area the plane appears as a single line (III).

12-5. Basic principles reviewed — pure shear

Two basic principles underlying the study of combined stresses have already been advanced in Chapter 5:

(1) The first principle concerns the development of mutually perpendicular shear stresses. If a plane passing through a point in a body has acting upon it a shearing unit stress, there is simultaneously induced on a plane perpendicular to it a shearing unit stress of equal magnitude (Fig. 12-3). These shear stresses act in a direction perpendicular to the line of intersection of the planes in which they operate.

If shearing stresses alone act on two perpendicular planes, the stress condition is identified as a state of *pure shear*, and it is under such a stress condition that the second Principle 2 is developed.

(2) When a state of pure shear exists at a point in a body, normal and shear stresses of varying intensity are developed *on all oblique planes* at that point. On those planes making 45° to the shear planes, the normal stresses are maximum stresses, *acting with no shear* and are equal in magnitude to the shearing stresses (Fig. 12-4). One maximum normal, or principal,

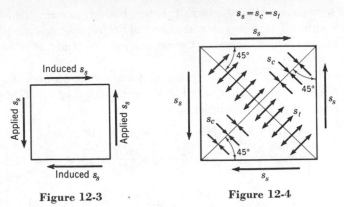

Figure 12-3   **Figure 12-4**

stress is always tension, the other, compression. The planes on which they act are perpendicular to each other.

12-6. Stresses induced by principal stresses

Occasionally a loaded member, such as the boiler of Fig. 12-1, is acted upon by readily computable principal stresses. For most other members, however, the principal stresses are not directly attainable and must be computed by combining the effects of two or more readily obtainable stresses such as Mc/I, Tr/J, P/A, and so forth. In any event, because these principal stresses induce other stresses which in some instances prove critical to the member being designed, their exact relationship to these stresses becomes an important fundamental in any stress analysis. We shall proceed with its formulation.

Consider the free body shown in Fig. 12-5(a), which is stressed in only two directions by principal stresses s_1 and s_2, the stress s_1 being greater than

(a)   (b)

Figure 12-5

s_2. Let us now pass a plane through this free body (trace revealed by line AC) which cuts off a triangular segment ABC represented in plan by Fig. 12-5(b), and which provides the means for the study of stresses on plane AC.

Because the direction of the equalizing force acting on area AC is unknown, it is shown acting obliquely having components $s_s \times AC$ and $s_n \times AC$. Balancing now the Y components, we may write

$$s_n \times AC = s_1 \times AB \times \cos\theta + s_2 \times CB \times \sin\theta$$

or

$$s_n = s_1 \times \frac{AB}{AC}\cos\theta + s_2 \times \frac{CB}{AC} \times \sin\theta$$

But

$$\frac{AB}{AC} = \cos\theta \text{ and } \frac{CB}{AC} = \sin\theta$$

$$\therefore \quad s_n = s_1 \cos^2\theta + s_2 \sin^2\theta$$

By substituting $1 - \sin^2\theta$ for $\cos^2\theta$ and $\frac{1}{2}(1 - \cos 2\theta)$ for $\sin^2\theta$, this equation may be changed to read

$$s_n = \frac{s_1 + s_2}{2} + \frac{s_1 - s_2}{2}\cos 2\theta \qquad (12.1)$$

Equating also the x components in Fig. 12-5(b) we have

$$s_s \times AC = s_1 \times AB \times \sin\theta - s_2 \times CB \times \cos\theta$$

or

$$s_s = s_1 \times \frac{AB}{AC} \times \sin\theta - s_2 \times \frac{CB}{AC} \times \cos\theta$$

$$= s_1 \sin\theta \cos\theta - s_2 \sin\theta \cos\theta$$

But since

$$\sin\theta \cos\theta = \frac{\sin 2\theta}{2}$$

we may write this equation as

$$s_s = \frac{s_1 - s_2}{2}\sin 2\theta \qquad (12.2)$$

With the development of Eqs. 12.1 and 12.2, it is revealed that a combination of shearing and normal stresses acts on every plane, making an angle with the principal planes. Each stress varies according to its respective equation, as angle θ is changed. It will be shown in the ensuing paragraphs that the resultant of the shear and normal stresses on any plane can never exceed the intensity of the maximum principal stress.

12-7. Mohr's circle — for determining stresses induced by principal stresses

The use of a Mohr's circle helps to establish firmly in mind the relationships given in Eqs. 12.1 and 12.2. On the coordinate axes of Fig. 12-6, the

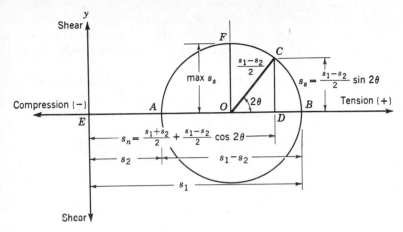

Figure 12-6

positive tensile stresses s_1 and s_2 are plotted as abscissas, and a circle whose center is on the x axis is drawn through their extremities A and B. The diameter AB of this circle will then be $s_1 - s_2$ and its radius equal to $\frac{1}{2}(s_1 - s_2)$.

If a radius OC is now drawn at a counterclockwise angle 2θ to the positive direction of the x axis, the ordinate DC to the end of the radius will equal $\frac{1}{2}(s_1 - s_2) \sin 2\theta$ or, as we have previously shown in Eq. 12.2, the shearing unit stress s_s. The abscissa DE to this point is

$$\frac{s_1 + s_2}{2} + \frac{s_1 - s_2}{2} \cos 2\theta$$

which, as revealed from Eq. 12.1, is equal to the normal unit stress s_n.

It cannot be emphasized strongly enough, however, that in order to correlate the values given by the Mohr's circle to those on the free body, the value of θ must always be the angle between the plane of the maximum principal stress and the plane on which the stresses are desired. That this must be so is shown as θ decreases to zero. The value of s_n, the normal stress acting on the diagonal plane, will then become equal to s_1 and the shear stress will equal zero.

In the event one or both of the principal stresses s_1 and s_2 are compressive, their values are plotted to the left (on the negative side) of the origin of the coordinate axes. The circle is always drawn through the extremities of s_1 and s_2 regardless of which side of the origin they may have to be placed.

In Fig. 12-7, s_1 is a tensile stress and s_2 is a compressive stress. If the stresses s_1 and s_2 were equal in magnitude to those used in the previous illustration, the circle would naturally be larger and produce greater shearing stresses.

Figure 12-7

Both s_1 and s_2 are shown as compressive stresses in Fig. 12-8. It is of interest to note that Mohr's circle becomes smaller in diameter as the values of s_1 and s_2 approach each other. Whenever both principal stresses are alike in both magnitude and direction, Mohr's circle becomes a point and renders the shearing unit stress on all planes equal to zero.

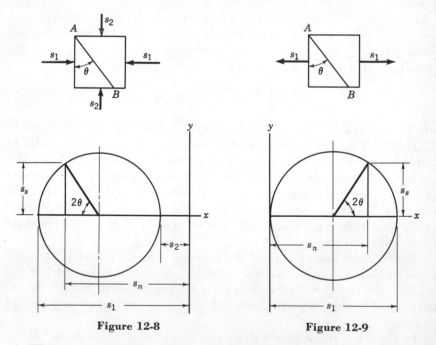

Figure 12-8   **Figure 12-9**

Whenever one of the principal stresses s_1 and s_2 equals zero (Fig. 12-9), Mohr's circle is tangent to the y axis and a state of axial stress results. Such a condition was previously discussed in § 2-8.

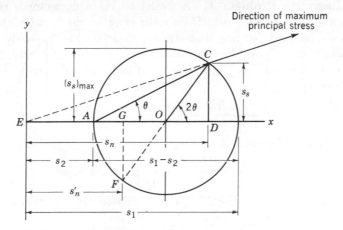

Figure 12-10

Maximum shearing stress. As radius OC of Fig. 12-10 is rotated about O, the ordinate of point C passes through a maximum value equal to $\frac{1}{2}(s_1 - s_2)$ when angle 2θ equals 90° and 270°, or when θ is equal to 45° and 135°. Since both of these shear stresses are equal and occur on mutually perpendicular planes, further substantiation is introduced of basic Principle 2 on the inducement of equal shear stresses given on page 388.

Maximum normal stress. Also of great significance and vital concern to the designer is the fact that the maximum principal stress is the greatest normal stress that can act at a point. This relieves his anxiety and helps expedite the problem of endeavoring to determine the most critical condition acting on a body. Of course, several critical points may have to be investigated, but as the principal stresses are found at each such point and the most critical condition is ascertained by comparison, no further concern about greater normal stresses acting on the body is necessary.

The justification for the above statements is based on the fact that the abscissa to point C, shown in Fig. 12-10, can never be greater than s_1.

Sum of normal stresses on mutually perpendicular planes. Another interesting relationship deduced from the Mohr's circle is that the sum of the normal stresses on any two mutually perpendicular planes remains constant for any angle θ. Referring again to Fig. 12-10, we note that

$$ED + EG = 2\,OE$$

Substituting the appropriate values of stress in this equation gives the substantiating statement

$$s_n + s'_n = s_1 + s_2 = (s_n)_x + (s'_n)_x \tag{12.3}$$

where $(s_n)_x$ and $((s'_n)_x$ are the normal stresses on any two mutually perpendicular planes.

Illustrative Problem 1. A boiler 60 in. in diameter is subjected to a steam pressure of 250 psi. If its walls are $\frac{1}{2}$ in. thick, calculate the maximum normal and shearing unit stresses that occur in the shell.

SOLUTION. From the thin-wall cylinder formulas derived in article 4-2, we may determine longitudinal and transverse stresses.

Transverse stress:

$$s_t = \frac{RD}{2t} = \frac{250 \times 60}{2 \times \frac{1}{2}} = 15{,}000 \text{ psi}$$

Longitudinal stress:

$$s'_t = \frac{RD}{4t} = \frac{250 \times 60}{4 \times \frac{1}{2}} = 7500 \text{ psi}$$

These stresses are principal stresses because they occur on planes unaccompanied by shear. They are shown in Fig. 12-11, acting on a small rectangular portion of the cylinder wall.

The third principal stress is produced by the internal pressure acting on the wall. It gradually decreases to zero as the outside of the wall is approached. On cubical free bodies *A* and *B* (lateral areas equal one unit of area) obtained from the inside and outside of the wall (Fig. 12-12) are shown the three principal stresses (or forces), the third stress being at full intensity on body *A* and zero on body *B*.

Figure 12-11

Figure 12-12

Having now ascertained the principal stresses, the computation of the maximum shear stress follows, using Eq. 12.2. Because compressive stresses are considered as negative tensile forces, Eq. 12.2, as applied to free body A, will produce a greater maximum shearing unit stress than the two-dimensional system at free body B. Substituting in this equation the maximum principal stress of 15,000 psi and the minimum principal stress of 250 psi, there results

$$(s_s) = \frac{s_1 - s_2}{2} \sin 2\theta$$

$(s_s)_{\text{max.}}$ occurs when $\theta = 45°$:

$$(s_s)_{\text{max.}} = \frac{s_1 - s_2}{2} = \frac{15,000 - (-250)}{2} = 7625 \text{ psi}$$

The traces of the planes on which the maximum shearing unit stress acts are shown as dash lines in Fig. 12-12(b). Both shearing planes are perpendicular to the plane containing the 15,000- and 250-lb forces and are located at a 45° angle to the maximum principal stress.

PROBLEMS

12-1. A cylindrical tank 48 in. in diameter is to be subjected to an internal pressure of 150 psi. If the plates are $\frac{3}{8}$ in. thick, what are the maximum normal and maximum shearing unit stresses developed in the shell of the tank?

12-2. A minute free body taken from a stressed member is shown in Fig. 12-13. Determine the shearing and normal unit stresses on a plane making 30° to the plane of the maximum principal stress. *Answer:* 5630 psi, 6750 psi.

12-3. Determine the shearing and normal unit stress in the previous problem if the minor principal stress of -3000 psi were changed to a tensile unit stress of $+8000$ psi.

Figure 12-13

12-4. If the angle used in Problem 12-2 were to be changed to 60°, what would the shearing and normal unit stresses be? *Answer:* 5630 psi, 250 psi.

12-5. Determine the maximum diameter for a sphere subjected to an internal gas pressure of 80 psi, fabricated from $\frac{1}{2}$-in. plates and limited in size by a maximum shearing unit stress of 12,000 psi in the shell. *Answer:* 49.8 ft.

THE SIMULTANEOUS APPLICATION OF A TENSION (OR COMPRESSION) AND SHEARING LOAD

12-8. *Preliminary considerations*

In contrast to the previous problem where principal stresses were found directly from well-known stress equations, such as Eqs. 4.3 and 4.4, the more general problem concerns the determination of the magnitude and location of the principal stresses in structural members to which two or more different types of loading (that is, axial, bending, twisting, and so forth) are applied simultaneously. In such a case, the critical stress induced by each type of loading is determined separately and combined through convenient stress relationships to find the principal stresses. We shall endeavor to obtain these relationships.

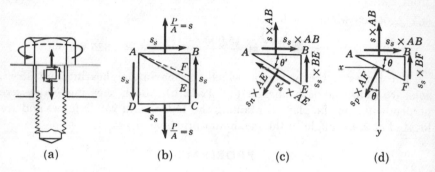

(a) (b) (c) (d)

Figure 12-14

One combined stress problem frequently encountered in engineering practice concerns the tightening of an engine stud bolt (Fig. 12-14a). In the final tightening operation, the bolt is twisted and placed in tension to hold the cylinder head to the cylinder block. A free body taken from a point just below the head of the bolt appears in Fig. 12-14(b). Our problem is now to find the principal stresses, since they are the maximum and minimum normal stresses and, as seen from § 12-6, produce the maximum shearing unit stress.

12-9. Finding the maximum principal stress

In view of the advantageous orientation of the free body (Fig. 12-14a), the shearing and normal (tensile) stresses, s_s and s, are easily obtained by

$$s = \frac{P}{A} \quad \text{and} \quad s_s = \frac{Tr}{J}$$

Since principal stresses, however, act on their planes unaccompanied by shearing unit stress, it is evident that the normal unit stress found above cannot be a principal stress. For this determination, we must select a particular plane AF (Fig. 12-14d), a principal plane, on which only the maximum normal stress is assumed to act. Note the difference between this plane and the general plane AE shown in Fig. 12-14(c), on which both a normal and shearing unit stress act simultaneously.

Equating the x and y components of the forces shown acting on this free body, we obtain the following expressions:

$$\Sigma F_x = s_s \times AB - s_p \times AF \times \sin \theta = 0 \qquad (12.4)$$
$$\Sigma F_y = s \times AB + s_s \times BF - s_p \times AF \cos \theta = 0 \qquad (12.5)$$

These equations may be simplified by dividing them by AF and noting that $AB/AF = \cos \theta$ and $BF/AF = \sin \theta$. Thus,

$$s_s \times \frac{AB}{AF} = s_p \sin \theta$$

from which
$$s_s \cos \theta = s_p \sin \theta \qquad (12.6)$$

and from which

$$s \times \frac{AB}{AF} + s_s \times \frac{BF}{AF} = s_p \cos \theta$$

$$s \times \cos \theta + s_s \times \sin \theta = s_p \cos \theta \qquad (12.7)$$

By rearranging Eq. 12.7 so that the cosine terms are on the left-hand side and the sine term on the right, there is obtained

$$(s_p - s) \cos \theta = s_s \sin \theta \qquad (12.8)$$

Equation 12.6 may now be divided into Eq. 12.8 to give

$$\frac{s_p - s}{s_s} = \frac{s_s}{s_p}$$

from which
$$s_p{}^2 - s \times s_p - s_s{}^2 = 0$$

and
$$s_p = \tfrac{1}{2}s \pm \tfrac{1}{2}\sqrt{s^2 + 4s_s{}^2} \qquad (12.9)$$

The two values obtained for s_p from this equation are the maximum and minimum principal stresses. There must, therefore, be two θ angles that satisfy Eqs. 12.4 and 12.5. *Because the value under the radical will always exceed the magnitude of $\tfrac{1}{2}s$, the maximum and minimum principal stresses will be of opposite types — that is, one a tensile stress, the other compressive.*

12-10. *Finding the planes of principal stress*

The planes on which these principal stresses act are found by solving Eq. 12.6 for s_p and substituting it in Eq. 12.7. The latter equation will then provide the value of θ in terms of the known stresses s and s_s.

$$s_p = s_s \times \frac{\cos \theta}{\sin \theta}$$

$$s \cos \theta + s_s \sin \theta = s_s \times \frac{\cos \theta}{\sin \theta} \times \cos \theta$$

$$s \sin \theta \cos \theta = s_s(\cos^2 \theta - \sin^2 \theta)$$

From our knowledge of double-angle trigonometric functions we obtain

$$s \times \frac{\sin 2\theta}{2} = s_s \cos 2\theta$$

from which
$$\tan 2\theta = \frac{2s_s}{s} \tag{12.10}$$

Again recalling our trigonometry, it is remembered that $\tan \theta$ has identical values of sign and magnitude for all pairs of angles separated by 180°. For instance, the values of $\tan 2\theta$ for angles $2\theta = 30°$ and for 210° are the same. Thus, if

$$\tan 2\theta = \tan 30° = \tan 210°$$

the angles that satisfy the equation are $\theta = 15°$ and $\theta = 105°$.

We may, therefore, state that two values of θ satisfy Eq. 12.10 and that they are 90° apart. Furthermore, these two values of θ define the planes on which the maximum and minimum principal stresses act.

Illustrative Problem 2. A steel shaft (Fig. 12-15), 2 in. in diameter, is acted upon by an axial tensile force of 50,000 lb and a twisting moment of 30,000 in.-lb. Calculate the maximum and minimum principal stresses and the planes on which they act.

Figure 12-15

SOLUTION. *The maximum and minimum principal stresses.* Let us first select a free body from the surface of the shaft, having a radial depth of unity (Fig. 12-15b). The values of s and s_s are then computed as

$$s = \frac{P}{A} = \frac{50,000}{\pi/4 \times 2^2} = 15,900 \text{ psi}$$

$$s_s = \frac{Tr}{J} = \frac{30,000 \times 1}{\pi/32 \times 2^4} = 19,100 \text{ psi}$$

Inserting these values in Eq. 12.9, there is obtained the maximum and minimum principal stresses

$$s_p = \tfrac{1}{2}s \pm \tfrac{1}{2} \sqrt{s^2 + 4s_s^2}$$

$$= \frac{15,900}{2} \pm \tfrac{1}{2} \sqrt{15,900^2 + 4 \times 19,100^2}$$

$$= 7950 \pm \frac{41,300}{2}$$

$$(s_n)_{max} = 28,600 \text{ psi}$$

$$(s_p)_{min.} = -12,700 \text{ psi}$$

These stresses and the planes in which they act are shown in Fig. 12-16.

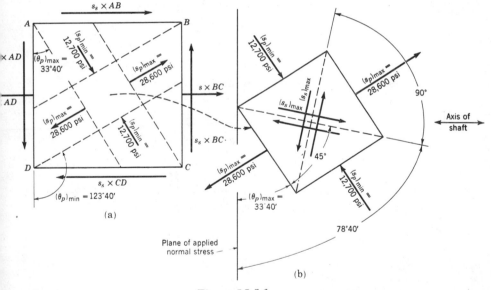

Figure 12-16

The principal planes. It is well to recall at this point that the angle θ in the previous derivation is the angle between the principal plane and the plane of the applied normal stress. However, two sets of planes may be drawn at an angle θ to the plane of applied normal stress and it becomes necessary to further qualify which θ is correct.

An easy method that may be employed in the determination of the correct value of θ is to find first the approximate location and magnitude of the resultant R' of both pairs of colliding shear forces (see Fig. 12-15). A further approximate combination of R' with the applied normal force, $s \times BC$, directs the resultant R in a direction approximately perpendicular to the plane of the maximum principal stress. It is this plane that is angle θ (magnitude below 90°) from the plane of the applied normal stress.

The value of θ may now be determined from Eq. 12.10.

$$\tan 2\theta = \frac{2s_s}{s} = \frac{2 \times 19{,}100}{15{,}900} = 2.4$$

$$2\theta = 67°20', \text{ or } 247°20'$$

$$\theta = 33°40', \text{ or } 123°40'$$

$$(\theta_p)_{\text{max.}} = 33°40', \qquad (\theta_p)_{\text{min.}} = 123°40'$$

12-11. *The maximum shearing stress*

As explained in § 12-7, the maximum shearing unit stress incurred by the application of two tensile principal stresses s_1 and s_2 acting at a single point in a body is equal to

$$(s_s)_{\text{max.}} = \frac{s_1 - s_2}{2} = \frac{(s_p)_{\text{max.}} - (s_p)_{\text{min.}}}{2}$$

and occurs on planes located 45° from the principal planes.

If the two principal stresses as derived in Eq. 12.9 are inserted in the above equation of maximum shearing unit stress, there results,

$$(s_s)_{\text{max.}} = \tfrac{1}{2}[\tfrac{1}{2}s + \tfrac{1}{2}\sqrt{s^2 + 4s_s^2} - (+\tfrac{1}{2}s - \tfrac{1}{2}\sqrt{s^2 + 4s_s^2})]$$

$$= \tfrac{1}{2}\sqrt{s^2 + 4s_s^2} \tag{12.11}$$

Illustrative Problem 3. Determine in Illustrative Problem 2 the maximum shearing unit stress and its location with respect to the plane of the applied normal stress s.

SOLUTION. The maximum shearing stress is equal to

$$(s_s)_{\text{max.}} = \tfrac{1}{2}\sqrt{s^2 + 4s_s^2} = \tfrac{1}{2}\sqrt{15{,}900^2 + 4 \times 19{,}100^2} = 20{,}650 \text{ psi}$$

It may also have been computed directly from the principal stresses as follows:

$$(s_s)_{\text{max.}} = \tfrac{1}{2}[28{,}600 - (-12{,}700)] = \tfrac{1}{2} \times 41{,}300 = 20{,}650 \text{ psi}$$

The location of the plane of maximum shearing stress with respect to the plane of the applied normal stress is

$$\theta_s = 33°40' + 45°00' = 78°40'$$

or

$$\theta_s = 33°40' + 135°00' = 168°40'$$

PROBLEMS

12-6. A stud bolt $\frac{3}{4}$ in. in diameter is to be tightened with a 50-lb force applied at the end of a 12-in. monkey wrench. If the tensile unit stress in the bolt at the time of the development of maximum torque is 10,000 psi, what are the maximum, principal, and shearing unit stresses in the body of the bolt? Locate the angles on which they act with respect to the cross section.

12-7. A hollow, steel hanger rod, $1\frac{1}{2}$ in. in outside diameter and 1 in. in inside diameter and 12 ft long, is subjected to a static load of 12,000 lb. If the rod is twisted 5°, what maximum normal and shearing stresses are incurred? *Answer:* 14,300 psi, 8200 psi.

12-8. The solid, circular steel shaft of a vertical hydraulic turbine is 30 in. in diameter. If the axial load supported by the shaft is 1,500,000 lb and the torque produced by the water wheel is 3,500,000 ft-lb, what maximum normal and shearing stresses are produced?

12-9. If the torque in Problem 12-8 were not given, what maximum value could it have withstood without exceeding a shearing stress of 10,000 psi, or a maximum principal stress of 15,000 psi? *Answer:* 4,380,000 ft-lb.

12-10. The 2-in.-diameter steel shaft of Fig. 12-17 is acted upon by force P of 400 lb. Determine the maximum and minimum principal stress, the maximum shearing unit stress, and the direction in which each acts. *Answer:* 10,600 psi, −400 psi, 5500 psi, 10°54′, 100°54′, 55°54′.

12-11. A shaft 2 in. in diameter is subjected to a torque of 600 ft-lb and a bending moment of 500 ft-lb. Determine the maximum normal and shearing unit-stresses in the shaft.

Figure 12-17

12-12. *Use of Mohr's circle for determining principal stresses*

From the computed normal and shearing unit stresses s and s_s, acting at any point in a body, the corresponding principal stresses can be obtained through the use of a Mohr circle diagram. Consider the solution of Illustrative Problem 2, the computed stresses of which are shown on the element of Fig. 12-18(a). The orientation of the element for purposes of solution by Mohr's circle should always be such that the normal stress acts horizontally. With such orientation, the stresses which act on the *right-hand face* of the element form the basis of a simple, straightforward method of finding the principal stresses.

Figure 12-18

The solution proceeds in the following manner. On a pair of rectangular coordinate axes, s and s_s, (Fig. 12-18b) lay off on the s axis the value of the normal stress, 15,900 psi. This, being a tensile stress, is considered positive and is laid off in the direction it appears on the right-hand side of the element. This locates point A. Now, erect at A a perpendicular AB equal to s_s (19,100 psi) also in the direction it appears on the right-hand side of the element.

Locate C at the mid-point of OA. Line CB is then equal to $\sqrt{\left(\dfrac{s}{2}\right)^2 + s_s^2}$. Then using CB as a radius, draw a circle with C as a center. If, now, we investigate the value of OD, we note that it is equal to the maximum principal stress, since

$$OD = OC + CD = \frac{s}{2} + \sqrt{\left(\frac{s}{2}\right)^2 + (s_s)^2}$$

$$= \frac{s}{2} + \frac{1}{2}\sqrt{s^2 + 4s_s^2} = (s_p)_{max.} = 28,600 \text{ psi}$$

This equation was derived in § 12-9. In like manner OE is shown to be equal to the minimum principal stress.

$$OE = OC - CE = \frac{s}{2} - \frac{1}{2}\sqrt{s^2 + 4s_s^2} = (s_p)_{min.} = -12,700 \text{ psi}$$

Because the maximum ordinate of a point on the circle is equal to the radius of the circle, its value is equal to the maximum shear stress.

$$(s_s)_{max.} = \sqrt{\left(\frac{s}{2}\right)^2 + (s_s)^2} = \frac{1}{2}\sqrt{s^2 + 4s_s^2} = 20,650 \text{ psi}$$

Furthermore, in Eq. 12.10 it was shown that the angle of inclination of the plane of principal stresses to the plane of the computed normal stress was given by the relationship

$$\tan 2\theta = \frac{2s_s}{s}$$

If this is written as $\tan 2\theta = \dfrac{s_s}{s/2}$, it reveals that angle BCA is equal to 2θ. Because angle BCA is a central angle cutting the arc BD, included angle BED, which cuts the same arc, is equal to one half of 2θ, or θ. This is the angle that the maximum principal stress plane makes with the plane of the given normal stress. It is also the angle between these two stresses. Since the direction of the given stress of 15,900 psi is known to be horizontal, the direction of EB locates the direction of the maximum principal stress. If EB is now extended outward and an element drawn symmetrically about it, (Fig. 12-18c) faces RT and SU perpendicular to the line are the planes of the maximum principal stress. The other two faces are the planes of the minimum principal stress ($-12,700$ psi), whose value is given by line OE on the Mohr's circle.

The orientation of the element required to produce the maximum shear stresses (45° to principal stresses) is shown in Fig. 12.18(d).

The procedure, as outlined in the paragraphs above, follows exactly any combined stress problem consisting of shear stress and one normal stress.

Figure 12-19

It is essential for the proper solution that the shear and normal stress on the *right-hand face* of the element be those used in forming the Mohr's circle. Another illustration of the formation of such a circle is shown in Fig. 12-19.

Should the normal and shear stress be desired on any other plane, use should be made of the theory presented in § 12-6 on elements subjected to principal stresses. Mohr's circle may also be drawn to obtain these same stresses by using the computed principal stresses and the proper 2θ angle.

PROBLEMS

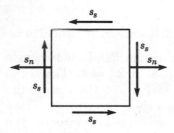

Figure 12-20

12-12. If a free body of a loaded member were stressed as shown in Fig. 12-20, with $s_s = 6000$ psi and $s_n = 10,000$ psi, what would the maximum and minimum normal and maximum shearing unit stresses be? What would the normal and shearing unit stresses be on a plane making 30° to the plane of s_n? Use mathematical analysis. *Answer:* 12,800 psi, −2800 psi, 7800 psi, 6750 psi, 8900 psi.

12-13. Solve Problem 12-12, assuming stress s_n to be reversed. Use mathematical analysis. *Answer:* −12,800 psi, +2800 psi, 7800 psi, 6750 psi, −8900 psi.

12-14. Solve Problem 12-12 using Mohr's circle.

12-15. Solve Problem 12-13 using Mohr's circle.

12-16. Solve Problem 12-10 using Mohr's circle.

12-17. Solve Problem 12-11 using Mohr's circle.

12-13. Combined stresses in beams

When a beam is loaded as shown in Fig. 12-21, flexural and shear stresses are developed throughout the beam in varying intensity according to the formulas $s = Mc/I$ and $s_s = (V/Ib)a\bar{y}$. The principal stresses resulting therefrom are also of varying magnitude and direction as shown. Further study reveals that below the neutral axis, the major principal stresses are in tension. Above the same axis, they are in compression. When a line such as ABA' is drawn tangent at all points to either the tensile or compressive principal stresses, it forms a *stress trajectory*. Many such stress trajectories can be drawn. If stress trajectories for the compressive principal stresses are drawn superimposed on corresponding stress trajectories for the tensile principal stresses, a system of orthogonal trajectories (intersections at right angles) is formed.

Note that the direction of the principal stresses on the neutral axis is the same, i.e., 45°. This is also true on the top and bottom surfaces, although

Figure 12-21. Variation of flexural and shearing stresses throughout a beam, disregarding localized effects of uniform load and concentrated reactions. Also shown are the principal stress directions and compressive stress trajectories.

the directions of the major principal stresses are at 0°. Lines connecting points of these or other *equal* directions of principal stress are called *isoclinics*.

The use of isoclinics and stress trajectories forms the basis for the study of photoelasticity. These lines are obtained from any stressed, temporarily refractive plastic model by two different settings of the photoelastic polariscope (see Fig. 13-11). From a superposition of one set of lines on the other, sufficient data are obtained to compute the magnitude and direction of all normal and shearing stresses occurring in the model and prototype.

PROBLEMS

12-18. In Fig. 12-22, determine the maximum normal and shearing unit stresses on the section 3 ft to the right of R_1 at 0, 2, 4, and 6 in. below the neutral axis. Determine the direction of each stress with respect to the horizontal.

Figure 12-22

12-19. A rectangular beam 4 in. by 10 in. in cross section (10 in. dimension vertical) is subjected to a positive bending moment of 43,000 in.-lb and a vertical shear of 3580 lb at a short distance from the left end of the beam. The beam is simply supported at the ends. Determine the magnitude and orientation of the principal stresses for a point in the cross section 2 in. below the centroidal axis of the beam. *Answers:* $(s_p)_{max.} = 301$ psi, $(s_p)_{min.} = -43$ psi, $\theta_p = 20.6°$.

12-20. A timber cantilever beam, 25 in. long, with a 2 in. by 12 in. cross section (12-in. vertical dimension), has a concentrated load of 800 lb at its free end. Determine the magnitude and orientation (with the horizontal) of the principal stresses for a point 2 in. above the neutral axis on the section 10 in. from the free end. *Answer:* $(s_p)_{max.} = 80.3$ psi, $(s_p)_{min.} = -24.7$ psi, $\theta_p = 29°$.

12-14. *Failure theories*

One of the first problems encountered in the study of the mechanics of materials concerned the design of a tension member. For this problem there was used an allowable stress based on the yield or ultimate strength of a tensile specimen made of a similar material. This procedure followed a seemingly logical reasoning because the action of the tension member was like that of the test specimen. Suppose, however, the member to be designed is subjected to a complicated combined stress system, the action of which is different from that of a tensile test. Can the yield or ultimate strength of the tension test still be employed as a basis for securing the maximum allowable design stress? Can the attainment of a certain maximum tensile stress be the only possible method of failure, and the only basis for its design? Would the development of the other stresses, shear and compression, or the resulting strains produce earlier failures? Or of even more significance, does the tensile test specimen which is used to determine the maximum allowable working stress in tension actually fail in tension?

The complete answers to these questions are still being sought. Various theories, based on experimental data, have been proposed. To date, no one theory has successfully explained the cause of failure in all materials. Some theories work well with brittle materials, others with ductile materials. None is perfect. Let us consider five of the more prominent theories that have been proposed, in the order of their development.

Maximum normal stress theory. The maximum normal stress theory, generally attributed to Lamé and Rankine, is based on the assumption that failure will occur when the maximum normal stress at any point attains the value of the limiting stress obtained by a simple tensile or compression test, regardless of the other stresses acting at the point. Failure may be considered to take place by excessive yielding or by fracture.

The dependency of this theory upon the tensile test is one reason for its inability to predict accurately the failure of ductile materials subjected to combined stress. Observation of a ductile tensile specimen during and after a test reveals that shear stresses contribute heavily to its failure. Test specimens of brittle material, however, show little or no shear deformation, and the test data obtained from them permit the application of the maximum normal stress theory with satisfactory accuracy.

The failure of an element subjected to axial stresses s_1 and s_2 may be shown graphically under the maximum normal stress theory by using a plot of s_1/s values as abscissas and s_2/s values as ordinates, s being either the ultimate or yield strength value in tension or compression, dependent on what mode of failure will take place. Failure will occur whenever $s_1/s = \pm1$ and $s_2/s = \pm1$. This condition is represented by the square plot shown as curve A in Fig. 12-23. According to this theory, any state of biaxial stress represented by a point within this square will not produce failure.

Figure 12-23

Maximum normal strain theory. The maximum normal strain theory, which was championed principally by Poncelet and Saint-Venant in the middle of the 19th century, is based on the assumption that failure occurs when the maximum normal strain at any point attains the value of the limiting strain obtained by a simple tension or compression test regardless of the stresses or other strains acting at the point. For an element acted on by principal stresses s_1 and s_2, it is expressed mathematically by

$$\epsilon_1 \pm \mu\epsilon_2 = \epsilon \quad \text{or} \quad \epsilon_2 \pm \mu\epsilon_1 = \epsilon$$

where ϵ is the strain attained at the proportional limit of a simple tension or compression test. Substituting stresses for the strains,

$$\frac{s_1}{E} \pm \mu\frac{s_2}{E} = \frac{s}{E} \quad \text{and} \quad \frac{s_2}{E} \pm \mu\frac{s_1}{E} = \frac{s}{E}$$

These may be reduced further to

$$\frac{s_1}{s} = 1 \pm \mu\frac{s_2}{s} \quad \text{and} \quad \frac{s_2}{s} = 1 \pm \mu\frac{s_1}{s}$$

Plotted on s_1/s and s_2/s axes, the graphs of these equations result in a diamond shaped figure (curve B, Fig. 12-23). The figure forms a boundary of limiting stress conditions outside of which failure will result.

Maximum strain energy theory. In an earlier chapter, it was shown that when a load acts on an axial member, there is stored in each elementary volume an amount of strain energy equal to $s^2/2E$ where s is a stress below the proportional limit created by the load. The maximum strain energy theory proposed by Maxwell, assumes that elastic failure takes place in a material whenever the strain energy per unit volume at any point exceeds the energy per unit volume absorbed by a tension or compression test specimen of similar material when stressed up to its proportional limit.

An element subjected to the same biaxial state of stress indicated previously produces a unit maximum energy absorption equal to

$$U = \frac{1}{2}s_1\epsilon_x + \frac{1}{2}s_2\epsilon_y$$

$$= \frac{1}{2}s_1(\epsilon_1 - \mu\epsilon_2) + \frac{1}{2}s_2(\epsilon_2 - \mu\epsilon_1)$$

$$= \frac{1}{2}s_1\left(\frac{s_1}{E} - \mu\frac{s_2}{E}\right) + \frac{1}{2}s_2\left(\frac{s_2}{E} - \mu\frac{s_1}{E}\right)$$

$$= \frac{1}{2}\frac{s_1^2}{E} + \frac{1}{2}\frac{s_2^2}{E} - \mu\frac{s_1s_2}{E}$$

According to the maximum strain energy theory, this energy produces failure when equal to that obtained in a tension or compression test. Thus

$$\frac{s_1^2}{2E} + \frac{s_2^2}{2E} - \mu\frac{s_1s_2}{E} = \frac{s^2}{2E}$$

or 　　　　　　　$$s_1^2 + s_2^2 - 2\mu\, s_1s_2 = s^2$$

Dividing through by s^2 gives

$$\left(\frac{s_1}{s}\right)^2 + \left(\frac{s_2}{s}\right)^2 - 2\mu\left(\frac{s_1}{s}\right)\left(\frac{s_2}{s}\right) = 1$$

If the proportional limit stresses in tension and compression, s_1 and s_2, are equal, this equation will form, when plotted graphically, an ellipse shown as curve C on Fig. 12-23. According to this theory, to remain within the ellipse guarantees elastic action.

Maximum shear stress theory. Proposed by J. J. Guest at the beginning of the 20th century, the maximum shear stress theory assumes that failure in a material will occur only when the maximum shear stress at any point reaches the value of the shear stress obtained at failure in a simple tension test of the same material. This condition expressed mathematically occurs when

$$(s_s)_{max.} = \tfrac{1}{2}s$$

In an element under a biaxial state of stress (Fig. 12-24a), where the principal stresses are s_1, s_2, and 0, the maximum shear occurs on different planes, depending on which projection of the element will give the maximum difference of the principal stresses, s_1, s_2, and 0. When s_1 and s_2 have like signs, the greatest difference will be between the greater of the s_1 and s_2 stresses and the zero stress, and will act on planes 45° to them. (See Fig. 12-24c.) Expressed mathematically, the relationship of these stresses at failure is presented by the following equation.

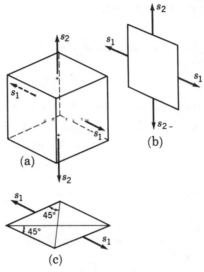

Figure 12-24

$$\pm \frac{s_1 - 0}{2} = \pm \frac{s_1}{2} = \frac{s}{2} \quad \text{or} \quad s_1 = \pm s$$

where s is the ultimate or yield strength value in tension or compression, dependent upon what mode of failure takes place. In a similar manner when s_2 is greater than s_1

$$s_2 = \pm s$$

Thus, when the signs of s_1 and s_2 are the same, this theory corresponds to the maximum normal stress theory.

When the signs of s_1 and s_2 are different, however, the greatest shear stress equals one-half their arithmetic sum (Fig. 12-24b, reverse sign of s_2 on side projection). Failure is then represented by the equation

$$\tfrac{1}{2}(\pm s_1 \pm s_2) = (s_s)_{max.} = \tfrac{1}{2}s$$
$$\pm (s_1 + s_2) = s$$
$$\frac{s_1}{s} + \frac{s_2}{s} = \pm 1$$

The graphs of this equation and those above enclose the area shown in Fig. 12-23 by D.

The maximum distortion energy theory. This theory, formulated independently by Von Mises and Hencky, and later supplemented by Huber, assumes that failure under combined stresses occurs when the amount of strain energy per unit volume due to shear (U_c) equals the strain energy per unit volume due to shear produced at the proportional limit of the same material subjected to a simple tension or compression test (U_t). Thus, the equality of energies

$$U_c = U_t$$

in a general state of stress becomes

$$\frac{1}{12G}\left[(s_1 - s_2)^2 + (s_1 - s_3)^2 + (s_2 - s_3)^2\right] = \frac{s^2}{6G}$$

or
$$(s_1 - s_2)^2 + (s_1 - s_3)^2 + (s_2 - s_3)^2 = 2s^2$$

in which s is the proportional limit stress, and s_1, s_2, and s_3 are the principal stresses. When $s_3 = 0$ (biaxial state of stress), this equation becomes

$$s_1^2 - s_1 s_2 + s_2^2 = s^2$$

or
$$\left(\frac{s_1}{s}\right)^2 - \left(\frac{s_1}{s}\right)\left(\frac{s_2}{s}\right) + \left(\frac{s_2}{s}\right)^2 = 1$$

A marked similarity is noted between the equation above and that derived for the maximum strain energy theory. It is indicated as curve E on Fig. 12-23.

Comparison of theories. On Fig. 12-23, where the graphs of the five theories are shown superimposed on the same set of axes, the typical results of combined stress tests of various materials are also plotted. Note that the maximum normal stress theory appears to be most correct for brittle materials and the maximum distortion energy theory for ductile materials.

12-15. Machine shafting

Most shafts are subjected to the combined action of twisting and bending forces. The tension and compression stresses produced by bending, applied simultaneously to the shearing stresses produced by twisting, develop the critical normal and shearing stresses expressed by formulas developed in § 12-9. No stresses with the possible exception of stresses produced at keyways, shrink fits, etc., occur elsewhere in the shaft to exceed them. In order to insure the safety of the shaft, these stresses, or the strain or strain energy that they produce, must be maintained at a safe level. The safe level is customarily determined as some percentage of the controlling feature of one of the five failure theories presented in the previous article.

The design of a typical shaft will now be presented. Each of the five failure theories will be used to determine its controlling diameter.

Illustrative Problem 4. In Fig. 12-25 a solid, circular, steel shaft, 80 in. long, has affixed to it a 15-in. and a 9-in. pulley and a 7-in. PD spur gear in the position shown. The belt tensions at each pulley are assumed

Figure 12-25

parallel, with $T_2 = 0.3T$, and $T_4 = 0.3T_3$. If the driven pulley A is rotated clockwise at 200 rpm by a 10-hp motor and has 8 and 2 hp tapped off at B and C, respectively, what will the diameter of the shaft have to be if based on developing one third of its elastic strength of 42,000 psi for each of the five previously mentioned failure theories? $\mu = 0.30$; $s_s = 0.50\ s_t$.

SOLUTION. The torques supplied at points A, B, and C are as follows (Eq. 5.6):

$$\text{hp} = \frac{2\pi Tn}{12 \times 33,000}$$

$$T_A = \frac{12 \times 33,000 \times 10}{6.28 \times 200} = 3150 \text{ in.-lb}$$

Because the sum of torques B and C equals 10 hp and they are respectively proportional to the horsepower tapped off, we may write

$$T_B = 3150 \times \tfrac{8}{10} = 2520 \text{ in.-lb}$$
$$T_C = 3150 \times \tfrac{2}{10} = 630 \text{ in.-lb}$$

The belt tensions on pulley A equal

$$7.5(T_1 - 0.3T_1) = 3150$$
$$T_1 = 600 \text{ lb}, \qquad T_2 = 180 \text{ lb}$$

The belt tensions on pulley B equal

$$4.5(T_3 - 0.3T_3) = 2520$$
$$T_3 = 800 \text{ lb}, \qquad T_4 = 240 \text{ lb}$$

The horizontal thrust on the gear at C is found from the expression

$$3.5 \times C_H = 630, \qquad C_H = 180 \text{ lb}$$

The effect of these applied loads in the horizontal and vertical planes is now determined. When the bending moments in each of these planes are found, those providing the greatest resultant effect are used in the determination of the proper size of the shaft.

$$T_1 + T_2 = 600 + 180 = 780 \text{ lb}$$
$$T_3 + T_4 = 800 + 240 = 1040 \text{ lb}$$
$$\text{Horizontal component} = 1040 \times 0.5 = 520 \text{ lb}$$
$$\text{Vertical component} = 1040 \times 0.866 = 900 \text{ lb}$$

Reactions are:

$$\Sigma M_{D_V} = 20 \times 780 = 15{,}600$$
$$= 50 \times 900 = \underline{45{,}000}$$
$$70E_V = 60{,}600$$
$$E_V = 866 \text{ lb}$$
$$D_V = 814 \text{ lb}$$
$$\Sigma M_{D_H} = 50 \times 520 = 26{,}000$$
$$80 \times 180 = \underline{14{,}400}$$
$$70E_H = 40{,}400$$
$$E_H = 577 \text{ lb}$$
$$D_H = 123 \text{ lb}$$

The critical stress condition, from observation of the two bending-moment diagrams (Fig. 12-26), is evidently at point B. The vector sum of the bending moments is their resultant and is found by

$$M_R = \sqrt{M_V{}^2 + M_H{}^2} = \sqrt{17{,}300^2 + 6150^2} = 18{,}360 \text{ in.-lb}$$

The solution has progressed to the point where the diameter must now be found by each of the five separate failure theories.

Maximum normal stress theory. According to this theory, elastic failure occurs when the maximum normal stress $(s_p)_{\text{max.}}$ attains the value of the limiting elastic strength s_t of the tensile test.

$$s_t = (s_p)_{\text{max.}} = \frac{s}{2} + \frac{1}{2}\sqrt{s^2 + 4s_s}$$

but $\qquad s = \dfrac{Mc}{I}, \quad s_s = \dfrac{Tr}{J}, \quad I = \dfrac{\pi d^4}{64}, \quad \text{and} \quad J = \dfrac{\pi d^4}{32}$

Figure 12-26

Therefore $\quad s_t = \dfrac{16}{\pi d^3} (M + \sqrt{M^2 + T^2})$

$$\frac{42,000}{3} = \frac{16}{3.14 \times d^3} (18,360 + \sqrt{18,360^2 + 3150^2})$$

$$d = 2.37 \text{ in.}$$

Maximum shear stress theory. According to the maximum shear stress theory, elastic failure occurs when the shearing elastic limit $(s_s)_{\text{max.}} = \frac{1}{2} \sqrt{s^2 + 4s_s}$. If $(s_s)_{\text{max.}} = 0.5s_t$ and substitutions are made for s and s_s in terms of M and T, then

$$0.5s_t = \frac{16}{\pi d^3} \sqrt{M^2 + T^2}$$

$$7000 = \frac{16}{\pi d^3} \sqrt{18,360^2 + 3150^2}$$

$$d^3 = \frac{16 \times 18,600}{3.14 \times 7000} = 13.52$$

$$d = 2.39 \text{ in.}$$

Maximum normal strain theory. From the discussion of this theory in ◄§ 12-14, elastic failure will occur if the maximum normal strain at any point attains the value of the limiting strain obtained by a simple tension test.

$$\epsilon = \epsilon_1 - \mu\epsilon_2 = \frac{s_1}{E} - \mu\frac{s_2}{E}$$

If, now, the values of maximum and minimum principal stresses s_1 and s_2 are substituted,

$$E\epsilon = \frac{s}{2} + \frac{1}{2}\sqrt{s^2 + 4s_s^2} - \mu\left(\frac{s}{2} - \frac{1}{2}\sqrt{s^2 + 4s_s^2}\right)$$

$$= \frac{(1-\mu)}{2}s + \frac{1+\mu}{2}\sqrt{s^2 + 4s_s^2}$$

A further substitution of Mc/I and Tr/J for s and s_s, respectively, gives

$$E\epsilon = \frac{32}{\pi d^3}\left(0.35M + 0.65\sqrt{M^2 + T^2}\right)$$

The value of ϵ is the strain that produces elastic failure in the tension test, namely $42,000/E$ psi. If substituted in the above equation, $E\epsilon$ becomes equal to the limiting stress of 42,000 psi. The allowable stress is 42,000/3 or 14,000 psi. Therefore

$$d^3 = \frac{32}{14,000 \times 3.14}\left(0.35 \times 18,360 + 0.65\sqrt{18,360^2 + 3150^2}\right)$$

$$d = 2.36 \text{ in.}$$

Maximum strain energy theory. Failure, according to this theory, is attained when the strain energy of any point under combined stress equals the strain energy of the tensile test at the elastic limit, namely $s_t^2/2E$. This is equal to $\frac{42,000^2}{2 \times 30 \times 10^6}$ or 29.4 in.^{3} If the elastic limit stress is now divided by the safety factor 3, this value becomes 3.27 in.^{3}. Thus, the design according to this theory states that

$$\frac{(s_t/3)^2}{2E} = 3.27 = \frac{1}{2E}(s_1^2 + s_2^2 - 2\mu s_1 s_2)$$

Inserting the equivalents of s_1 and s_2 in terms of the initially computed normal and shearing stresses provides

$$2E \times 3.27 = \left(\frac{s}{2} + \frac{1}{2}\sqrt{s^2 + 4s_s^2}\right)^2 + \left(\frac{s}{2} - \frac{1}{2}\sqrt{s^2 + 4s_s^2}\right)^2 -$$

$$2\mu\left(\frac{s}{2} + \frac{1}{2}\sqrt{s^2 + 4s_s^2}\right)\left(\frac{s}{2} - \frac{1}{2}\sqrt{s^2 + 4s_s^2}\right)$$

$$6.54E = \frac{s^2}{2} + \frac{1}{2}(s^2 + 4s_s^2) - \frac{\mu s^2}{2} + \frac{\mu}{2}(s^2 + 4s_s^2)$$

$$= \frac{(1-\mu)}{2}s^2 + \frac{(1+\mu)}{2}(s^2 + 4s_s^2)$$

To further simplify the expression for use in designing shafts, let Mc/I and Tr/J be substituted for s and s_s, respectively. There follows

$$\sqrt{6.54E} = \frac{32}{\pi d^3} \sqrt{0.35M^2 + 0.65(M^2 + T^2)}$$

Now, inserting the numerical values of M and T, let us find d.

$$d^3 = \frac{32 \times 18,550}{14,000 \times \pi}, \qquad d = 2.37 \text{ in.}$$

Maximum distortion energy theory. Placing the fundamental equation of this theory

$$(s_t)^2 = s_1{}^2 + s_2{}^2 - s_1 s_2 = (s_p)^2{}_{\text{max.}} + (s_p)^2{}_{\text{min.}} - (s_p)_{\text{max.}} (s_p)_{\text{min.}}$$

in terms of the initially calculated shear and normal stress yields

$$s_t{}^2 = s^2 + 3s_s{}^2 = M^2 \left(\frac{32}{\pi d^3}\right)^2 + 3T^2 \left(\frac{16}{\pi d^3}\right)^2$$

or

$$s_t = \frac{32}{\pi d^3} \sqrt{M^2 + \frac{3}{4} T^2}$$

Substituting numerical values with the factor of safety of 3 gives

$$d^3 = \frac{32}{\pi \times 14,000} \sqrt{18,360^2 + \sqrt[3]{4}\,3150^2}$$

$$d = 2.38 \text{ in.}$$

Note: The closeness of the answers to this problem indicates a condition of stress represented on Fig. 12-23 by the near intersection of all five failure theories. A change in the relative magnitudes of maximum bending moment and torque would unquestionably have caused greater differences in diameter.

PROBLEMS

12-21. Two pulleys 15 and 12 in. in diameter are placed at the third points of a 6-ft shaft operated at 200 rpm by a 20-hp motor. If one pulley is driven and the other is the driver, what diameter of shaft is necessary if elastic failure occurs in shear at 24,000 psi, and in normal stress at 48,000 psi? Assume the tension on one side of each pulley to be 0.3 of the other. Factor of safety = 3.0. $\mu = 0.3$. Use all five theories presented.

12-22. Determine the diameter of the shaft shown in Fig. 12-27 if elastic failure occurs at shearing and normal unit stresses of 24,000 and 40,000 psi, respectively. Use factor of safety of 4.0. $\mu = 0.3$. Use all five failure theories presented. *Answer:* 1.363 in.

12-23. Determine the diameter of the shaft shown in Fig. 12-28 if elastic failure occurs at shearing and normal unit stresses of 24,000 psi and 42,000 psi, respectively. Use factor of safety of 3.0. $\mu = 0.3$. Use all five theories presented.

Figure 12-27

12-24. What would be the diameter of the shaft of Problem 12-23 if the pulley *B* were removed and a vertical load of 4000 lb placed midway between the bearings? The torque produced at *A* is to be dissipated at *C*. Consider all design conditions to be the same. Use all five theories presented. *Answer:* 2.67 in.

Figure 12-28

12-25. Determine the diameter of solid circular shaft required to operate the pulley system of Fig. 12-29. Design is governed by a maximum allowable shearing unit stress of 8000 psi.

12-16. *The most general two-dimensional stress system*

When an element of a body has acting upon it a coplanar system of shear and normal forces, and when projected has stresses resulting from these

Figure 12-29

forces acting on each of its sides, it is subjected to the most general two
dimensional stress system (see Fig. 12-30a, b). To investigate the possibility of a more critical stress condition existing within the element, a still
smaller free body is secured by passing the diagonal plane $ECC'E'$ through
it perpendicular to its front face. Using the projected free body

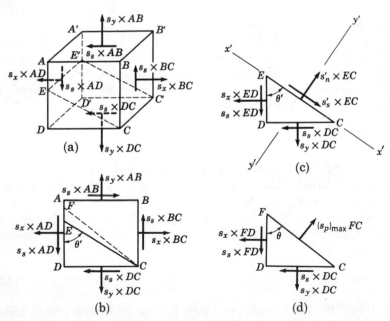

Figure 12-30

(Fig. 12-30c), equilibrium in the y'-y' direction is given by the following expression

$$s'_n \times EC = s_x \times ED \times \cos \theta' + s_y \times DC \times \sin \theta'$$
$$+ s_s \times ED \times \sin \theta' + s_s \times DC \times \cos \theta'$$

Dividing each side of the equation by EC and setting $ED/EC = \cos \theta'$ and $DC/EC = \sin \theta'$, there results

$$s'_n = s_x \cos^2 \theta' + s_y \sin^2 \theta' + s_s \sin 2\theta' \qquad (12.12)$$

Similarly, the value of s'_s is obtained by equating the components parallel to the x'-x' axis.

$$s'_s \times EC = s_x \times ED \times \sin \theta' - s_y \times DC \times \cos \theta'$$
$$- s_s \times ED \times \cos \theta' + s_s \times DC \times \sin \theta'$$

$$s'_s = s_x \sin \theta \cos \theta' - s_y \sin \theta \cos \theta' - s_s \cos^2 \theta' + s_s \sin^2 \theta'$$

$$s'_s = \frac{(s_x - s_y)}{2} \sin 2\theta' - s_s \cos 2\theta' \qquad (12.13)$$

Planes of maximum normal and shear stress. Were the two general equations of normal and shear stress (Eqs. 12.12 and 12.13) now differentiated with respect to θ and set equal to zero, the planes of maximum and minimum intensities would be defined. Those planes defining the maximum and minimum normal stress are indicated by the derivative

$$\tan 2\theta = \frac{2s_s}{s_x - s_y} \qquad (12.14)$$

This expression is satisfied by two values of 2θ between $0°$ and $360°$, which are $180°$ apart. Therefore, the two values of θ indicating the planes of *the maximum and minimum normal stresses are separated by $90°$.*

The planes of maximum shear stress, obtained by differentiating Eq. 12.13, are defined by the expression

$$\tan 2\theta = \frac{s_x - s_y}{2s_s} \qquad (12.15)$$

This expression, also, is satisfied by two values of 2θ between $0°$ and $360°$, which are $180°$ apart. The two values of θ which are $90°$ apart, however, define planes of maximum shear stress.

Were the general shear equation (Eq. 12.13) set equal to zero, and solved for θ, the plane of zero shear stress would be obtained. The result of this operation gives

$$\tan 2\theta = \frac{2s_s}{s_x - s_y} \qquad (12.16)$$

which defines the same angles as those for the maximum and minimum normal stress.

It must therefore be concluded, in verification of our previous statement, that *the maximum and minimum normal stresses act on planes where the shearing stress is zero* (Fig. 12-30d).

Maximum and minimum normal stresses. The maximum and minimum normal stresses are obtained by inserting the value θ of the plane on which they occur (Eq. 12.14), in the general normal stress equation (Eq. 12.12). These principal stresses are therefore

$$(s_p)^{\text{max.}}_{\text{min.}} = \frac{s_x + s_y}{2} \pm \sqrt{\left(\frac{s_x - s_y}{2}\right)^2 + (s_s)^2} \qquad (12.17)$$

Maximum shearing stress. Similarly, the maximum shearing stress is obtained by substituting the value θ of the plane on which that stress occurs (Eq. 12.15) in the general shearing stress equation (Eq. 12.13). There results

$$(s_s)_{\text{max.}} = \pm \sqrt{\left(\frac{s_x - s_y}{2}\right)^2 + (s_s)^2} \qquad (12.18)$$

The $\pm$ sign in front of the radical indicates that there are two equal maximum shearing stresses which occur in a general two-dimensional stress system. As indicated by Eq. 12.15, these maximum stresses act on planes 90° apart.

Directional considerations. By substituting each of the two angles derived from Eq. 12.14 into Eq. 12.12, an accurate analytical determination can be made to connect the proper principal plane with the maximum or minimum normal stress. A more simple determination, however, may be made by sketching to an approximate scale the resultants of the shear and normal forces on one side of the two diagonals passing through the element. The greater total resultant will be the maximum principal stress and the plane on which it acts will be the maximum principal plane. See discussion at end of § 12-10.

12-17. Mohr's circle for general two-dimensional stress system

The procedure to be followed in drawing Mohr's circle for the general two-dimensional stress system includes those steps used in drawing previous circle diagrams. The normal stresses s_x and s_y are plotted first (Fig. 12-31b), care being taken to plot the tensile stresses on the right of the origin and the compression stresses on the left. The shear stress s_s is plotted perpendicular to the x axis at the extremity of s_x in the direction it appears on the right face of the element, Fig. 12-31(a). Then selecting a center on the x axis $\frac{1}{2}(s_x + s_y)$ away from the origin, draw a circle passing through the free end of the shear stress ordinate s_s.

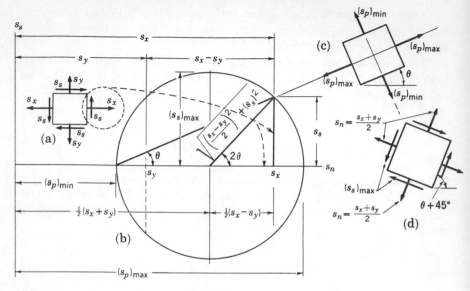

Figure 12-31

The principal stresses, maximum shear stress, and the directions of the planes on which each acts are determined in accordance with the discussion given in § 12-12.

12-18. General stress condition

The most general stress condition that may be developed on any element of a body occurs when normal and component shear stresses act on each of its faces (Fig. 12-32a). Because of the three-dimensional character of this stress system, any investigation of a more critical stress condition existing within the element involves complications heretofore unencountered. Consider the small free body (Fig. 12-32c) obtained by passing the diagonal plane $ECC'E'$ through the element perpendicular to its front face. When projected into the XY plane, several of its forces (Fig. 12-32b) are reduced to zero effect. However, these forces can still produce stresses on plane $ECC'E'$, a truth which is revealed by projecting the element into other planes.

Referring momentarily to the elementary body, note that the shear forces created by $(s_s)_1$ and $(s_s)_2$ on the front face are balanced by like forces on the rear face and may be eliminated from equilibrium considerations. The force created by $(s_s)_2$ on the left face, however, has no balancing force except on plane $ECC'E'$ because the right face was removed in obtaining the wedge-shaped free body. A similar condition also exists relative to the shear force developed by $(s_s)_1$ on the bottom face. It is evident, therefore,

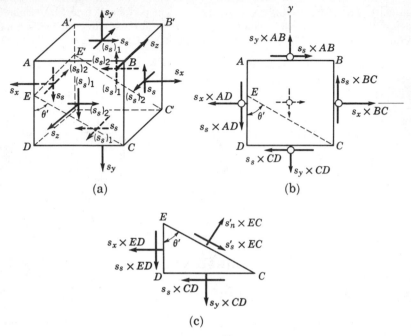

Figure 12-32

that to find the total stress condition, their combined effect must be added to the stresses found acting on plane $ECC'E'$ from the two-dimensional analysis. Furthermore, in order to obtain the maximum effect of all the active stresses, plane $ECC'E'$ must be rotated not only about line CC' but also about line EC.

Because of these complications, the determination of the principal stresses within the element due to the general stress system is beyond the scope of this text.

PROBLEMS

12-26. A horizontal cylindrical tank is subjected to an internal pressure which causes a longitudinal tensile stress $s_x = 5,000$ psi, and a circumferential tensile stress $s_y = 10,000$ psi, at a point on the external surface. An external torque applied to the cylindrical tank causes a shearing unit-stress $s_s = -1500$ psi at the point.

Determine the principal stresses (magnitude and sign) and draw a small sketch showing how the principal stresses are inclined with the horizontal (i.e., the x) axis. State the angle in terms of its natural function. *Answers:* $(s_p)_{max.} = 10,420$ psi, $(s_p)_{min.} = 4580$ psi, $(\theta_p)_{min.} = +15°30'$.

12-27. In each of the following sketches (Fig. 12-33), an element is shown with normal and shearing unit stresses acting on each peripheral face. Determine for each element the magnitude, character, and orientation of the principal and maximum shear stresses. Use Mohr's circle for each solution. *Answers:*

(a) $(s_p)_{max.} = 12.0$; $(s_p)_{min.} = -8.0$; $(s_s)_{max.} = 10.0$; $\theta = \tan^{-1} -\frac{6}{18}$;

(b) $(s_p)_{max.} = 14.3$; $(s_p)_{min.} = 1.7$; $(s_s)_{max.} = 6.3$; $(\theta_p)_{max.} = 54.1°$;

(c) $(s_p)_{max.} = -12.0$; $(s_p)_{min.} = +8.0$; $(s_s)_{max.} = 10.0$; $\theta = \tan^{-1} +\frac{6}{18}$

Figure 12-33

COMBINED STRAINS

12-19. *Importance of study of strains*

As revealed in the preceding sections, the theoretical determination of combined stresses and their use in design is, without question, of great importance. Yet the accuracy of their determination is dependent on the degree to which the equations used and the assumptions made in their derivation depict the actual conditions present. It often occurs that the calculated and existing stresses vary considerably. What is even more serious, a theoretical analysis may prove to be very difficult, if not altogether impossible.

Whether theory must be correlated with actual conditions present, or a stress analysis required where a theoretical solution is unobtainable, recourse may be taken to an *experimental* stress analysis based on indirect measurements of strain. These strain measurements are obtained by the correlated measurements of resistance changes of electric strain gages (Fig. 12-34) cemented to the surface of the body at the point where the stresses are desired. From a suitable number of such strain measurements, the complete combined stress picture at that point may be obtained. The relationships of strain and stress required to make such a study possible are presented in the ensuing paragraphs.

12-20. *Two-dimensional strain relationships*

Linear strains. Consider the infinitesimal surface element *ABCD* shown in Fig. 12-35(a) to be taken from a point on an unstressed body and

Figure 12-34

having inscribed upon it line DE, oriented at any angle θ with respect to line DC, an arbitrary datum. If the member is loaded and a unit tensile strain ϵ_x applied to the element, line DE will move to line DE', assuming DA to remain stationary. The total elongation in AE would then equal EE', and if DE'' is made equal to DE, $E'E''$ will be the total elongation in DE. The unit strain applied to line DE will therefore equal

$$\epsilon_\theta = \frac{E'E''}{DE''} = \frac{EE'\cos\theta}{DE} = \frac{EE'\cos\theta}{AE/\cos\theta} = \frac{EE'}{AE}\cos^2\theta = \epsilon_x\cos^2\theta \qquad (12.19)$$

(a)

(b)

Figure 12-35

If, in like manner, a unit tensile strain ϵ_y is applied in the y direction (Fig. 12-35b), the unit strain applied to line DE will equal

$$\epsilon_\theta = \frac{E'E''}{DE''} = \frac{EE' \sin \theta}{DE} = \frac{EE' \sin \theta}{EF/\sin \theta} = \frac{EE'}{EF} \sin^2 \theta = \epsilon_y \sin^2 \theta \qquad (12.20)$$

Considering both tensile strains ϵ_x and ϵ_y to be applied simultaneously, the strain on line DE will be

$$\epsilon_\theta = \epsilon_x \cos^2 \theta + \epsilon_y \sin^2 \theta \qquad (12.21a)$$

$$= \frac{\epsilon_x + \epsilon_y}{2} + \frac{\epsilon_x - \epsilon_y}{2} \cos 2\theta \qquad (12.21b)$$

It is important to note that ϵ_x and ϵ_y are principal strains and that Eq. 12.21 has been obtained for the strain of *any* line DE oriented at an angle θ with CD the plane of minimum principal strain.

Shear strains. Let us now consider the magnitude of the shear strain produced by the two principal strains ϵ_x and ϵ_y.

In Fig. 12.36(a) is shown the infinitesimal element $ABCD$ upon which has been drawn the rectangle $EFGH$. If now the element is subjected to a

Figure 12-36

tensile strain ϵ_x, the resulting shear strain on a plane making θ to plane CD of the element will be indicated by the angular change in the angles of the rectangle $EFGH$ (§ 2-12). Let us consider the angle EHG. After being subjected to the horizontal tensile strain of ϵ_x, the angle is increased by the angles $G''H'G'$ and $H'EH$. The sum of these two angles is equal to the shear strain associated with angle θ.

Expressed mathematically, this shear strain is equal to

$$\gamma_\theta = \text{angle } G''H'G' + \text{angle } H'EH$$

$$= \frac{G''G'''}{G''H'} + \frac{HH''}{EH}$$

$$= \frac{\epsilon_x x_2 \, dx \, \sin \theta}{x_2 \, dx / \cos \theta} + \frac{\epsilon_x x_1 \, dx \, \cos \theta}{x_1 \, dx / \sin \theta}$$

$$= \epsilon_x \sin \theta \cos \theta + \epsilon_x \sin \theta \cos \theta$$

$$\gamma_\theta = \epsilon_x \sin 2\theta \qquad (12.22)$$

In like manner, the shear strain γ_θ due to an applied tensile strain in the y direction (Fig. 12-36b) is equal to

$$\gamma_\theta = \frac{EE''}{HE} + \frac{GG''}{HG}$$

$$= \frac{\epsilon_y y_2 \, dy \, \sin \theta}{y_2 \, dy / \cos \theta} + \frac{\epsilon_y y_1 \, dy \, \cos \theta}{y_1 \, dy / \sin \theta}$$

$$= \epsilon_y \sin \theta \cos \theta + \epsilon_y \sin \theta \cos \theta$$

$$\gamma_\theta = \epsilon_y \sin 2\theta \qquad (12.23)$$

Because the tensile strain in the x direction enlarges angle EHG and the tensile strain in the y direction decreases the angle, their combined effect will create a subtraction of the shear strains. Assuming that enlarging the angle produces positive strain,

$$\gamma_\theta = (\epsilon_x - \epsilon_y) \sin 2\theta \qquad (12.24)$$

An analysis of Eq. 12.24 reveals that if both tensile principal strains were equal to each other, no shear strain or angular distortion could be developed within its field of action. It is also to be noted that, if the principal strains were of different character, one of tension, the other of compression, their corresponding shear strains would be additive regardless of their character. The maximum shear strain would, however, be found occurring on an angle of 45° to the principal strains.

12-21. Mohr's circle of strain

A comparison of Eqs. 12.21b and 12.24 with those for shear and normal stress developed on diagonal planes by maximum and minimum principal stresses, namely,

$$s_n = \frac{s_1 + s_2}{2} + \frac{s_1 - s_2}{2} \cos 2\theta = \frac{s_x + s_y}{2} + \frac{s_x - s_y}{2} \cos 2\theta \qquad (12.1)$$

$$s_s = \frac{s_1 - s_2}{2} \sin 2\theta = \frac{s_x - s_y}{2} \sin 2\theta \qquad (12.2)$$

reveals a marked degree of mathematical similarity. The one major difference is the omission of the 2 in the denominator of the shear strain equation.

In order to make the right-hand sides of both shear equations similar, let the shear strain equation be divided by 2, thus:

$$\frac{\gamma_\theta}{2} = \frac{\epsilon_x - \epsilon_y}{2} \sin 2\theta \qquad (12.25)$$

Now because similar trigonometric relationships exist for s_n and ϵ_θ, and s_s and $\gamma_\theta/2$, a Mohr's circle of strain similar to Mohr's circle of stress may be drawn on rectangular axes ϵ and $\gamma/2$ (Fig. 12-37) having a radius equal

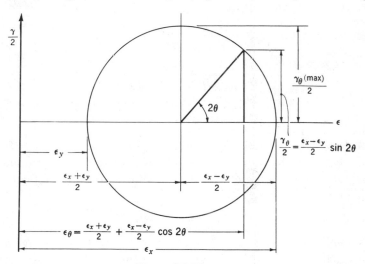

Figure 12-37

to $(\epsilon_x - \epsilon_y)/2$ and its center located at $(\epsilon_x + \epsilon_y)/2$. To find the shear and normal strain on any plane making an angle θ with the minimum principal strain, in this case ϵ_y, a radius is drawn making an angle 2θ to the positive end of the normal strain axis, measured counterclockwise. The coordinates to the intersection of the radius and circle equal the normal and shear strains desired.

Illustrative Problem 5. The principal strains at a certain point on a stressed body (Fig. 12-38a) are $\epsilon_x = 0.00060$ in. per inch and $\epsilon_y = -0.00040$ in. per inch. Determine the shear and normal strain on a plane making $\theta = 30°$ with the direction of minimum principal strain. Determine the maximum shear strain.

SOLUTION. On the rectangular axes ϵ and $\gamma/2$ (Fig. 12-38b), plot the value of $\epsilon_x = 0.00060$ and $\epsilon_y = -0.00040$. Find the mid-point of these two values which equals $(\epsilon_x + \epsilon_y)/2 = 0.00010$ and plot on the ϵ axis. This is the center of the strain circle whose radius is equal to $(\epsilon_x - \epsilon_y)/2 = 0.00050$. After drawing the circle, lay off radius at $2\theta = 60°$. The intercept of the radius with the circle reveals $\epsilon_{30°} = 0.00035$ and $\gamma_{30°} = 0.000866$.

Figure 12-38

The maximum shear strain, which is equal to the diameter of the circle, is equal to 0.001000.

PROBLEMS

12-28. Two mutually, perpendicular strains ϵ_x and ϵ_y equal to 0.000600 and -0.000200, occur with no accompanying shear strain. Calculate the strain condition existing on a plane making an angle of $60°$ with the plane on which the 0.000600 strain acts. *Answers:* $\epsilon_{60°} = 0$, $\gamma_{60°} = 0.000693$.

12-29. The maximum shear strain at a point in a body is equal to 0.000400. If the maximum principal strain is equal to 0.000600, what is the minimum principal strain?

12-22. General strain condition

The most general strain condition that may act on any surface element of a body includes both shear and normal strains on all four faces. Because of the shear strains, the normal strains are not principal strains. The principal strains must, therefore, be produced at a different orientation from that given.

The development of linear strain. Consider the element shown in Fig. 12-39(c) acted upon by shear and normal strains. To obtain the linear and angular unit deformation ϵ_θ and γ_θ on any line DE under this general

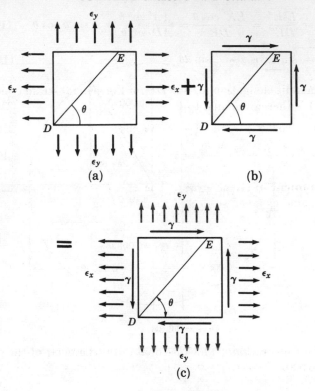

Figure 12-39

strain condition, those deformations for the biaxial strain condition (Fig. 12-39a) previously considered are superimposed and algebraically added to those produced for the shear condition (Fig. 12-39b), as yet undetermined.

The unit elongation for line DE located on the element subjected to shear as shown in Figs. 12.39(b) and 12.40(a) is equal to

Figure 12-40

$$\epsilon_\theta = \frac{E'E''}{DE''} = \frac{EE'\cos\theta}{DE} = \frac{AA'\cos\theta}{AD/\sin\theta} = \gamma\sin\theta\cos\theta \qquad (12.26a)$$

$$\epsilon_\theta = \sin\theta\cos\theta = \frac{\gamma}{2}\sin 2\theta \qquad (12.26b)$$

The net total unit elongation for line DE for the general strain condition of Fig. 12-39(c) is therefore equal to

$$\epsilon_\theta = \epsilon_x\cos^2\theta + \epsilon_y\sin^2\theta + \gamma\sin\theta\cos\theta \qquad (12.27a)$$

$$\epsilon_\theta = \frac{\epsilon_x + \epsilon_y}{2} + \frac{\epsilon_x - \epsilon_y}{2}\cos 2\theta + \frac{\gamma}{2}\sin 2\theta \qquad (12.27b)$$

The development of shear strain. The shear strain associated with angle θ of the same element subjected to shear (Fig. 12-40b) is equal to

$$\begin{aligned}
\gamma_\theta &= -(\alpha - \beta) \\
&= -\left(\frac{E'E''}{E'H} - \frac{GG''}{GH}\right) \\
&= -\left(\frac{EE'\cos\theta}{ED/\cos\theta} - \frac{GG'\sin\theta}{GC/\sin\theta}\right) \\
&= -(\gamma\cos^2\theta - \gamma\sin^2\theta) \\
&= -\gamma(\cos^2\theta - \sin^2\theta) = -\gamma\cos 2\theta \qquad (12.28)
\end{aligned}$$

Adding this strain algebraically to the shear strain obtained for the same element subjected to biaxial strain gives the net shear strain due to the general strain condition, namely

$$\gamma_\theta = (\epsilon_x - \epsilon_y)\sin 2\theta - \gamma\cos 2\theta \qquad (12.29)$$

Maximum linear and shear strain. The maximum strains occurring in an element subjected to a general strain condition occur, as did the principal stresses, on specific planes, obtained by differentiating the expressions for ϵ_θ and γ_θ with respect to θ. Thus Eq. 12.27(b) becomes, after differentiating,

$$\frac{d\epsilon_\theta}{d\theta} = -\frac{\epsilon_x - \epsilon_y}{2}\frac{\sin 2\theta}{2} + \frac{\gamma}{2}\frac{\cos 2\theta}{2}$$

Set equal to zero and solved for $\tan 2\theta$, this equation gives

$$\tan 2\theta_p = \frac{\gamma}{\epsilon_x - \epsilon_y} \qquad (12.30)$$

The two angles θ_p which satisfy this expression identify the planes on which the maximum or minimum linear strains, otherwise known as the *principal strains*, occur. If the values of $\sin 2\theta$ and $\cos 2\theta$ derived from the expression for $\tan 2\theta$, are inserted in the general strain equation 12.27, these principal strains become

$$(\epsilon_p)_{\substack{\text{max.} \\ \text{min.}}} = \frac{\epsilon_x + \epsilon_y}{2} \pm \sqrt{\left(\frac{\epsilon_x - \epsilon_y}{2}\right)^2 + \left(\frac{\gamma}{2}\right)^2} \qquad (12.31)$$

It is of interest to note that the directions of the principal strains correspond to those of the principal stresses.

In a similar manner, the maximum shear strain is found to equal

$$\gamma_{max.} = \sqrt{\left(\frac{\epsilon_x - \epsilon_y}{2}\right)^2 + \left(\frac{\gamma}{2}\right)^2} \tag{12.32}$$

and acts on planes 45° to the planes of principal strain.

Mohr's circle for general strain condition. The expressions for ϵ_θ and γ_θ, as given in Eqs. 12.27 and 12.29, may be represented by a Mohr's circle of strain similar to that explained in the previous article. Thus for the element subjected to the general strain condition shown in Fig. 12.41(a), the

Figure 12-41

values of ϵ_x and ϵ_y are laid off with algebraic magnitude on the ϵ axis and the $\gamma/2$ value is laid off parallel to the $\gamma/2$ axis in the direction indicated on the right-hand side of the element, upwards considered positive. The value of $(\epsilon_x + \epsilon_y)/2$ is then located (point A) and a circle scribed using AD as a radius. The line OB will then be the maximum principal strain, OC the minimum principal strain, and AE the maximum shear strain.

The previously discussed diagram can be considered as that resulting from the following illustrative problem.

Illustrative Problem 6. At a point on the surface of a stressed body mutually perpendicular normal strains ϵ_x and ϵ_y found to equal 0.00040 and -0.00020, respectively, occur with a positive* shear strain (shown in Fig. 12-41a) of 0.00080. Determine the magnitude of the principal strains and the maximum shear strain, and the angles on which they act.

SOLUTION. Supplementary to the previous discussion, there are plotted on the $\gamma/2$ and ϵ axes, first, the values of ϵ_x (0.00040,0) and ϵ_y (-0.00020,0). Then noting the positive direction of the shear strain vector acting on the right-hand face of the element, the value of $\gamma/2 = 0.00040$ is erected (line FD) in the corresponding positive direction at ϵ_x, the normal strain occurring on the same face. The mid-point between ϵ_x and ϵ_y, which is equal to $(\epsilon_x + \epsilon_y)/2$ is then plotted at point A (0.00010,0) and used as the center of a circle whose radius is AD (0.00050). The maximum principal strain is then equal to $OB = 0.00060$ and the minimum principal strain equal to OC or 0.00040. Line AE, the maximum ordinate, is equal to one half of the maximum shear strain or 0.00050. The maximum shear strain is therefore equal to 0.00100. Angle DAE is equal to $2(\theta_p)_{max.}$ having its tangent equal to

$$\frac{\gamma}{\epsilon_x - \epsilon_y} \quad \text{or} \quad \frac{0.00080}{0.00060} = 1.33$$

The direction of the maximum principal strain is obtained by drawing line CD, C being that point of intersection of the circle and the ϵ axis on the opposite side of O from the maximum principal strain, and D being at the end of the given shear strain line. By geometry, angle DCA is equal to $(\theta_p)_{max.}$, the angle between the planes perpendicular to the maximum principal strain and ϵ_y. The minimum principal strain occurs at right angles to the maximum principal strain with the maximum shear strain occurring at angles of 45° with each of them.

PROBLEMS

12-30. Two mutually perpendicular strains ϵ_x and ϵ_y are equal to 0.000600 and -0.000200. If they are accompanied by a positive shear strain of 0.000800, determine the maximum and minimum principal strains, the maximum shear strain, and the angles at which each acts relative to the direction of ϵ_x. *Answers:* $\epsilon_{pmax.} = 0.000766$, $\epsilon_{pmin.} = -0.000366$, $\gamma_{max.} = 0.001133$, $\theta_{pmax.} = 22.5°$.

* A positive shear strain produces upward shear stress on the right-hand face of the element.

12-31. In Fig. 12-39(c), ϵ_x, ϵ_y, and γ are respectively equal to 0.000800, 0.000200, and 0.000800. Determine the maximum and minimum principal strains, the maximum shear strain and the angles at which each acts relative to the direction of ϵ_x.

12-32. Solve Problem 12-31, using ϵ_x, ϵ_y, and γ equal to -0.000800, $+0.000200$, and 0.000800, respectively. *Answers:* $\epsilon_{\text{max.}} = -0.000940$, $\epsilon_{\text{min.}} = 0.000340$, $\gamma_{\text{max.}} = 0.001280$, $(\theta_p)_{\text{max.}} = 160°40'$.

12-33. Solve Problem 12-31 using ϵ_x ϵ_y, and γ equal to 0.000800, -0.000200, and -0.000800, respectively.

12-23. *The experimental determination of stresses by electric resistance gages — strain rosette*

The purpose of a strain gage is to measure the deformation that occurs over the test length of the gage, from which the unit strain may be calculated. Of the many kinds of strain gages now available, one of the most refined and widely applicable is the electric resistance gage. It consists of a grid of very fine wire (Fig. 12-34) which is bonded to the surface of a member at a point where a stress study is desired. When the member is subjected to load, the gage deforms exactly the same amount as the surface to which it is attached. Because wire, when deformed longitudinally, changes its resistance to the flow of electricity, and because the deformation per inch and the corresponding resistance change can easily be calibrated, the strain at the point in question may be obtained by measuring the change in resistance of the gage through the use of a Wheatstone bridge.

Figure 12-42

Should a resistance gage be bonded lengthwise to a tensile test bar which is thereafter loaded axially, the unit stress in the bar would be equal to the product of its longitudinal unit strain and modulus of elasticity. If, however, the same gage were to be placed in a biaxial state of strain in the direction of one of the principal strains (Fig. 12-42), the product of strain reading and modulus would not be equal to the principal stress. Its stress would be influenced by the action of the lateral strain, as indicated previously in Eq. 3.10.

$$(s_p)_{\text{max.}} = \frac{(\epsilon_x + \mu\epsilon_y)E}{1 - \mu^2} = \frac{E(\epsilon_{p\text{max.}} + \mu\epsilon_{p\text{min.}})}{1 - \mu^2} \tag{12.33}$$

$$(s_p)_{\text{min.}} = \frac{(\epsilon_y + \mu\epsilon_x)E}{1 - \mu^2} = \frac{E(\epsilon_{p\text{min.}} + \mu\epsilon_{p\text{max.}})}{1 - \mu^2} \tag{12.34}$$

Thus to obtain the principal stresses occurring in a biaxial state of strain, two strain gages would have to be placed at the point in question, in the direction of the principal strains. The simultaneously obtained strain readings introduced into the above equations give the principal stresses acting at the point.

Strain rosette. Ordinarily, however, the directions of the principal strains are not discernible on the surface of a body subjected to combined stress. Either an alternate means must first be employed to determine their orientation—such as the use of a brittle coating (see § 13-5)—or, as is commonly done, a more general use of strain gages is instituted, for which no prior knowledge of strain direction is required.

This more general method is based on the threefold use of Eq. 12-27a, at the designated point. Thus, the equations

UNKNOWNS

$$\epsilon_{\theta 1} = \epsilon_x \cos^2 \theta_1 + \epsilon_y \sin^2 \theta_1 + \gamma \sin \theta_1 \cos \theta_1 \qquad (12.35)$$

$$\epsilon_{\theta 2} = \epsilon_x \cos^2 \theta_2 + \epsilon_y \sin^2 \theta_2 + \gamma \sin \theta_2 \cos \theta_2 \qquad (12.36)$$

$$\epsilon_{\theta 3} = \epsilon_x \cos^2 \theta_3 + \epsilon_y \sin^2 \theta_3 + \gamma \sin \theta_3 \cos \theta_3 \qquad (12.37)$$

MEASURABLE

indicate for such a point the linear strains along three different lines making angles of θ_1, θ_2 and θ_3 *with some arbitrary axis*. The values of $\epsilon_{\theta 1}$, $\epsilon_{\theta 2}$ and $\epsilon_{\theta 3}$ are linear strains measured by means of three resistance gages superimposed

Figure 12-43. Strain rosettes being used in experimental stress analysis. (Courtesy of Baldwin-Lima-Hamilton Corp.)

on one another. These gages comprise a unit called a *strain rosette* (Fig. 12-43). Occasionally a fourth gage is added to serve as a check on the measurements obtained by the other three.

Because the values of ϵ_θ and θ are measurable quantities, the three common unknowns ϵ_x, ϵ_y and γ may be obtained by the solution of these three simultaneous equations. The values of ϵ_x, ϵ_y and γ, in turn, may be used either in a Mohr's circle of strains or in Eqs. 12.30 and 12.31 to obtain the principal strains and their orientation. Once these strains are obtained, the principal stresses are computed from the Eqs. 12.33 and 12.34.

To simplify the calculation of the values of ϵ_x and ϵ_y and γ, the gages of the strain rosette are set at predetermined angles, the trigonometric values of which are well known. The angles most frequently used are 0°, 45°, and 90°. The name assigned to the combination of gages set at these angles is *the rectangular strain rosette* (Fig. 12-44).

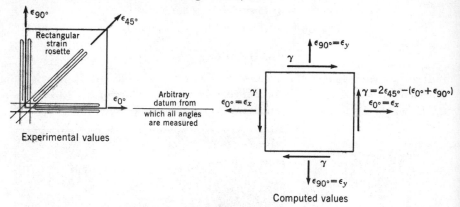

Figure 12-44

Inserting these angles in Eqs. 12.35, 12.36, and 12.37 results in

$$\epsilon_{0°} = \epsilon_x, \qquad \epsilon_{90°} = \epsilon_y \qquad\qquad (12.38)$$

$$\epsilon_{45°} = \frac{\epsilon_x}{2} + \frac{\epsilon_y}{2} + \frac{\gamma}{2}$$

from which

$$\gamma = 2\epsilon_{45°} - (\epsilon_x + \epsilon_y)$$

and

$$\gamma = 2\epsilon_{45°} - (\epsilon_{0°} + \epsilon_{90°}) \qquad\qquad (12.39)$$

Another strain rosette used employs the angles of 0°, 60° and 120°. This is the *equiangular strain rosette*. Should these values be substituted into Eqs. 12.35, 12.36, and 12.37 and properly simplified, the result would be

$$\epsilon_x = \epsilon_{0°} \qquad\qquad (12.40)$$

$$\epsilon_y = \frac{1}{3}(2\epsilon_{60°} + 2\epsilon_{120°} - \epsilon_{0°}) \tag{12.41}$$

$$\gamma = \frac{2}{\sqrt{3}}(\epsilon_{60°} - \epsilon_{120°}) \tag{12.42}$$

The use of a strain rosette may best be illustrated by a practical problem.

Illustrative Problem 7. The principal stresses are desired at a certain critical location on a web of a steel crankshaft. The strain readings of its three gages are $\epsilon_{0°} = 0.00040$, $\epsilon_{45°} = 0.00050$ and $\epsilon_{90°} = -0.00020$. $\mu = 0.30$. $E = 30 \times 10^6$ psi.

SOLUTION. From the simplified linear strain equations, there are obtained from the strain readings

$$\epsilon_x = \epsilon_{0°} = 0.00040$$
$$\epsilon_y = \epsilon_{90°} = -0.00020$$
$$\gamma = 2\epsilon_{45°} - (\epsilon_{0°} + \epsilon_{90°})$$
$$= 2 \times 0.00050 - (0.00040 - 0.00020)$$
$$= + 0.00080 \text{ (acts upward on right-hand face of element)}$$

To obtain the principal strain relative to this condition, use may be made of a Mohr's circle of strains (shown in Fig. 12.41) or direct computation may be made using Eq. 12.31. Using the latter method,

$$(\epsilon_p)_{\text{max.}} = \frac{0.00040 - 0.00020}{2} + \sqrt{\left(\frac{0.00040 + 0.00020}{2}\right)^2 + \left(\frac{0.00080}{2}\right)^2}$$
$$= 0.00060$$

$$(\epsilon_p)_{\text{min.}} = \frac{0.00040 - 0.00020}{2} - \sqrt{\left(\frac{0.00040 + 0.00020}{2}\right)^2 + \left(\frac{0.00080}{2}\right)^2}$$
$$= -0.00040$$

The principal stresses may now be obtained using Eqs. 12.33 and 12.34.

$$(s_p)_{\text{max.}} = \frac{E}{1 - (0.30)^2} \times [0.00060 + 0.3(-0.00040)]$$
$$= \frac{30 \times 10^6}{0.91} \times 0.00048 = 15,820 \text{ psi}$$

$$(s_p)_{\text{min.}} = \frac{E}{1 - (0.30)^2} [-0.00040 + 0.3(0.00060)]$$
$$= 7260 \text{ psi}$$

The direction of the maximum principal strain (stress) is given by Eq. 12.30.

$$\tan 2\theta = \frac{\gamma}{\epsilon_x - \epsilon_y} = \frac{0.00080}{0.00040 + 0.00020} = 1.33$$
$$2\theta = 49°, \qquad \theta = 24.5°$$

PROBLEMS

12-34. The strain readings obtained on the $0°$, $45°$, and $90°$ gages of a rectangular strain rosette are respectively 0.000300, 0.000400, and 0.000100. Determine the principal stresses, the maximum shear stress, and the angles on which each acts, relative to the direction of the $0°$ gage. $E = 30 \times 10^6$ psi. $\mu = 0.30$. *Answers:* $(s_p)_{max.} = 13,750$ psi, $(s_p)_{min.} = 3400$ psi, $(s_s)_{max.} = 5180$ psi, $(\theta_p)_{max.} = 31°43'$.

12-35. Solve problem 12-34 using gage readings of -0.000300, 0.000400, $+.000100$.

12-36. Solve problem 12-34 using gage readings of -0.000300, -0.000400, $+0.000100$. *Answers:* $(s_p)_{max.} = -12,600$ psi; $(s_p)_{min.} = +4030$ psi; $(s_s)_{max.} = 8320$ psi; $(\theta_p)_{max.} = 28°9'$.

12-37. An equiangular strain rosette placed on the surface of a stressed machine part reveals strains along the $\epsilon_{0°}$, $\epsilon_{60°}$, and $\epsilon_{120°}$ directions equal to 0.000600, 0.000200 and -0.000400, respectively. If $E = 10.6 \times 10^6$ psi and $\mu = 0.33$, determine the principal stresses and their directions relative to the assumed $0°$ direction. *Answers:* $(s_p)_{max.} = 6740$ psi; $(s_p)_{min.} = -2530$ psi; $(s_s)_{max.} = 4635$ psi; $(\theta_p)_{max.} = 18°18'$.

12-38. Solve Problem 12-37 using gage readings of -0.000600, 0.000200, and -0.000400.

12-39. Solve Problem 12-37 using gage readings of 0.000600, -0.000200, and 0.000400. *Answers:* $(s_p)_{max.} = 8070$ psi; $(s_p)_{min.} = 428$ psi; $(s_s)_{max.} = 3830$ psi; $(\theta_p)_{max.} = -23°5'$.

12-40. Will two strain gages placed parallel and perpendicular to the longitudinal axis of a thin walled cylinder give readings in the ratio of 1:2 when the cylinder is under pressure? Give reason for your answer.

Chapter Thirteen

FATIGUE STRENGTH — STRESS CONCENTRATIONS

13-1. *The phenomena of fatigue*

Perhaps our first introduction to the subject of the fatigue strength of materials took place when, in order to remove a nail from the surface of a piece of wood, we wiggled the nail back and forth until it broke. Although at the time the term *fatigue* may have had no significance to us other than a purely physical one, we are now to apply it to the *gradual reduction of strength in a material subjected to repeated stresses.*

In our wiggling operation, we may have noticed that a greater sweep to and fro produced a quicker failure. Expressed in engineering terms, rupture is hastened by increasing the range of the applied stresses. Furthermore, *unless we balance* the cycles of stress, such that each point in the member has alternate tensile and compressive stresses of equal magnitude, *the effectiveness of the range of stress* in producing fatigue failure will be increased. Such a balanced stress reversal is called a *completely reversed cycle of stress.* It may be contrasted with an *incomplete cycle of stress,* whose extremes of magnitude are not alike and which may prove to be more critical.

Many members employed in structures and machines, *such as crankshafts, axles, turbine disks,* and so forth, are subjected to complete or incomplete cycles of stress. Some of the magnitudes of the stress reversals may be small and of little significance to the life of structural or machine parts. Others may be large and cause the design of members to be made dependent upon a contemplated reduction of strength with use.

13-2. *s-N curves — the endurance limit*

Of invaluable assistance to the designer in such problems is the so-called *s-N* curve, *s* indicating unit stresses in lb per sq in., plotted as ordinates, and *N* signifying the number of completely reversed cycles of stress plotted as abscissas (Fig. 13-1). To gather information from one material for the plotting of such a curve requires a series of fatigue tests, each employing a different unit stress. Each test is run to failure, the number of cycles required for rupture being equal to N and the corresponding maximum unit stress being equal to s. When these values are plotted, they locate one point on the curve. A sufficient number of similar tests must be performed to provide the points necessary for a well-defined graph.

Figure 13-1

The s-N curve of Fig. 13-1, which is typical for many materials, shows that as the unit stress is decreased, the number of cycles required for failure is increased. This increase in N is rather rapid for the lower values of s, making the s-N curve asymptotic to a horizontal line. Should a completely reversed stress be imposed upon a specimen of a magnitude less than that of the asymptote, it would not fail regardless of the number of stress cycles to which it was subjected. That maximum unit stress which may be applied to a material through an indefinite number of completely reversed stress cycles without failure is called its *endurance limit*.

Because of the numerous tests required, the construction of an s-N curve is necessarily time-consuming. It is seldom that one can obtain definite assurance of an endurance limit with less than 10,000,000 cycles. Should the presence of the endurance limit still be questioned, this number of stress cycles would have to be further increased. To include the widely scattered data of an s-N curve on one graph sheet, a semi-logarithmic, or a log-log, plot is used (Fig. 13-2). Such plots indicate the presence of an endurance limit more clearly than an ordinary Cartesian plot.

Figure 13-2

Figure 13-3

In Fig. 13-3 are drawn the s-N curves of a few common metals. Those curves representing ferrous materials generally show a clearly defined

TABLE 10
FLEXURAL ENDURANCE-LIMIT STRESSES

Material	Flexural Endurance Limit* (psi)
Plain carbon steel:	
0.25% carbon, as rolled.............................	26,000
0.50% carbon, normalized..........................	33,000
0.75% carbon, annealed.............................	38,000
1.25% carbon, normalized..........................	50,000
Alloy steels:	
Nickel steel, not quenched..........................	50,000
Nickel steel, quenched..............................	65,000
Chrome-nickel steel, not quenched....................	50,000
Chrome-nickel steel, quenched.......................	68,000
Cast iron..	11,000
Aluminum, rolled....................................	10,500
Duralumin, rolled....................................	18,000
Magnesium forgings.................................	16,000
Bronze, 95-5 annealed...............................	23,000
Bronze, cold-rolled..................................	22,500
Brass, 70-30, cold-rolled.............................	17,500
Copper, annealed....................................	10,000
Copper, cold-rolled..................................	16,000
Beryllium copper, heat-treated.......................	45,000
Douglas fir...	3,900
Spruce...	1,700

* Flexural endurance limits are approximately one half of the ultimate tensile strength.

endurance limit. However, some nonferrous materials, notably those containing aluminum or magnesium, have not as yet been shown to have a clearly defined endurance limit even after 500,000,000 complete stress reversals. It is reasonable to assume that even these materials will reveal an endurance limit if sufficient time is taken for such a study. Table 10 gives the flexural endurance-limit stresses for a number of commonly used materials.

13-3. *Other methods of producing fatigue failure*

A fatigue failure is not only possible by the action of repeated flexural stresses, but by repeated torsional and direct stresses as well. In fact, combinations of the above methods are common in the design of machine parts and frequently prove to be of primary significance. The endurance-limit ratio in torsion to that in bending has an average value of about 0.56. The fatigue strength for axially applied stress is approximately equal to that for bending.

Illustrative Problem 1. A rod that activates the cantilever arm of a valve mechanism pushes and pulls with the same intensity of force at a rate of 120 complete cycles per minute. If the maximum activating force is 500 lb and the rod made of unquenched chrome-nickel steel is 12 in. long, what diameter must the rod have if operation is to be on the basis of an 8-hr day for a minimum of 10 yr? Use a factor of safety of 2.

SOLUTION. Number of complete cycles of stress anticipated equals

$$120 \times 60 \times 8 \times 365 \times 10 = 210,000,000$$

Since this number exceeds the 10,000,000 cycles generally required for an endurance limit, the design of the valve mechanism must be based on the 50,000 psi endurance limit. See Table 10.

The working stress is, therefore, equal to

$$\frac{50,000}{2} = 25,000 \text{ psi}$$

$$\text{Area required} = \frac{500}{25,000} = 0.02 \text{ sq in.}$$

$$\text{Diameter required} = \sqrt{\frac{4 \times 0.02}{\pi}} = 0.16 \text{ in.}$$

PROBLEMS

13-1. The axle of a freight car is expected to perform its intended function 8 hr a day or 10 yr. If during this period the loading is as shown in Fig. 13-4, and the speed of the freight car averages 20 mph, calculate the diameter of the axles. The axle is made of normalized 0.50 per cent carbon steel. Use a factor of safety of 2.5. *Answer:* 4.40 in.

13-2. A 2-in. diameter circular shaft made of 0.25 per cent carbon steel is 6 ft long and is freely supported in bearings placed at each end. If several million completely reversed cycles of stress are applied at its mid-point, what maximum value of load may be applied without rupture? Use factor of safety of 2.

Figure 13-4

13-3. A beryllium-copper spring, 0.25-in. wire diameter, is to be subjected to millions of complete cycles of torsional stress. What maximum load may be fluctuated if the coil diameter is 1.5 in., the number of coils is 10, and the factor of safety is 2? *Answer:* 56.0 lb.

13-4. Why materials fail in fatigue

Fatigue failures are the result of the poor transmission of stress developed by discontinuities both in the body and in the design of the working part. The discussion of internal and external discontinuities follows.

Internal discontinuities. No natural or synthetic material is ever homogeneous. If you were to peer into a microscope at the surface of a polished and etched piece of metal you would see that it consisted of a tightly packed and irregular granular structure (Fig. 13-5). A plastic, which might be considered more uniform, is still not homogeneous because of the large irregular molecules that make up its structure. Wood is an even more irregular material, consisting of a highly complex and non-uniform cell structure.

Figure 13-5. Photomicrograph of prestressed structural steel surface (200X). (Courtesy of Oliver E. Olsen)

Because of their non-homogeneity, regular geometrically shaped stress-bearing members do not have imposed upon their cross sections the theoretical stress patterns we assume to be present. Take, for example, the ordinary uniform cross-sectioned tension member. If loaded axially, the stress theoretically applied to each cross section is P/A. This, however, is an average stress, perfectly adapted for ordinary engineering design. On the other hand, if we were to investigate this stress across the various minute components of the cross section, we would find a distribution of

$$s = \frac{P}{A}$$

Figure 13-6

stress pictorially represented by Fig. 13-6.

Those points more highly stressed than the others may pass through their proportional limit and suffer some mechanical weakening even though held from straining further by the adjoining understressed material. If this weakening action takes place in a metal, it usually takes place across the grains, along so-called *slip planes*. When a slip plane is developed, it forms a source of incipient failure. Repeated stresses gradually cause the slip planes of adjoining grains to form a line perpendicular to the direction of the principal stress or parallel to the direction of the maximum shear stress, whichever is the more critical. With a decrease in the resisting area occurring with the development of each slip plane, failure is hastened.

This type of failure is caused by an internal discontinuity and is possible in every engineering material.

External discontinuity. Whenever the resisting portion of a stressed member has its cross section suddenly changed, another type of structural discontinuity is developed that is even more serious than that previously described. We shall call such a discontinuity an *external discontinuity*. The more common examples of this type of discontinuity are screw threads, rivet holes, keyways, re-entrant corners, and so forth, although even the peculiar shapes of many engineering members have discontinuities that may result in fatigue failure.

The seriousness accorded this type of discontinuity is apparent when it is discovered that at points of abrupt cross-sectional change the stress is materially increased, oftentimes to three or four times that obtained with the ordinary stress formulas derived in the earlier portions of this book. It is at such stress concentrations that most fatigue failures take place. Should such a stress concentration be unavoidable, the designer should correctly evaluate its magnitude and reduce the design stresses accordingly. The corrected axial, torsional, and bending formulas giving stresses at stress concentrations are

$$s = k\frac{P}{A}, \qquad s_s = k\frac{Tr}{J}, \qquad s = k\frac{Mc}{I} \qquad (13.1)$$

where k is the stress concentration factor.

Ductile materials, when subjected to static loads, are not as seriously affected by stress concentrations as are more brittle materials. This is due to the fact that ductile materials yield sufficiently to reduce the potentially high-stress concentration. When subjected to repeated loads, however, ductile materials fare only slightly better.

Theoretical stress concentration factors caused by various types of design discontinuities are recorded in Table 11.

TABLE 11

STRESS CONCENTRATION FACTORS*

I		Tension: $k = \dfrac{3d}{a+d}$ approximately.

Uniaxial Stress, Hole Centrally Located in Flat Plate.

Bending: approximately the same as for tension.

II

Tension: $k = 1 + 2\dfrac{a}{b}$

(for wide plate).

Elliptical Hole, Centrally Located in Flat Plate.

III(a)

Rectangular Bar, Reduced Section, Square Shoulder.

Tension:

$\dfrac{D}{d} \diagdown \dfrac{r}{d}$	$\dfrac{1}{16}$	$\dfrac{1}{8}$	$\dfrac{3}{16}$	$\dfrac{1}{4}$	$\dfrac{3}{8}$	$\dfrac{1}{2}$
3.0	3.10	2.66	2.28	2.00	1.76	1.60
2.0	2.66	2.29	1.97	1.74	1.52	1.41
1.25	1.96	1.84	1.66	1.50	1.32	1.26

III(b)

Bending:

$\dfrac{h}{r} \diagdown \dfrac{r}{d}$	0.05	0.10	0.20	0.25	0.50	1.0
0.5	1.61	1.49	1.39	1.34	1.22	1.07
1.5	2.00	1.73	1.50	1.39	1.22	1.08
3.5		1.76	1.54	1.40	1.23	1.10

* Compiled from the following sources:

Roark, R. J., *Formulas for Stress and Strain*, New York: McGraw-Hill Book Co., Inc., 1938, pp. 298-311.

Moore, H. F. and Henward, P. E. "The Strength of Screw Threads under Repeated Tension," Univ. of Ill. *Eng. Exp. Sta. Bull.* **264**, 1934.

Moore, R. R. "Effect of Grooves, Threads and Corrosion upon the Fatigue of Metals," *Proc. A.S.T.M.* **26**, 1926, Part II, p. 255.

TABLE 11 (*Cont.*)

IV

Circular Shaft, Reduced Section,
Square Shoulders.

Tension: Approximately the same as tension for the rectangular bar of case III.

Bending: Approximately the same as bending for rectangular bar of case III.

Torsion:

$\dfrac{D}{d}\ \backslash\ \dfrac{r}{d}$	0.005	0.01	0.02	0.03	0.06
2.00		3.00	2.25	2.00	1.05
1.20	3.00	2.50	2.00	1.75	1.50
1.09	2.20	1.88	1.53	1.40	1.20

V

Semicircular Notch in Circular
Shaft.

Tension: Approximately the same as for the elliptical hole in the plate of case II, tension

Bending: Approximately the same as for the elliptical hole in the plate of case II, tension

Torsion: $k = \dfrac{2D}{D + 2r}$

VI

Radial Hole in Circular Shaft.

Bending:

$\dfrac{a}{d}\ \backslash\ d$	2	3
0.0625	1.84	1.65
0.125	1.50	1.70
0.250	1.37	1.46

Torsion: for $\dfrac{a}{d}$ very small, $k = 4$

VII   Screw Threads

Tension: $D = 0.375$ in., 0.300% C steel
    Whitworth thread.. 1.76
    U. S. Standard... 2.84
    Rolled.. 2.15
Bending: $D = 0.375$ in., $h = 0.0271$ in. 24 threads per in., 0.43% C steel
    Continuous thread... 1.38
    Single notch.. 2.42

Illustrative Problem 2. A long tension member having a cross section $\frac{1}{2}$ in. thick by 4 in. wide has a 1-in. diameter hole bored through its

longitudinal axis. Determine the maximum tensile stress at the sides
of the hole if the load applied is 30,000 lb. Stress concentration factor is 2.

SOLUTION. The cross section of the bar through the hole is $A = \frac{1}{2}(4 - 1) = 1.5$ sq in.

The average stress on this cross section is

$$s = \frac{P}{A} = \frac{30,000}{1.5} = 20,000 \text{ psi}$$

However, due to a stress concentration factor of 2 at the side of the hole,
the actual stress at this point will be

$$s = k\frac{P}{A} = 2 \times \frac{30,000}{1.5} = 40,000 \text{ psi}$$

It follows that the actual stress at the outside edge of the cross section
will be less than 20,000 psi, since the average stress on the cross section
must remain the same.

PROBLEMS

13-4. The rolled Duralumin shaft shown in Fig. 13-7 is subject to millions of
complete cycles of flexural load applied at its mid-point. If the stress concentration
factor is 2, determine the maximum load that may be applied. Reactions at ends.
Answer: 147 lb.

Figure 13-7

13-5. What maximum load P may be applied to the 95-5 annealed-bronze shaft
shown in Fig. 13-8, if it is to fluctuate through many millions of reversed cycles?
Use a stress concentration factor of 2.

Figure 13-8

13-6. If the stress concentration at the oil hole (Fig. 13-9) equals 3, how far must it be placed from R_1 to create a stress equal to that obtained at the fillet? *Answer:* 21.4 in.

Figure 13-9

13-7. A Steatite insulator $\frac{3}{4}$ by $1\frac{1}{2}$ by 6 in. long is to be made with a hole placed 1 in. from either end for connection purposes. If the hole were made elliptical with its major axis of $\frac{3}{8}$ in. coincidental with the longitudinal axes of the insulator and its minor axis equal to $\frac{1}{4}$ in., what load could be safely applied through millions of axial stress reversals? Endurance limit under imposed conditions of direct stress is 1000 psi. Use stress concentration factor of 2.

13-8. What load could be sustained by the insulator of Problem 13-7, if the hole were $\frac{1}{4}$ in. in diameter? *Answer:* 182 lb.

13-9. A plaster of Paris specimen (Fig. 13-10) is loaded at the third points. If rupture takes place in the threaded portion when both loads equal 50 lb, what stress concentration is present? Root diameter is 1.25 in. Modulus of rupture of plaster of Paris is 1100 psi.

Figure 13-10

13-5. Methods of obtaining stress concentration factors

Various methods are employed to determine the stress concentration factor at an external discontinuity. Among the methods employed are:

(1) The strain-gage method.
(2) The plaster of Paris method.
(3) The brittle-lacquer method.
(4) The photoelastic method.

(5) The fatigue method.

(6) The mathematical method.

The strain gage method. By methods discussed in Chapter 12, the strains occurring at any point on a stressed surface can be used to obtain the *average* normal stress occurring in any direction. The smaller the gage length of the strain recorder, the closer will be the agreement between the actual and average stress.

The electric strain gage, manufactured in lengths as small as $\frac{1}{8}$ in., is conveniently employed for stress concentration determinations at fillets and other sharp changes in surface contour. *The stress concentration factor* equals the experimental normal stress (s_a) acting in any desired direction divided by the theoretical stress (s_t) acting in the same direction and at the same load obtained by the simple strength theory $(k = s_a/s_t)$. It indicates the relative speed of stress increase at the stress concentration over that of a similarly located point having no stress concentration.

The plaster of Paris method. Plaster of Paris, if properly hardened, has a fairly straight stress-strain graph when stressed in tension. When subjected to load, it will, as most other brittle materials, fail along the planes of maximum normal tensile stress. Thus, when a model of a load-bearing member made from plaster of Paris is stressed to its breaking point, the failure stress is equal to ultimate unit stress on the tensile stress-strain graph.

By comparing the experimental or actual stress with the theoretical stress produced by the same load, the stress concentration factor may be found.

The brittle-lacquer method. When a mechanical part is coated with a brittle lacquer and subjected to load, the strain of the load-bearing material will, when it exceeds the ultimate tensile strain of the lacquer coating, cause the lacquer to crack in the direction of the tensile principal stress. Furthermore, if at the same time a small calibrating cantilever beam is similarly coated and given a substantial known deflection at its free end, it will show cracks in its lacquered surface from the point where the strain of the beam exceeded the ultimate tensile strain of the lacquer. By simple calculation of the flexure formula, the stress in the calibrating beam at the beginning of the lacquer failure can be obtained. Correlating this finding to the point on the mechanical part where lacquer failure begins affords a simple means of ascertaining the stress at that location caused by the applied load.

Comparing once again the experimental and theoretical stress at the same point provides a simple means of determining the stress concentration factor.

At the present time, industry uses the brittle-lacquer method more extensively for the determination of the direction of the principal stresses rather than for the computation of their magnitude. Electric strain gages, oriented accurately by the cracks in the lacquer, are employed for the actual stress determination. The greater accuracy of the electric strain gage has prompted this arrangement.

The photoelastic method. When a doubly refracting, isotropic, two-dimensional body, such as a glass, celluloid or cast-Bakelite plate, and so forth is stressed and placed in a polariscope (Fig. 13-11), dark lines

Figure 13-11

passing through the body are viewed on the projecting screen and are proportional to the difference of the principal stresses. Under the same loading condition, the change in thickness of the plate, which is proportional to the sum of the principal stresses, is determined A solution of the two resulting simultaneous equations, including the terms $s_1 + s_2$ and $s_1 - s_2$, may then be made to obtain the principal stresses.* A detailed discussion of the optical problems involved is beyond the scope of this book. Knowing the actual stresses and those obtained by the simple strength formulas, the computation of the stress concentration factor is readily obtained.

The fatigue method. When s-N curves are obtained for two series of specimens similar in every detail with the exception of a stress concentration, the ratio of the endurance limits approximates the stress concentration factor. Because of the yielding of the material at the stress concentration, the value of k is less for more ductile materials. The value of k obtained is of real importance, however, for members subjected to repeated stress.

The mathematical method. Stresses at certain external discontinuities, such as circular and elliptical holes, may be determined mathematically. Comparing the exact theoretical unit stress with that obtained from the application of the simple theory provides the stress concentration factor.

* Other methods can be used to afford a solution of the s_1 and s_2 stresses, as found in the $s_1 - s_2$ equation, which do not require a determination of the change of model thickness. The reader is referred to any textbook on photoelasticity for further explanation.

13-6. *Incomplete stress reversals*

On many occasions, mechanical parts are subjected to incomplete stress reversals. Under such conditions, the endurance limit will be higher as the range of stress decreases. The limiting value is, of course, the static strength.

Of invaluable assistance in ascertaining the endurance limit for various cycles of stress is a diagram of the type shown in Fig. 13-12. It is con-

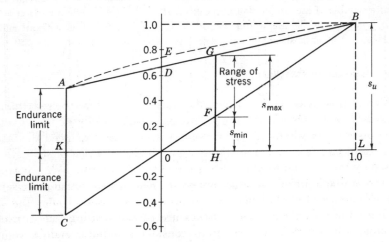

Figure 13-12

structed by plotting along a convenient straight line, such as COB, the values of the minimum stresses used in various incomplete stress cycles. If, then, the maximum unit stresses are plotted along their corresponding minimum stress ordinates, they conform to a slightly curved line AEB, which for practical purposes can be substituted with the straight line ADB. The endurance limit, therefore, for any incomplete cycle of stress having a minimum normal tensile stress equal to HF, is GH.

Such a diagram employing endurance limit values for completely reversed stress of $0.33s_u$ was developed independently by Goodman and J. B. Johnson and is commonly known as the Goodman-Johnson diagram. Greater accuracy is obtained, however, if the actual endurance limit is used.

PROBLEMS

13-10. A simple, grey cast-iron beam, $\frac{1}{2}$ in. thick by $1\frac{1}{2}$ in. wide by 24 in. long, is subjected to an incomplete load reversal at its center having as its maximum and minimum downward values 500 and 200 lb, respectively. Will it last indefinitely if the $1\frac{1}{2}$-in. dimension is kept vertical? Prove your answer. Ultimate flexural unit stress is 25,000 psi. *Answer:* Yes.

Hint. Construct Goodman-Johnson diagram using ultimate stress and the endurance limit for completely reversed cycles of stress. Determine the endurance limits for the incomplete cycles of stress from the conditions of the problem.

13-11. A cantilever beam is subjected to millions of incomplete load reversals. If it is to be made from a 1-in. diameter steel (0.25 per cent C) rod, 12 in. long, and has a minimum downward load of 30 lb, what maximum downward load can it take if a factor of safety of 2 is used?

13-12. A 1-in. diameter quenched nickel-steel rod is twisted through an indefinite number of incomplete loading cycles. If the torque in one direction is 1500 in.-lb, what can be the maximum torque in the opposite direction without rupture occurring? Ultimate shearing unit stress is 75,000 psi. *Answer:* 10,220 in.-lb.

13-7. Corrosion fatigue

The corrosion of metals proceeds more rapidly for stressed than for unstressed materials. McAdam, in his exhaustive study of the effects of stress on corrosion, found that corrosion without stress reduced the fatigue strength of metals as much as 30 per cent. This reduction of strength was caused by the pits and irregularities formed on the surface. When corrosion and stress were applied simultaneously, the results were much more serious than when either acted alone.

Since the experimental *s-N* curves are obtained using finely polished specimens, it would be necessary to consider a reduced endurance limit should parts be designed to perform in a corrosive atmosphere. A reduction of over 50 per cent in the endurance limit of steel may be expected when the repeated stress is developed in the presence of salt water.

Chapter Fourteen

THE APPLICATION OF ENERGY RELATIONSHIPS

14-1. Introduction

Energy, by definition, is the ability or capacity of doing work. A force performs work when it is displaced along the direction of its action line. For instance, when a force is gradually applied to an elastic body, its magnitude varies in proportion to the resistance encountered, and the work it performs on the body is measured by the product of its average magnitude and the displacement it produces. This work is classified as *external* work. Because *energy* can neither be created nor destroyed, the resistive forces acting within the body passing through internal deformations must produce an equivalent amount of *internal* work.

The more dynamic form of energy, such as that accruing to a falling weight, produces stresses of a much greater magnitude upon impact than those produced by the same weight applied gradually. Although the same equality of external and internal work must persist, the kinetic energy of the load before impact is generally so large as to make the additional external energy produced during deformation of minor importance.

The succeeding articles will discuss in detail the external and internal energies resulting from gradually applied and impact loads, and their use in determining deformations and stresses.

ENERGY DEVELOPED BY GRADUALLY APPLIED LOADS

14-2. External energy

When a load P is gradually applied to an elastic body, it produces a gradually increasing deformation which attains a maximum value at the time of full load application (see Fig. 14-1). The product of the average load $(P/2)$ applied or transferred to the body and the deformation Δ_{max}.

Figure 14-1

produced by the full load P is the measure of the external energy *put into* the body. Derived mathematically,

$$\text{external energy} = \int_0^{\Delta_{\text{max.}}} P_y \, d\Delta$$

But
$$P_y = \frac{P}{\Delta_{\text{max.}}} \Delta$$

$$\text{external energy} = \int_0^{\Delta_{\text{max.}}} \frac{P}{\Delta_{\text{max.}}} \Delta \, d\Delta = \frac{P}{\Delta_{\text{max.}}} \left[\frac{\Delta^2}{2} \right]_0^{\Delta_{\text{max.}}} = \frac{P\Delta_{\text{max.}}}{2} \quad (14.1)$$

The value of $\frac{1}{2}P\Delta_{\text{max.}}$ should be recognized as the area under the load deformation curve up to full load.

In a similar fashion, the work performed by a gradually applied couple T acting on an elastic body is equal to $\frac{1}{2}T\theta_{\text{max.}}$ (Fig. 14-1).

14-3. *Internal energy*

Whereas those forces producing external energy are *externally applied*, those producing internal energy are *internally applied*. Internally applied forces are those resisting forces (viz., C-T couples, T_R, etc.), which are induced by the action of the external forces. When developed by gradually applied external forces, the internal forces must, of course, also be gradually applied. The internal energy developed must therefore also equal an average force or couple times its maximum internal deformation.

Internal or resisting forces are of four different kinds, namely, axial, bending, torsional, and shear. Each produces its own type of deformation and magnitude of internal energy. They will now be considered separately.

Axial. An axial load P produces an equal and opposite resisting load P_R on every cross section of the body (Fig. 14-2). Every incremental length dx of the body is subjected to the same deformation $P\,dx/AE$

Figure 14-2

(Eq. 2.10), assuming A and E to remain constant. When P is gradually applied, each incremental length resists with an amount of internal energy equal to $\dfrac{P}{2}\dfrac{P\,dx}{AE}$. If the total energy is now obtained for all the incremental lengths we find that the

$$\begin{matrix}\text{total internal energy due}\\ \text{to an axially applied load}\end{matrix} = \int_0^l \frac{1}{2}\frac{P_R^2\,dx}{AE} = \frac{1}{2}\frac{P_R^2 l}{AE} = \frac{1}{2}\frac{P^2 l}{AE} \qquad (14.2)$$

Bending. The C-T couples produced on the cross sections of a member subjected to bending can produce only rotational deformation. These deformations produce relative rotations of the opposite sides of each segment in the beam equal to $d\theta$ (Fig. 14-3). From Chapter 8 it was learned that $d\theta = (M/EI)\,dx$. If now a bending moment M is gradually applied to a segment of a beam whose internal C-T couple or M_R twists that segment through an angle $d\theta$, there is developed within that segment an internal energy equal to

$$\frac{M_R}{2} \times \frac{M_R\,dx}{EI}$$

Figure 14-3

If the energy from every such segment is added together, there results

$$\begin{matrix}\text{total internal energy}\\ \text{due to bending}\end{matrix} = \int_0^l \frac{M_R^2\,dx}{2EI} = \int_0^l \frac{M^2\,dx}{2EI} \qquad (14.3)$$

Figure 14-4

Torsional. When a shaft is twisted about its longitudinal axis by a couple T, every cross section of that shaft has acting on it an equalizing couple T_R (Chapter 5). These couples rotate about the longitudinal axis. The relative rotation of one side of a segment dx in length with respect to its other side is equal to $(T_R/GJ) \, dx$ (Fig. 14-4). Adding the energies of all the disk-like segments included in length l yields

$$\text{total internal energy} \atop \text{due to torsion} = \int_0^l \frac{T_R^2 \, dx}{2GJ} = \int_0^l \frac{T^2 \, dx}{2GJ} \quad (14.4)$$

Figure 14-5

Shear. When two adjacent parallel surfaces dx distance apart are subjected to shearing forces, the shear strain is equal to de_s/dx. Assuming the shear stress to be uniformly distributed, the total deformation is then equal to

$$de_s = \epsilon_s \, dx = \frac{s_s}{G} \, dx = \frac{V_R}{A_s G} \, dx$$

The internal energy exerted by the element in resisting shear is equal to $\dfrac{V_R}{2} \times \dfrac{V_R \, dx}{A_s G}$ (Fig. 14-5). The total internal shear energy exerted by all the shearing forces is then equal to

$$\text{total internal energy} \atop \text{due to shear} = \int_0^l \frac{V_R^2}{2A_s G} \, dx = \int_0^l \frac{V^2 \, dx}{2A_s G} \quad (14.5)$$

14-4. *Equivalence of external and internal energy*

Whenever an elastic body is subjected to a system of force and couples producing internal energies of the four types discussed in the previous article, the law of conservation of energy is used to produce highly important relationships between these forces and their displacements. This law, which states that energy can neither be created nor destroyed, makes the external energy equal to the internal energy. Therefore, discounting the effects of friction and hysteresis, the following general statement drawn from the preceding derivations may be written for any elastic body subjected to a general force system.

$$\text{external energy} = \text{internal energy}$$

$$\sum \frac{P\Delta}{2} + \sum \frac{T\theta}{2} = \sum \int \frac{M^2\,dx}{2EI} + \sum \int \frac{P^2\,dx}{2AE} + \sum \int \frac{T^2\,dx}{2GJ} + \sum \int \frac{V^2\,dx}{2AG} \quad (14.6)$$

Of course, not all bodies are subjected to all kinds of external and internal energy. Also, under certain conditions of loading, some terms may be relatively small. In such cases those terms in Eq. 14.6 not applicable or inconsequential to the analysis may be deleted.

A simple illustration will reveal its usefulness.

Illustrative Problem 1. Determine the maximum deflection of a cantilever beam loaded at its free end with a concentrated load. Omit internal shear energy as being negligible.

SOLUTION. Assuming the origin of the x and y axes to be at the free end of the beam, the value of M_x at any point is equal to $-Px$. Writing the equation of internal and external energy gives

$$\frac{P\Delta}{2} = \int_0^l \frac{M^2\,dx}{2EI} = \int_0^l \frac{(-Px)^2\,dx}{2EI} = \frac{Pl^3}{6EI}$$

from which

$$\Delta = \frac{Pl^3}{3EI}$$

14-5. Disadvantages of using full energy equation

If the foregoing cantilever beam had an additional load applied to its mid point, the energy equation (omitting internal shear energy) would be written as

$$\frac{1}{2}P_1\Delta_1 + \frac{1}{2}P_2\Delta_2 = \int_0^{l/2} \frac{M^2\,dx}{2EI} + \int_{l/2}^l \frac{M^2\,dx}{2EI}$$

To obtain the values of Δ_1 and Δ_2 would require another relationship between them. The difficulty involved in obtaining this relationship and the simplicity with which either deflection may be obtained by other methods have resulted in the almost complete abandonment of the full energy equation in determining deflections. The virtual work method, based on an energy equation of a dummy or virtual load, the superposition method, or that based on Castigliano's theorem, have superseded the use of the full energy expression. Only the latter method will be discussed here.

14-6. Castigliano's theorem

Where an elastic body is deformed under the action of a general force system, Castigliano's theorem states that the derivative of the strain energy with respect to any one of the forces or couples included in the force system is equal to the displacement of that force or couple. The proof of this statement follows:

Figure 14-6

Proof. Let there be applied to the beam shown in Fig. 14-6 a differential load dP_1 creating an internal strain energy equal to dU. If loads P_1 and P_2 are added to the beam, the additional internal energy developed in the beam will be equal to

$$U_1 = \frac{P_1 y_1}{2} + y_1\, dP_1 + \frac{P_2 y_2}{2}$$

Had only P_1 and P_2 been added (dP_1 omitted), the internal energy of the beam would have equaled

$$U_2 = \frac{P_1 y_1}{2} + \frac{P_2 y_2}{2}$$

Taking the difference of these two energies, there results

$$dU = U_1 - U_2 = \frac{P_1 y_1}{2} + y_1\, dP_1 + \frac{P_2 y_2}{2} - \frac{P_1 y_1}{2} - \frac{P_2 y_2}{2}$$

$$dU = y_1\, dP_1$$

$$\frac{dU}{dP_1} = y_1 \tag{14.7}$$

Had a differential dP_2 been used at the location of P_2, a similar equation could have been written:

$$\frac{dU}{dP_2} = y_2 \tag{14.8}$$

Upon further analysis, this equation states that the differentiation of the entire internal energy of an elastic body produced by some external force system with respect to any one of the forces in that system is equal to the elastic displacement of that force in the direction of its action line. In a similar manner, had a torque T been acting in place of either of the forces, and dT been used as its differential, the result would have been

$$\frac{dU}{dT} = \theta \tag{14.9}$$

where θ is the rotational displacement of T.

The versatility of these equations will be demonstrated first by the use of some simple problems.

In the case of an axial loaded tensile bar, the internal energy equals $P^2 l / 2AE$ (§ 14.2). The derivative of this expression with respect to P is equal to Pl/AE, or the elongation of the bar due to P as derived in Chapter 2.

The internal energy of a shaft twisted by a torque T is equal to $T^2l/2GJ$. Its derivative with respect to T is equal to Tl/GJ, or θ, the angle of twist caused by T (see Chapter 5).

The maximum deflection of a cantilever beam loaded at its free end with a load P is equal, disregarding shear, to the derivative of its internal flexural energy

$$\Delta_P = \frac{dU}{dP} = \frac{d}{dP}\int_0^l \frac{(-Px)^2\,dx}{2EI} = \frac{d}{dP}\left(\frac{P^2l^3}{6EI}\right) = \frac{Pl^3}{3EI}$$

In problems such as these, it is generally much more convenient to perform the differentiation first, then the integration.

$$\Delta_P = \frac{dU}{dP} = \frac{d}{dP}\int_0^l \frac{M^2\,dx}{2EI} = \int_0^l \frac{M\,\dfrac{dM}{dP}\,dx}{EI} = \int_0^l \frac{(-Px)(-x)\,dx}{EI} = \frac{Pl^3}{3EI}$$

When the deflection desired occurs at a point where there is no load, a dummy load or couple is placed at that point. The strain energy equation is then written including the dummy load or couple and differentiated with respect to it. This load or couple is then reduced to zero and the integration performed to obtain the answer.

Illustrative Problem 2. Determine by Castigliano's theorem the deflection at the free end of a uniformly loaded cantilever beam. Consider flexural energy alone (Fig. 14-7).

$P =$ dummy load
w lb/ft
$M_x = -Px - \dfrac{wx^2}{2}$

Figure 14-7

SOLUTION.

$$M_z = -Px - \frac{wx^2}{2}$$

$$U = \int_0^l \frac{M^2\,dx}{2EI} = \int_0^l \frac{\left(-Px - \dfrac{wx^2}{2}\right)^2 dx}{2EI}$$

$$\Delta_P = \frac{dU}{dP} = \int_0^l \frac{\left(-Px - \dfrac{wx^2}{2}\right)(-x)\,dx}{EI}$$

If, now, P is reduced to zero,

$$\Delta_P = \int_0^l \frac{\dfrac{wx^3}{2}\,dx}{EI} = \left[\frac{wx^4}{8EI}\right]_0^l$$

$$\Delta_P = \frac{wl^4}{8EI}$$

Illustrative Problem 3.   Determine by Castigliano's theorem the vertical displacement of point C of the member having an I cross section shown in Fig. 14-8. Use all energies. $A = 10$ sq in., $I = 100$ in.^{4}, $E = 30 \times 10^6$ psi, $G = 12 \times 10^6$ psi, area of web, $A_s = 5$ sq in.

Figure 14-8

SOLUTION. Because of the necessity of differentiating with respect to the load, let us consider the load as P.

FORCES ACTING ON AB	FORCES ACTING ON BC
Moment $= Px$	Moment $= PR(1 - \cos \theta)$
Shear $= P$	Shear $= P \sin \theta$
Axial $= 0$	Axial $= P \cos \theta$

The signs of these effects are all considered positive, inasmuch as their contributory displacements are all similarly directed, i.e., downwards.

$$U = \int_{30}^{78} \frac{M^2 \, dx}{2EI} + \int_{30}^{78} \frac{V^2 \, dx}{2A_sG} + \int_{30}^{78} \frac{P^2 \, dx}{2AE} + \int_0^{\frac{\pi}{2}} \frac{M^2 \, ds}{2EI} + \int_0^{\frac{\pi}{2}} \frac{V^2 \, ds}{2A_sG}$$
$$+ \int_0^{\frac{\pi}{2}} \frac{P^2 \, ds}{2AE}$$

$$U = \int_{30}^{78} \frac{(Px)^2 \, dx}{2EI} + \int_{30}^{78} \frac{P^2 \, dx}{2A_sG} + 0 + \int_0^{\frac{\pi}{2}} \frac{[PR(1 - \cos \theta)]^2 R \, d\theta}{2EI}$$
$$+ \int_0^{\frac{\pi}{2}} \frac{(P \sin \theta)^2 R \, d\theta}{2A_sG} + \int_0^{\frac{\pi}{2}} \frac{(P \cos \theta)^2 R \, d\theta}{2AE}$$

$$\Delta_c = \frac{dU}{dP} = \int_{30}^{78} \frac{2(Px)(x) \, dx}{2EI} + \int_{30}^{78} \frac{2P \, dx}{2A_sG}$$
$$+ \int_0^{\frac{\pi}{2}} \frac{2[PR(1 - \cos \theta)][R(1 - \cos \theta)]R \, d\theta}{2EI}$$
$$+ \int_0^{\frac{\pi}{2}} \frac{2(P \sin \theta)(\sin \theta) R \, d\theta}{2A_sG} + \int_0^{\frac{\pi}{2}} \frac{2(P \cos \theta)(\cos \theta)R \, d\theta}{2AE}$$

After integrating, inserting the limits, and setting $P = 1000$ lb,

$$\Delta_c = 0.0537 \text{ in.}$$

PROBLEMS

NOTE: Use Castigliano's theorem. Consider only flexural energy except where noted.

14-1. Determine the vertical displacement at the mid-point of a simple beam uniformly loaded. *Answer: $5wl^4/384\ EI$.*

14-2. Find the slope at the end of the beam of Problem 14-1.

14-3. A simple beam is loaded at one of its third points by a concentrated load P. Determine the displacement at the other third point. *Answer: $\frac{7}{486}(Pl^3/EI)$.*

14-4. Find the slope at the end of the beam of Problem 14-3 farthest from the load P.

14-5. A steel I beam having the shape of a quarter circle (radius $= R$) has its fixed end placed horizontally and its load P acting vertically downward on its free end. Free end is below fixed support. Determine the vertical displacement of the load in terms of R and P. Use all energies. $A = 10$ sq in. $A_s = 5$ sq in. $I = 10$ in.^{4} *Answer: $(1.18PR^3 + 1.57PR)10^{-8}$.*

14-6. Determine the displacement and slope of the free end of the quarter circle beam of Problem 14-5 if its fixed end is placed vertically and is above the applied load, which acts vertically downward at its free end. Use all energies.

14-7. The solution of statically indeterminate members by Castigliano's theorem

Any statically indeterminate member may be solved by means of Castigliano's theorem by the simple method of

(1) Replacing a sufficient number of redundant forces with *variable, movable* forces to make the member or structure statically determinate. Stability must, of course, be maintained.

(2) Writing the expression for internal energy over the *entire* structure including the effect of all the movable, variable redundant forces.

(3) Taking the partial differential of the expression with respect to the force (or forces) whose magnitude is desired. Generally, there will be as many differentiations as there are redundant forces.

(4) Setting the differential(s) equal to zero inasmuch as a fixed point cannot move.

(5) Solving the equations so obtained to determine the redundant.

These steps will best be illustrated by the following problems.

Illustrative Problem 4. Find the reactions at A and B for the bracket shown in Fig. 14-9 by Castigliano's theorem using flexural energy alone. E and I are constant.

Figure 14-9

SOLUTION. Replace the reaction at B with a variable movable unknown R_B. Then as

$$M_{CD} = -2x; \quad M_{CB} = -12; \quad M_{AB} = (-12 + R_B x)$$

$$U = \int_0^6 \frac{(-2x)^2 \, dx}{2EI} + \int_0^{10} \frac{(-12)^2 \, dx}{2EI} + \int_0^{10} \frac{(-12 + R_B x)^2 \, dx}{2EI}$$

$$\Delta_B = \frac{dU}{dR_B} = 0 + 0 + \int_0^{10} \frac{(-12 + R_B x)(x) \, dx}{2EI}$$

$$\Delta_B = 0 = \frac{1}{EI} \left[\frac{-12x^2}{2} + \frac{R_B x^3}{3} \right]_0^{10}$$

$$R_B = 1.8 \text{ kips}$$

from which $H_A = 1.8$ kips, $V_A = 2.0$ kips, $M_A = +6.0$ ft-kips.

Illustrative Problem 5. Determine the components of the reaction at C acting on the beam shown in Fig. 14-10 by Castigliano's theorem. Use only flexural energy.

Figure 14-10

SOLUTION. Assume the beam to be disengaged from the hinge at C and supplied with two variable component forces R_x and R_y at that same point.

Under this loading

$$M_{AB} = R_y(x + 7.07) - 7.07R_x - 10x$$
$$M_{BC} = (0.707sR_y - 0.707sR_x)$$

The expression for energy is then equal to

$$U = \int_0^5 \frac{[R_y(x + 7.07) - 7.07R_x - 10x]^2}{2EI}\, dx + \int_0^{10} \frac{(0.707sR_y - 0.707sR_x)^2}{2EI}\, ds$$

from which

$$\frac{\delta U}{\delta R_x} = \int_0^5 \frac{[R_y(x + 7.07) - 7.07R_x - 10x]}{EI}(-7.07)\, dx$$
$$+ \int_0^{10} \frac{[0.707s(R_y - R_x)]\,(-0.707s)\, ds}{EI} = 0$$

Now integrating and simplifying we obtain

$$\left[-7.07R_y\frac{x^2}{2} - 50R_yx + 50R_zx + 70.7\frac{x^2}{2} \right]_0^5 + \left(-0.5\frac{s^3}{3}(R_y - R_x) \right)_0^{10} = 0$$

from which

$$+20.20\,R_y - 16.67R_x = +35.35 \tag{A}$$

Now, taking the partial differential of U with respect to R_y and setting it equal to zero, there follows

$$\frac{\delta U}{\delta R_y} = \int_0^5 \frac{[R_y(x + 7.07) - 7.07R_x - 10x](x + 7.07)}{EI}\, dx$$
$$+ \int_0^{10} \frac{[0.707s(R_y - R_x)](0.707s)}{EI}\, ds = 0$$

$$\left[\frac{R_yx^3}{3} + 14.14R_y\frac{x^2}{2} + 50R_yx - 7.07R_x\frac{x^2}{2} - 50R_xx - \frac{10x^3}{3} - 70.7\frac{x^2}{2} \right]_0^5$$
$$+ \left[0.5\frac{s^3}{3}(R_y - R_x) \right]_0^{10} = 0$$

$$25.41R_y - 20.20R_x - 52.0 = 0 \tag{B}$$

Then by solving Eqs. A and B simultaneously,

$$R_x = 10.0 \text{ kips} \quad \text{and} \quad R_y = 10.0 \text{ kips.}$$

PROBLEMS

14-7. Determine by means of Castigliano's theorem the restraining moment on a uniformly loaded beam of span l, fixed at one end and simply supported at the other. *Answer:* $-wl^2/8$.

14-8. Determine the reactions acting on the frame shown in Fig. 14-11, using Castigliano's theorem. *Answers:* $A_H = 6.67$ kips; $A_V = 16.67$ kips.

14-9. If the support at A shown in Fig. 14-11 were fixed, find the reactions acting on the frame using Castigliano's theorem. *Answers: $A_H = 4.00$ kips, $A_V = 22.0$ kips, $M_A = -80.0$ ft-kips.*

Figure 14-11

IMPACT LOADS

14-8. *The difference between static and impact loads*

When a blacksmith forges a red-hot piece of steel, he subjects the steel to repeated blows from his heavy hammer. These blows, delivered with tremendous force, cause large deformations which form the material into its desired shape. It is evident that the faster the blacksmith can propel the hammer, the greater the energy he possesses and the greater will be the resultant deformation. The force which is produced by the hammer *by virtue of its sudden change of velocity is called an impact load* as differentiated from the force of the dead weight of the hammer, which is called its *static load.*

14-9. *Stress-strain diagram — static and impact loading*

With the introduction of the static load stress-strain diagram in Chapter 3, it was shown that for many materials the unit stress is proportional to the unit strain below the proportional limit (Fig. 14-12). All the basic design relationships employing static loads are dependent upon the proportionality of stress and strain. Through the use of modern strain gages, it has been shown that this important relationship is approximately equal for either static or impact loads. It is thus possible to use the proportionality of stress and strain as given by the static load stress-strain diagram in formulating the principles used in designing members subjected to impact loading.

A further study of Fig. 14-12 shows that, although the stress-strain diagram for impact loading will have a higher yield point and ultimate unit stress than that recorded for a static loading, the amount of elongation is appreciably less. The moduli of resilience and toughness for both static and

Figure 14-12

impact tests are sufficiently similar, however, for interchangeable use in either type of design (cf. §§ 3-7 and 3-8).

14-10. *When kinetic energy is delivered to a resisting member*

When a moving load is suddenly stopped by a resisting member, its kinetic energy is dissipated into all those bodies taking part in the collision. These bodies include not only the members that took the full force of the impact, but every supporting, loading, or restraining member no matter how lightly stressed. Even the surrounding air acts as a means of dissipating this heat energy generated by the impact. The uncertainty of the nature and magnitude of the dissipation of energy makes the design of structural and machine members less accurate than those subjected to static loads only.

Assuming, however, that the net energy of a resisting member could be accurately found, its diffusion into the volume of this member would be of next concern. If the member were of uniform cross section and the applied energy were spread uniformly throughout its interior, it would be capable of sustaining the maximum amount of energy for a member of that volume. This ideal situation is complicated in practice with the inclusion of irregular cross sections, holes, screw threads, and many other forms of stress concentrations. Since the stress increases more rapidly at a stress concentration than elsewhere in the member, it arrives at the ceiling value of permissible energy absorption before points of lower stress. This condition curtails the amount of energy absorption that the other portions of material included in the member are capable of withstanding.

14-11. *Calculation of impact stresses in tension or compression member of uniform cross section*

Figure 14-13

Consider the steel rod AB of Fig. 14-13 to have a uniform cross section a, a length l, and to be suspended from some stationary point A. If weight W were now allowed to fall onto the flange at B from a height h, its kinetic energy at the time of impact would be Wh. However, owing to the elongation e, the weight will have moved a distance of $(h + e)$ before coming to rest. The total energy derived from the fall is, therefore, $W(h + e)$.

Although some energy will have been absorbed by the weight and the air during impact, let us suppose a complete transfer into the rod. Assume also the maximum stress incurred to be below the elastic limit and to be acting on each cubic inch of material in the rod. The kinetic energy applied by the weight will then be equal to the total internal energy absorbed by the rod as given by the following relationship.

$$U = W\,(h + e) = \frac{1}{2}\frac{s^2}{E}\,al \tag{14.10}$$

Solving for s, we obtain

$$s = \sqrt{\frac{2UE}{al}} = \sqrt{\frac{2WE\,(h + e)}{al}} \tag{14.11}$$

If, under the conditions of impact, e is insignificant when compared to h, it may be eliminated from Eq. 14.11. This permits the equation to be solved, since e is dependent on s.

Should the deformation e be appreciable, a solution is obtainable by substituting for W/a the static stress s_q and for E/l its equal s/e. Equation 14.13 thus becomes

$$s = 2s_q\left(\frac{h}{e} + 1\right) \tag{14.12}$$

Recalling the proportionality between unit stress and unit strain below the proportional limit, we may write

$$\frac{s}{\epsilon} = \frac{s_q}{\epsilon_q}$$

in which ϵ_q is the static strain caused by the weight W. Dividing each side by l gives

$$\frac{s}{\epsilon l} = \frac{s_q}{\epsilon_q l}$$

which is equal to

$$\frac{s}{e} = \frac{s_q}{e_q} \quad \text{or} \quad e = \frac{se_q}{s_q}$$

Substituting this value into Eq. 14.12 and rearranging gives

$$s^2 - 2s\,s_q + s_q{}^2 = s_q{}^2 + \frac{2s_q{}^2 h}{e_q}$$

from which

$$s = s_q + s_q\sqrt{1 + \frac{2h}{e_q}} \tag{14.13}$$

Equation 14.13 reveals that the stress developed by a falling weight acting on a uniform cross-sectioned tension or compression member may greatly exceed that obtained by the same weight when gradually applied.

To obtain the deformation of a tension or compression member when acted upon by an axially applied energy load, the values of $s = Ee/l$ and $s_q = Ee_q/l$ are substituted in Eq. 14.15. Thus

$$e = e_q + e_q\sqrt{1 + \frac{2h}{e_q}} \tag{14.14}$$

14-12. *Axially applied impact loads on tension or compression members of nonuniform cross section*

Let us compare the permissible energy loads of the two tension members of Fig. 14-14 whose static strengths are equal.

The uniform cross-sectional bar of Fig. 14-14(a) will, upon the application of an impact stress s to any cross section, have an imposed energy load of $\frac{1}{2}(s^2/E)al$.

In the member of Fig. 14-14(b), however, the stress in the upper and lower sections will be equal to one half of that in the middle section. If the stress in the middle section is s, the total energy in the member will be

Figure 14-14

$$U = \frac{1}{2}\frac{s^2}{E}a\frac{l}{2} + 2 \times \frac{1}{2}\frac{s^2}{4E}2a\frac{l}{4}$$

$$= \frac{s^2}{4E}al + \frac{s^2}{8E}al = \frac{3}{8}\frac{s^2}{E}al \tag{14.15}$$

which is less than that for the uniform cross-sectioned bar of lesser volume.

The reduction of the permissible energy load in the larger member can be traced to the fact that in the enlarged ends, the stress decreases to $s/2$ as the area increases to $2a$. The energy-per-unit volume, being proportional to s^2, decreases to one fourth of that value in the middle portion, whereas its volume only increases twice.

The foregoing discussion reveals the startling fact that members subjected to impact loading must be designed not only on the basis of static loading but on energy loading as well. It is also shown that those members possessing maximum impact resistance have each unit of volume equally stressed. Adding material at certain cross sections may weaken rather than increase the resistance of a member to impact loads. Conversely, the removal of material from an axially loaded member may increase its impact resistance. An excellent example of such an increase in impact strength is revealed in the reduction of the shank diameter of threaded bolts. The larger diameter threads cause severe stress concentrations. By making the shanks smaller, the stress more nearly approximates the maximum stress at the concentration, thereby increasing the energy resistance of the bolt.

PROBLEMS

14-10. A load of 600 lb falls 2 in. onto a stop at the end of a vertical steel rod 12 ft long and 1 sq in. in cross section. Compute the stress and elongation produced in the bar.

14-11. Find the greatest height from which the weight in Problem 14-10 can fall without exceeding an allowable working unit stress of 20,000 psi in the bar. *Answer:* 1.6 in.

14-12. A weight of 60 lb drops 12 in. onto the top of a cast-iron cylinder 6 in. in diameter by 12 in. high. If the loading is axial, what compressive stress is induced?

14-13. What would the compressive unit stress be in Problem 14-12 if the cylinder were 4 in. in diameter by 6 in. high? *Answer:* 16,900 psi.

14-14. How long would a 1-in. diameter steel rod have to be to absorb the energy load of a 50-lb weight falling 4 ft and to attain a maximum tensile stress of 20,000 psi? Suppose the rod were bronze?

14-15. A steel rod must elongate 0.010 in. when subjected to a falling weight of 50 lb. If its diameter is $\frac{3}{4}$ in. and the weight is dropped the full length of the rod, how long must it be?

14-16. Which of the two bodies shown in Fig. 14-15 will absorb the most energy when acted upon by the same energy load and limited to a maximum stress equal to s?

14-17. An internal explosion in the chamber shown in Fig. 14-16 resulted in the rupture of the short 1-in. diameter (2-in. active length) bolts. Would the use of longer bolts (14-in. active length), passing through both plates, be more resistant to

Figure 14-15   Figure 14-16

a similar energy load? Prove your answer. *Answer:* The smaller bolt will have 2.64 times more stress than the larger bolt.

14-13. *Effect of impact loads on beams*

Because the energy of resistance in any body depends on the stress applied to it, it follows that the resisting energy of a beam depends on the moment diagram of the loads applied to it. This means that the distribution of load as well as the type of beam used makes a considerable difference in the resistance of the beam to impact loads.

It should also be noted that because of the stress variation on every cross section of a beam, it is not possible to expect as high an impact resistance in a beam as it would be in a tension member of the same dimensions.

Consider a simple beam having a rectangular cross section on which a concentrated load W falls on its mid-point from a height h. The external energy will be equal to $U = W(h + \Delta)$, where Δ is the maximum deflection of the beam. This maximum deflection will be equal to $\Delta = \frac{1}{48} Pl^3/EI$ (Chapter 8), P being the equivalent static load required to produce it. The maximum moment produced by load P is, of course, equal to $Pl/4$. Placing these expressions in $\frac{1}{2}P\Delta$, the external energy developed by the equivalent static load, there results

$$U = \frac{1}{2}P\Delta = \frac{1}{2} \times \frac{4M}{l} \times \frac{1}{48}\frac{Pl}{EI}$$

$$= \frac{1}{6}\frac{s^2}{c^2}\frac{Il}{E} \tag{14.16}$$

Inserting the value of $I = \frac{1}{12} bd^3$ for a rectangular beam, there is obtained

$$U = \frac{1}{18}\frac{s^2}{E}al = \frac{1}{9}\left(\frac{s^2}{2E}\right)al \tag{14.17}$$

A comparison of Eqs. 14.10 and 14.17 reveals the relative ineffectiveness of a constant cross-sectioned beam in developing internal flexural energy when contrasted to a tension member of similar size. When it is realized that the maximum stress is developed theoretically at only two points in the beam, and all others will have $s^2/2E$ values less than that they are capable of carrying, it is not surprising that the resistance offered is so low.

In order to improve the energy carrying capacity of beams, I sections are used so that a greater volume of the material will be subjected to a higher stress. Beams are also made with varying section moduli approximately proportional to the moment diagram of the applied loads.

PROBLEMS

14-18. Derive the expression for the energy that a circular cross-sectioned simple beam can withstand when subjected to an impact load applied at its midpoint. *Answer:* $U = \frac{1}{12}(s^2/2E)al$.

14-19. Compare Eq. 14.17 with the energy developed in a cantilever beam of similar size subjected to an impact load at its free end.

Chapter Fifteen

MISCELLANEOUS TOPICS

CURVED BEAMS

15-1. Introduction

In contrast to an ordinary straight beam, the theory of which is presented in § 7-2, a curved beam when subjected to bending, produces flexural stresses which do not vary directly with the distance from the neutral axis (Fig. 15-1). Neither does the neutral axis coincide with the centroidal axis. As will be shown by the theory presented in the succeeding paragraphs, the magnitudes of these divergences are dependent on the ratio of the depth of the beam to its degree of curvature.

15-2. Non-linear stress variation explained

Let Fig. 15-1 represent an infinitesimal portion of a curved beam located between the two radii AO and CO. Consider it also to have a constant cross section which is symmetrical about the plane of bending (or vertical axis). As such, the horizontal centroidal axes of all the intervening sections would form a plane curve.

Suppose, now, the couples M are applied to the beam in the plane of bending. The radial sections AB and CD, which are assumed to remain plane under stress, will rotate through an angle $d\alpha$ with respect to each other. Section AB will move to its new position $A'B'$ producing deformations which vary linearly. The unit strains, however, cannot vary linearly since the fibers between sections AB and CD vary in length. Because the total deformations and the lengths of the fibers vary simultaneously and with different linear patterns, the unit strains reveal a non-linear variation.

Figure 15-1

Assuming the unit strain to be proportional to the unit stress ($E =$ constant), the unit stresses, naturally, must vary in the same manner as the strains (Fig. 15-1).

15-3. *The curved beam theory*

Expressed mathematically, the unit strain for any fiber y distance from the neutral axis is equal to

$$\epsilon_y = \frac{e_y}{l_y} = \frac{y \, d\alpha}{(R_n + y) \, d\theta}$$

where y is positive above the neutral axis and negative below. Assuming Hooke's law to hold, the stress on this fiber is equal to

$$s_y = E\epsilon_y = \frac{E \, d\alpha}{d\theta} \times \frac{y}{R_n + y} \tag{15.1}$$

An analysis of this equation reveals that for any one section, all of its terms with the exception of y are constants. The ratio $y/(R_n + y)$ indicates, therefore, the variable nature of the stress.

Since the normal forces on any section must equal zero to insure equilibrium,

$$\int_{R_2}^{R_1} s_y \, dA = \frac{E \, d\alpha}{d\theta} \int_{R_2}^{R_1} \frac{y}{R_n + y} \, dA = 0$$

Because the term $E \, d\alpha/d\theta$ is constant, it must necessarily follow that

$$\int_{R_2}^{R_1} \frac{y}{R_n + y} \, dA = 0 \tag{15.2}$$

Placing $y = R - R_n$, there is obtained

$$\int_{R_2}^{R_1} \frac{(R - R_n)}{R} \, dA = 0, \quad \text{from which} \quad R_n = \frac{A}{\int_{R_2}^{R_1} \frac{dA}{R}}$$

and

$$\bar{y} = R_g - \frac{A}{\int_{R_2}^{R_1} \frac{dA}{R}} \tag{15.3}$$

It is thus revealed that in bending a curved beam the neutral axis shifts away from the horizontal centroidal axis and toward the axis of curvature of the beam. The integral appearing in the equation is evaluated by placing dA in terms of dR.

It is also true that the resisting moment of the normal forces acting on the section (C-T couple) must equal the applied moment. This statement may be expressed by

$$\int_{R_2}^{R_1} y s_y \, dA = \frac{E \, d\alpha}{d\theta} \int_{R_2}^{R_1} \frac{y^2 dA}{R_n + y} = M \tag{15.4}$$

The expression within the integral may be simplified as follows

$$\int_{R_2}^{R_1} \frac{y^2 dA}{R_n + y} = \int_{R_2}^{R_1} y - R_n \left(\frac{y}{R_n + y} \right) dA = \int_{R_2}^{R_1} y \, dA - R_n \int_{R_2}^{R_1} \frac{y}{R_n + y} \, dA$$

From Eq. 15.2 previously derived, the second integral was shown to equal zero, thus making

$$\int_{R_2}^{R_1} \frac{y^2 \, dA}{R_n + y} = \int_{R_2}^{R_1} y \, dA = \bar{y} A$$

Inserting this simplified expression in Eq. 15.4

$$\frac{M}{\bar{y} A} = \frac{E \, d\alpha}{d\theta}$$

in which case, Eq. 15.1 may be written

$$s_y = \frac{M}{\bar{y} A} \times \frac{y}{R_n + y} \tag{15.5}$$

This is a general expression for flexural stress in a curved beam. If the values of $y = c_1$ and $y = c_2$ are inserted in the above formula to obtain the outside fiber stresses, there are obtained

$$s_1 = \frac{M c_1}{\bar{y} A R_1} \tag{15.6}$$

and

$$s_2 = \frac{M c_2}{\bar{y} A R_2} \tag{15.7}$$

The value of the greater of the two stresses, s_2, will be located on the inside of the beam. It should be remembered that these stresses are developed by the application of pure bending only.

Illustrative Problem 1. A critically stressed rectangular cross section of a steel crane hook (Fig. 15-2) has a width of 1 in. and a depth of 4 in. If R_1 and R_2 at this section are respectively 10 and 6 in., and $M = 50,000$ in.-lb, determine its maximum tensile and compressive stresses. Compare these stresses to those obtained with the straight beam formula.

Figure 15-2

SOLUTION. The position of the neutral axis must first be located.

$$\bar{y} = R_g - \frac{A}{\int_{R2}^{R_1} \dfrac{dA}{R}} = 8'' - \frac{4}{\int_{R2}^{R_1} \dfrac{1 \times dR}{R}} = 8 - \frac{4}{\ln R \Big]_{R2}^{R_1}}$$

$$= 8 - \frac{4}{2.3026 \log (10/6)} = 8 - \frac{4}{2.3026 \times (1.000 - 0.788)}$$

$$= 8 - 7.83 = 0.17 \text{ in.}$$

The maximum fiber stresses are now found from Eqs. 15.6 and 15.7.

$$s_1 = \frac{50,000 \times 2.17}{0.17 \times 4.0 \times 10} = 15,950 \text{ psi}$$

$$s_2 = \frac{50,000 \times 1.83}{0.17 \times 4.0 \times 6} = 22,400 \text{ psi}$$

Straight beam comparison:

$$s = \frac{50,000 \times 2.0}{\frac{1}{12} \times 1 \times 4^3} = 18,750 \text{ psi}$$

Comments. It is observed from the above illustrative problem that the stress on the inner radius of a curved beam increases as its initial curvature increases. Contrariwise, the stress on the outer radius decreases. The variation of these stresses to the ratio of d/R_2 is shown in Fig. 15-3. The percentage of change in position of the neutral axis as the curvature increases is also shown.

It becomes apparent as a study is made of Fig. 15-3, that a beam, as commonly used, could have a considerable curvature before the ordinary

Figure 15-3

flexure formula need be discarded. It is only as a relatively deep beam is bent into a C shape or a portion thereof that one need pay particular attention to curved beam theory.

It should be carefully noted that these curves apply to rectangular beams subjected to bending moment only. Should curved beams of other cross sections be subjected to bending, the theory would have to be applied specifically to them by a proper use of Eq. 15.3.

PROBLEMS

15-1. In Problem 10-17, the stresses incurred were obtained in using the straight beam flexure theory. Apply the curved beam theory to obtain the maximum normal stresses acting on a cross section, if the inside radius of the T section is 6 in. *Hint:* for each rectangular section set $\int \frac{dA}{R} = \int \frac{b \, dR}{R} = b \log_e R$. *Answers:* -1660 psi, $+2300$ psi.

15-2. A curved beam has a rectangular cross section 1 in. thick and 2 in. deep with an inside radius of 3 in. Show the variation of normal stress over a cross section of the curved portion of the beam if the moment is 5000 in.-lb.

15-3. A 2-in. diameter steel rod is to be bent into a circular shape. To what mean radius must it be bent for a maximum stress of 20,000 psi to develop on a cross section when subjected to a moment of 11,820 in.-lb. *Answer:* 3.0 in.

15-4. Derive the general expression for the location of the neutral axis of a curved beam of circular cross section.

15-5. Determine the maximum normal stress occurring on section A-A of the C frame shown in Fig. 10-13 if the inside radius is equal to 8 in. *Answers:* -5920 psi, $+6410$ psi.

NON-HOMOGENEOUS BEAMS

15-4. Introduction

Beams made of different materials are commonly used in practice. For instance, timber beams are often reinforced by steel plates. Concrete beams are reinforced by steel rods to overcome their weakness in tension. Plastic materials are strengthened by gluing aluminum sheets to their surfaces. The addition of these stronger supplementary materials to beams made of cheaper and weaker materials provides a flexibility in design which may result in appreciable economy. The theory relative to the flexural design of non-homogeneous beams will now be presented.

15-5. Composite beams — theoretical design principles

Let us consider the composite beam of Fig. 15-4, which consists of a timber beam reinforced with steel plates firmly fixed to its sides. When subjected to load P, every longitudinal element of the composite beam, dx

Figure 15-4

in length, is deformed in direct proportion to the distance from the neutral axis. The linear variation of this deformation produced without regard to the materials encountered implies that the unit strains across these materials will also vary in like manner. The flexure stresses, however, while varying linearly within each material ($s = \epsilon E$), do not vary at the same rate because of the difference of their moduli of elasticity. (See Fig. 15-4d.) If $n = E_{st}/E_w$, the stress in the higher modulus material will be n times the other.

Because of the dissimilar stress pattern on the cross section of the composite beam, the flexure formula cannot be used directly (see assumption, § 7-3). A modification of the cross section, however, will make its use possible. Let us investigate this interesting possibility.

The resisting moment of the entire cross section is obviously the sum of the resisting moments of the steel and wood. These individual resisting moments (see derivation of flexure formula) are

$$(M_R)_w = \frac{s_w I_w}{c} \quad \text{and} \quad (M_R)_{st} = \frac{s_{st} I_{st}}{c}$$

where I_w and I_{st} are the moments of inertia of the wood and steel cross section, respectively. Their total equals

$$M = M_R = \frac{s_w I_w}{c} + \frac{s_{st} I_{st}}{c}$$

But $s_{st} = n s_w$, which makes

$$M = \frac{s_w I_w}{c} + \frac{n s_w I_{st}}{c}$$

or

$$M = \frac{s_w}{c}(I_w + n I_{st})$$

This equation is now a combined flexural formula providing the resisting moment of a *transformed cross section* whose moment of inertia is $I_w + n I_{st}$ and whose maximum stress is s_w. The section may be considered as that obtained by expanding the steel section laterally n times — on either side of the given wood section. By that transformation it will act as though it were made entirely of wood (Fig. 15-4e).

Suppose, however, the reinforcing plates were placed on its top and bottom surfaces. Would the beam be stronger? Let us investigate.

Once again, the strains are proportional to the distance from the neutral axis, regardless of the material involved. At the interfaces, the strains ϵ_2 in both materials are the same. The corresponding stresses will be $\epsilon_2 E_1$ and $\epsilon_2 E_2$ and if $E_1/E_2' = n$, the stress in the higher modulus material will be n times the other.

Because of the discontinuity in stress across the composite cross section, it must be modified to permit the use of the flexure formula. Let us investigate this interesting possibility.

The C and T resisting forces developed on the cross section (Fig. 15-5) are the forces of two couples whose moments $C_1(d + t)$* and $C_2(\tfrac{2}{3}d)$, or $T_1(d + t)$ and $T_2(\tfrac{2}{3}d)$, equal the total resisting moment of the cross section. Their sum must remain the same for the modified cross section to insure equilibrium.

Let us use only the moment $C_1(d + t)$ or, more specifically, its factor C_1 in modifying our cross section, since the moment arm $(d + t)$ remains constant. The value of C_1, as given by Fig. 15-5, is equal to

---

* The moment arm $(d + t)$ is approximate due to the variation of stress across the thickness of the steel plates. It is sufficiently accurate, however, for most engineering problems when the plates are relatively thin, as is the case in this illustration.

$$ns_1 = \epsilon_1 E_1$$
$$ns_2 = \epsilon_2 E_1$$

$$M_1 = C_1(d+t)$$
$$M_2 = C_2(\tfrac{2}{3}d)$$

Figure 15-5

$$C_1 = T_1 = \left(\frac{ns_1 + ns_2}{2}\right)A_1 \tag{15.8}$$

This may be modified by making

$$C_1 = T_1 = \left(\frac{s_1 + s_2}{2}\right)nA_1 \tag{15.9}$$

If we considered the steel sections to be expanded laterally n times, their areas would equal nA_1 and their centers of gravity would still be $(d + t)$ apart (Fig. 15-6). Holding C_1 constant, *the stresses on this trans-*

Figure 15-6

formed area would then be reduced n times to make its stress variation similar to that of the wood section. The straight line stress variation assumed in the derivation of the flexure formula would now be attained, permitting its use for the transformed section. As mentioned in the previous analysis, the transformed section will act as though it were made entirely of wood. The resisting moment of the cross section would then be equal to

$$M = C_2 \times \frac{2}{3}d + C_1 (d + t) = \frac{s_1 I_T}{c_T} \tag{15.10}$$

where $s_1 =$ the maximum flexural stress in the transformed section, $I_T =$ the moment of inertia of the transformed section about its neutral axis, and

c_T = the distance from the neutral axis to the extreme fiber of the transformed section, i.e., $(d + 2t)/2$.

In a similar manner, the section may have been transformed by decreasing the width of the wood section n times, making the rate of stress increase similar to that of the steel plate. The beam would then act as though it were made entirely of steel and would have a transformed section as shown in Fig. 15-7. Its limiting stress would be ns_1 and its moment of inertia would be that of the shaded area taken about the neutral axis.

Figure 15-7   **Figure 15-8**

The foregoing analysis may also be applied to members reinforced on the bottom (or top) only. The actual stress on the reinforcing plate may be reduced to vary with that of the wood by expanding it laterally by the ratio of their moduli (Fig. 15-8). Or the wood may be decreased in width by the same ratio as indicated in the previous paragraph. In any event, the flexure formula would apply to the transformed section. The center of gravity axis of the transformed section would have to be found, of course, and the moment of inertia taken about that axis.

Shear investigation. The investigation of critical shear stresses proceeds in the same manner as that for homogeneous beams, using Eq. 7.6 and the transformed section.

Illustrative Problem 2. A timber beam 6 in. wide and 12 in. deep is reinforced by affixing a 6-in. by $\frac{1}{4}$-in. steel plate to its bottom face (Fig.

(a)   (b)   (c)

Figure 15-9

15-9). If the allowable flexure stresses in the wood and steel are 1400 psi and 20,000 psi, respectively, what is the resisting moment of the cross section? $E_w = 2,000,000$ psi, $E_{st} = 30,000,000$ psi, $n = 15$.

SOLUTION. The center of gravity of the transformed section shown in Fig. 15-9(b) is first obtained by taking moments about the x-x axis:

$$
\begin{array}{ccc}
A & y & Ay \\
6 \times 12 = 72.0 \times 6.25 & = & 450.0 \\
90 \times \dfrac{1}{4} = 22.5 \times 0.125 & = & 2.8 \\
\hline
94.5 & & 452.8
\end{array}
$$

$$\bar{y} = \frac{452.8}{94.5} = 4.79 \text{ in.}$$

The moment of inertia about the center of gravity (neutral) axis is then equal to

$$
\begin{aligned}
I_w &= \tfrac{1}{12} \times 6 \times (12)^3 &=&\quad 864 \\
(Ad^2)_w &= 72 \times \overline{1.46}^2 &=&\quad 154 \\
I_{st} &= \tfrac{1}{12} \times 90 \times \left(\tfrac{1}{4}\right)^3 &=&\quad 0.117 \quad \text{(negligible)} \\
(Ad^2)_{st} &= 22.5 \times \overline{4.63}^2 &=&\quad \underline{482} \\
& & & \quad 1500 \text{ in.}^4
\end{aligned}
$$

To determine the resisting moment, the allowable stresses must be checked to ascertain perchance whether the attainment of one stress will cause the other to be exceeded. Suppose the maximum allowable stress of 20,000 psi (ns_1) were to be attained in the steel. The corresponding s_1 stress will then be 1333 psi. By similar triangles, the maximum stress in the timber (s_3) is equal to $1333 \times 7.46/4.79$ or 2080 psi. This exceeds the allowable stress of 1400 psi in the wood. The stress of 20,000 psi in the steel, therefore, is impossible to attain without overstressing the wood. If, on the other hand, the maximum stress in the wood (s_3) is set at its allowable value of 1400 psi, the corresponding maximum stress in the steel will be $1400 \times 4.79/7.46 \times 15 = 13,500$ psi. Although neither material is overstressed, the stress in the steel is far below its maximum allowable value. The maximum resisting moment will be

$$M_R = \frac{s_w I_T}{c_T} = \frac{1400 \times 1500}{7.46} = 281,000 \text{ in.-lb}$$

PROBLEMS

15-6. A simply supported timber beam, 10 ft long, has a cross section 4 in. wide by 10 in. deep. If $\tfrac{1}{4}$-in. by 3-in. steel plate, also 10 ft long, were fastened to the top and bottom faces, what maximum flexural stresses would be developed in the timber and the steel due to a load of 5000 lb applied at the center of the span? $E_{\text{w.}} = 1.5 \times 10^6$ psi, $E_{\text{st.}} = 30 \times 10^6$ psi. *Answers:* $s_{\text{w.}} = 805$ psi, $s_{\text{st.}} = 16,900$ psi.

15-7. What maximum uniform load could be applied to the beam of Problem 15-6 if the maximum allowable stresses for the steel and timber are 20,000 psi and 1500 psi, respectively? Moduli of elasticity are the same.

15-8. A sheet of plastic laminate $\frac{3}{8}$ in. thick, 12 in. wide and 36 in. long is to be strengthened by bonding sheets of Duralumin 0.05 in. thick to its top and bottom surfaces. What maximum concentrated load may be placed at its mid-section if the sheet is simply supported at its ends and the maximum allowable stresses for the laminate and Duralumin are 2500 and 10,000 psi respectively? $E_L = 2,000,000$ psi, $E_D = 10,500,000$ psi. Consider flexure alone. *Answer:* 301 lb.

Steel strip $\frac{1}{2}''$ thick $\times$ 2'' wide

12"

6"

Figure 15-10

15-9. A timber beam 6 in. wide by 12 in. deep has recessed into its upper face a steel strip $\frac{1}{2}$ in. thick by 2 in. wide (Fig. 15-10). If the beam is 10 ft long and is simply supported at each end, what maximum uniform load can it carry? Allowable stresses in timber and steel are 1200 psi and 20,000 psi respectively. $E_{\text{t.}} = 2 \times 10^6$ psi and $E_{\text{st.}} = 30 \times 10^6$ psi. What uniform load could it have carried if no steel had been used and the cross section had been the full 6 in. by 12 in. deep?

15-10. A beam consists of a timber 6 ft by 12 in. with a 12-in. by $\frac{1}{4}$-in. steel plate fastened to each of the 12-in. sides. What is the resisting moment of this section about the short axis under the following assumptions? Steel and timber act together without slipping. $E_{\text{st.}} = 30 \times 10^6$ psi, $E_{\text{w.}} = 1,200,000$ psi, maximum allowable stress in steel $= 18,000$ psi, in timber $= 1000$ psi. *Answer:* 319,000 in.-lb.

15-11. A rectangular cross section timber beam having a width of 6 in. and a depth of 10 in. is used as a cantilever, 8 ft long. If steel plates, 6 in. by $\frac{1}{4}$ in. in cross section are placed on the top and bottom faces, and the maximum allowable stress in the wood is 1000 psi, what is the maximum unit stress in the steel and the permissible uniform load on the beam? $E_{\text{st.}} = 30 \times 10^6$ psi, $E_{\text{w.}} = 2 \times 10^6$ psi. *Answer:* 15,750 psi, 875 lb per ft.

15-12. Compute the needed thickness of a pair of steel side plates 10 in. in depth in order to reinforce an 8-in. by 12-in. (nominal) timber beam to carry an applied moment of 50 kip-ft. Assume the timber to have dressed dimensions $7\frac{1}{2}$ in. by $11\frac{1}{2}$ in. Assume allowable flexure strength of timber to be 1600 psi, and that for steel to be 18,000 psi. $n = 20$. Each plate to be centered on the $11\frac{1}{2}$ in. side. Disregard effect of bolt hole.

REINFORCED CONCRETE BEAMS

15-6. Reinforced concrete beams

A concrete beam is reinforced with steel rods to overcome its weakness in tension. Its flexural resistance is determined by using a transformed section obtained by expanding laterally the area of the steel rods by the ratio of the moduli of steel to concrete ($n = E_{st.}/E_c.$) and by *disregarding the strength of the tensile concrete*, Fig. 15-11. If the compressive concrete and tensile steel

Figure 15-11

are stressed to their maximum allowable values *simultaneously*, the design of the beam is said to be *balanced* and its resisting moment (see Fig. 15.11) is equal to that developed by either stress.

$$M_R = \tfrac{1}{2}f_c bkd jd = \tfrac{1}{2}f_c kjbd^2 = Kbd^2 \qquad (15.11)$$

$$= nA_s\frac{f_s}{n}jd = A_s f_s jd \qquad (15.12)$$

Because of the simultaneous attainment of maximum allowable stresses in a balanced beam, it is also most economical and used whenever possible.

The design of a balanced beam is greatly simplified through the use of pertinent design data given in Table 12 for various values of f_c and f_s.

TABLE 12
CHARACTERISTICS FOR USE IN DESIGN OF
REINFORCED CONCRETE BEAMS

f'_c	n	f_c	f_s	k	j	p	K
3750	8	1688	20,000	0.403	0.866	0.0170	294
			18,000	0.429	0.857	0.0201	310
3000	10	1350	20,000	0.403	0.866	0.0136	235
			18,000	0.429	0.857	0.0161	248
2500	12	1125	20,000	0.403	0.866	0.0113	196
			18,000	0.429	0.857	0.0134	207
2000	15	900	20,000	0.403	0.866	0.0091	157
			18,000	0.428	0.857	0.0107	165

f'_c = ultimate strength of concrete in 28 days, $f_c = 0.45\,f'_c$, $K = \tfrac{1}{2}f_c jk$, $p = A_s/bd$

With the values of K and M (or M_R) known, the dimensions of a rectangular beam are easily obtained from Eq. 15.11. The value of p may also be used instead of Eq. 15.12 to obtain the steel area required.

Simply supported slabs, reinforced in one direction only, are also designed using the above procedure. A 1-ft width of slab is used as the design unit, it being typical of every other 1-ft width.

15-7. Unbalanced flexural design

Under extraordinary circumstances one may be forced to use an unbalanced design in which the allowable stresses for the compressive concrete and tensile steel are *not* attained simultaneously. In such instances, Eqs. 15.11 and 15.12 cannot be used, and new values similar to k and j, as well as the actually impressed f_c and f_s stresses must be introduced to obtain a corrected resisting moment equation. Moreover, all investigations of existing or already designed concrete beams must be made on the assumption that their design is unbalanced.

An unbalanced condition encountered in either design or investigation usually involves the determination of the *critical stress*. Because the maximum allowable stresses in concrete and steel are not attained simultaneously, one of these materials must be stressed to its maximum critical value, the other to a value *less* than the allowable. When it is determined what these stresses are, the resisting moment may be obtained by finding the new values of k and j and introducing them into formulas similar to 15.11 and 15.12. Of invaluable aid in the determination of the value of k is its relationship with p and n. It is derived as follows, using Fig. 15.12.

Figure 15-12

Knowing the neutral axis to be the center of gravity axis, regardless of the magnitude of stresses f_c and f_s we may write

$$bkd\frac{kd}{2} = nA_s(d - kd)$$

Inserting $A_s = pbd$ and simplifying,

$$\frac{k^2}{2}bd^2 = npbd^2 - npkbd^2$$

and $$k^2 = 2np - 2npk$$

from which $$k = \sqrt{2np + (np)^2} - np \qquad (15.13)$$

15-8. Shear investigation

In § 7-14, it was shown that the vertical shear stress at any point in a beam develops an equal horizontal shear stress at the same point. The combined effect of these two shearing stresses produces an equal maximum tensile stress on a 45° plane to these shears. The effect of this tensile stress, which occurs in addition to the flexural tensile stress, must be curtailed, if excessive, with the use of steel reinforcement placed across the lines of potential cracking. The maximum tensile stress which is developed in a beam subject to shear forces is de-termined as follows:

Let Fig. 15-13(a) represent a section of a loaded reinforced con-crete beam, dx in length and b in width, acted upon by flexural and shear forces. Taking moments about point A, there is obtained

Figure 15-13

$$dT\, jd = V\, dx \qquad (15.14)$$

The use of the smaller free body (Fig. 15-13b) reveals that

$$dT = v\, dx\, b \qquad (15.15)$$

Substituting dT into the previous equation produces

$$v\, dx\, bjd = V\, dx$$

or $$v = \frac{V}{bjd} \qquad (15.16)$$

The value of the shear stress obtained by Eq. 15.16 is equal to the maximum tensile stress and is generally restricted by code to 0.03 times the ultimate strength of the concrete, if no shear reinforcement is used.

15-9. Bond investigation

Of equal importance to the shear stress in the design of reinforced con-crete beams is the bond stress which occurs between the concrete and the steel bars. Generally, it must not be permitted to exceed a maximum al-lowable value. The magnitude of the bond stress may be derived as follows.

In Fig. 15.13, the unit bond stress occurring on the reinforcing rods is equal to the differential excess load dT divided by the peripheral area ($\Sigma\, 0 \times dx$) of the rods.

$$u = \frac{dT}{\Sigma 0 \times dx}$$

Inserting the value of dT obtained in Eq. 15.14 there is obtained

$$u = \frac{V}{\Sigma 0 \times jd}$$

The bond stress is limited by code to a value, for most cases, equal to 0.10 times the ultimate strength of the material, if deformed reinforcing bars are used, but not to exceed 350 psi.

Illustrative Problem 3. A simply supported reinforced concrete beam (Fig. 15-14) having a length of 12 ft has applied to it a uniformly distributed live load of 2000 lb per ft. If it is to have a rectangular cross section in which $b = d/2$, what will its dimensions be if the maximum allowable f_s and f_c equal 20,000 psi and 1125 psi, respectively? Check shear and bond stresses.

The maximum design load is equal to

$$\begin{array}{ll} 2000 \text{ lb per ft} & \text{live load} \\ \underline{170} & \text{dead load (assumed)} \\ 2170 \text{ lb per ft} & \text{total weight of beam} \end{array}$$

This load will produce a maximum moment of

$$M_{\text{max.}} = \frac{wl^2}{8} = \frac{2170 \times 144}{8} = 39,000 \text{ ft-lb}$$

SOLUTION. From Table 12 those design factors corresponding to the given f_s and f_c stresses are as follows:

$$k = 0.403, \ j = 0.866, \ p = 0.0113, \ K = 196$$

Inserting the values of $M_{\text{max.}}$ and K into Eq. 15.11 there is obtained

$$bd^2 = \frac{M}{K} = \frac{39,000 \times 12}{196} = 2390 \text{ in.}^3$$

The corresponding b and d will then be

$$d = 16.88 \text{ in., say 17 in.}$$
$$b = \ 8.44 \text{ in., say 8.5 in.}$$

Using a $1\frac{1}{2}$ in. cover of concrete and $\frac{7}{8}$ in. round bars, the practical overall dimension of the beam will be 8.5 in. wide by 19.0 in. deep (see Fig. 15-14).

Check on Assumed Weight. The weight of this beam per foot (based on concrete = 150 lb per ft³) will then be $\dfrac{8.5 \times 19.0 \times 12}{1728} \times 150 = 169$ lb per ft, which checks the assumed within a sufficient degree of accuracy.

Figure 15-14

Steel Required:

$$A_s = \frac{M}{f_s jd} = \frac{39,000 \times 12}{20,000 \times 0.866 \times 17} = 1.59 \text{ sq in. required}$$

A good selection might then be $3 - \frac{7}{8}$ in. round bars at 0.60 sq in. $= 1.80$ sq. in.

Shear Investigation:

$$v = \frac{V}{bjd} = \frac{wl/2}{bjd} = \frac{2170 \times 6}{8.5 \times 0.866 \times 17} = 104.0 \text{ psi}$$

Because this value of shear exceeds 0.03 times the ultimate strength of the concrete, viz., $2500 \times 0.03 =$ psi, shear reinforcement will be required.

Bond Investigation:

$$u = \frac{V}{\Sigma 0jd} = \frac{2170 \times 6}{3 \times 2.75 \times 0.866 \times 17} = 107.2 \text{ psi}$$

This value does not exceed the 250 psi (0.1×2500) permitted, indicating that the steel perimeter is satisfactory for the required bond resistance.

Illustrative Problem 4. Determine the maximum stresses in the concrete and steel of the rectangular reinforced concrete beam shown in Fig. 15-15 if the maximum bending moment is 800,000 in.-lb. $n = 12$.

SOLUTION. This is obviously an investigation problem. Since the stresses in either the concrete or steel are unknown, the neutral axis must be located using Eq. 15-13.

Figure 15-15

$$k = \sqrt{2np + (np)^2} - np$$

$$p = \frac{A_s}{bd} = \frac{3.0}{14 \times 20} = .0107$$

$$k = \sqrt{2 \times 0.0107 \times 12 + (12 \times 0.0107)^2} - 12 \times 0.0107$$

$$k = 0.525 - 0.129 = 0.396$$

$$kd = 0.396 \times 20 = 7.92 \text{ in.}$$

$$jd = d - \frac{kd}{3} = 20 - \frac{7.92}{3} = 17.36 \text{ in.}$$

If now the moment of the compressive force in the concrete is taken about the center of the steel,

$$M = \tfrac{1}{2}f_c b \times kd \times jd =$$
$$800,000 = \tfrac{1}{2} \times f_c \times 14 \times 7.92 \times 17.36$$
$$f_c = 832 \text{ psi}$$

The corresponding stress in the steel is

$$f_s = \frac{M}{A_s jd} = \frac{800,000}{3.0 \times 17.36} = 15,400 \text{ psi}$$

Illustrative Problem 5. Suppose the beam of Illustrative Problem 4 is to be subjected to an increased bending moment of 1,300,000 in.-lb. (a) What maximum stresses would then be induced in the concrete and steel? (b) If these stresses exceed the allowables of 20,000 psi in the steel and 1125 psi in the concrete ($n = 12$), what additional reinforcement must be added to make the beam safe? The dimensions of the beam are not to be altered.

SOLUTION. (a) Because the transformed section is the same as in Illustrative Problem 4, the location of the neutral axis will not change. Moreover, the stresses in the steel and concrete will be proportional to the bending moment since j, k, b, and d will not change.

$$f_s = 15,400 \times \frac{1,300,000}{800,000} = 25,000 \text{ psi}$$

$$f_c = 832 \times \frac{1,300,000}{800,000} = 1,350 \text{ psi}$$

(b) The above stresses, being in excess of the allowables, must be reduced by the addition of further steel. This conclusion is evident when it is realized that the location of the T and C resultant forces on the maximum moment section does not change but their magnitude does. In order for the T resultant to be counteracted without exceeding the 20,000 psi limiting stress, its area must be increased. In the upper or compression portion of the beam, however, it is impossible to increase the resultant C force beyond $\frac{1}{2} \times 1125 \times 7.92 \times 14.0 = 62,400$ lb without exceeding the maximum allowable concrete stress of 1125 psi.

Since there is no way to increase the compressive concrete area, compression steel must be added to supplement the concrete. This steel will be stressed to a value n times the stress on that concrete corresponding to its level in the beam.

Figure 15-16

The solution to this problem proceeds in three steps (Fig. 15-16a), namely:

(1) The determination of the bending moment the beam can carry assuming its design to be balanced.

(2) The determination of the amount of tensile and compression steel required to produce the additional moment required.

(3) The algebraic summation of the steel and concrete areas to provide the cross section required to resist the total moment.

The value of K for the balanced design of this beam is equal to 196 (see Table 12), making the corresponding resisting moment

$$M_B = 196 \times 14 \times 20^2 = 1{,}097{,}000 \text{ in.-lb}$$

Resisting this moment will be a tensile steel area of

$$(A_s)_B = .0113 \times 14 \times 20 = 3.17 \text{ sq in.}$$

The supplementary moment (ΔC, ΔT couple) will therefore be

$$\Delta M = M_T - M_B$$

$$= 1{,}300{,}000 - 1{,}097{,}000 = 203{,}000 \text{ in.-lb}$$

Proceeding now to the reinforcement in the compression concrete, let us assume this steel to be placed 2 in. from the top surface. Assuming the maximum allowable stresses in steel and concrete to be maintained, the concrete stress at this level will be

$$f''_c = 1125 \times \frac{7.92 - 2.00}{7.92} = 839 \text{ psi}$$

The steel stress in the compression steel, therefore, cannot exceed

$$f''_s = 839 \times 12 = 10{,}080 \text{ psi}$$

The area of compression steel required at this stress is thus

$$A'_s = \frac{\Delta C}{nf''_c} = \frac{\Delta M}{(kd - e)f''_s}$$

$$= \frac{203{,}000}{18 \times 10{,}080} = 1.12 \text{ sq in.}$$

The tensile steel area required to support the extra moment is

$$\Delta A_s = \frac{\Delta T}{f_s} = \frac{\Delta M}{(d - e)f_s}$$

$$= \frac{203{,}000}{(20 - 2) \times 20{,}000} = 0.56 \text{ sq in.}$$

making the total area of tensile steel required

$$A_s = (A_s)_B + \Delta A_s = 3.17 + 0.56 = 3.73 \text{ sq in.}$$

The cross section of the strengthened beam is shown in Fig. 15-16(b).

PROBLEMS

15-13. Find the dimensions of a rectangular reinforced concrete beam, if the maximum moment is 60,000 ft-lb. $E_c = 2 \times 10^6$ psi, $f_c = 900$ psi, $f_s = 20,000$ psi, $n = 15$. Find area of steel. Make $b = \frac{1}{2}d$. *Answers:* $b = 10.5$ in., $d = 21.0$ in., $A_s = 1.98$ sq in.

15-14. Solve Problem 15-13 using $f_c = 1688$ psi, $f_s = 20,000$ psi, and $n = 8$.

15-15. Solve Problem 15-13 using $f_c = 1125$ psi, $f_s = 20,000$ psi, and $n = 12$.

15-16. The width of a reinforced concrete beam is 8 in. and the depth to the center of steel is 10 in. The beam is 10 ft long and is loaded with 650 lb per ft. Area of steel $= 1.0$ sq in. Calculate the unit stress in the concrete and the steel. $n = 15$. *Answers:* $f_c = 737$ psi, $f_s = 13,100$ psi.

15-17. Calculate the areas of the compressive and tensile steel for the beam shown in Fig. 15-17. Bending moment $= 180,000$ ft-lb. Allowable stresses: concrete $= 900$ psi, steel $= 18,000$ psi, and $n = 15$. *Answers:* $A'_s = 2.98$ sq in., $A_s = 5.12$ sq in.

15-18. A reinforced concrete beam subjected to a bending moment of 1,500,000 in.-lb is restricted to 12 in. in width and 24 in. total depth. Design section for $f_s = 1000$ psi, $f_s = 18,000$ psi, and $n = 12$. Keep steel 2 in. away from nearest surface. *Answers:* $A'_s = 2.67$ sq in., $A_s = 4.30$ sq in.

Figure 15-17

15-19. Design a simply supported reinforced concrete slab having a span of 8 ft and carrying a superimposed load of 500 lb per sq ft. The maximum allowable stresses in the steel and concrete are 18,000 psi and 650 psi, respectively. $n = 15$. Check shear and bond. *Answers:* $d = 7.0$ in., $A_s = 0.517$ sq in. per width of slab.

15-20. Design a simply supported reinforced concrete slab on a 12 ft span to carry a live load of 500 lb per sq ft. Assume allowable stresses of 800 psi in the concrete, 18,000 psi in the steel, and take n as 12. Disregard bond and shear.

15-21. Design a cinder-concrete floor slab on a simple span of 6 ft to carry a live load of 250 lb per sq ft. using the following data: allowable compressive stress in cinder concrete, 200 psi, allowable tensile stress in steel reinforcement, 18,000 psi; $n = 30$. Assume weight of cinder concrete as 105 lb per cu ft, and use $\frac{3}{4}$-in. cover under reinforcement.

PRESTRESSED CONCRETE

15-10. *Pre-tensioning; post-tensioning*

To further develop the bending or tensile resistance of reinforced concrete, its reinforcing steel may be placed in tension, i.e., prestressed, before the design loads are applied. This, in effect, produces deformations in the concrete of opposite character to those subsequently introduced by the applied forces. In this way, undesirable tensile stresses are avoided. See Fig. 15-18 as applied to beams and pipes.

Figure 15-18

Prestressing may be done in one of two ways, namely, by either *pre-tensioning* or by *post-tensioning*.

Pre-tensioning employs the use of a stressing bed to place the reinforcement in tension before the concrete is poured around it. After the concrete is cured sufficiently to provide good bond, the force applied by the stressing bed is released. With the release, the steel wires (rods are not generally used) attempt to contract to a zero stress condition but are prevented from doing so by the bond and compressive resistance of the concrete. The development of a compressive stress prior to the application of tension increases the range of tensile stress that may safely be applied and consequently its load-carrying capacity.

Post-tensioning, on the other hand, employs wrapped or sheathed, bond-free reinforcement which is placed in tension after the concrete has been cured. Because the steel is not bonded to the concrete, the tensile force applied to it is developed by pushing against the concrete. This compressive force counteracts the effects of the tensile stresses produced in the concrete by the applied loads, thereby increasing the resistance of the member

Figure 15-19 Freyssinet prestressing jack. (Courtesy of Freyssinet Co.)

to tension or bending. After the tensioning has been completed, the reinforcing wires are grouted to the beam to promote bond and provide resistance to corrosion.

15-11. *Internal deformations due to prestressing*

When the load developed by a straining frame is transferred to the concrete of a pre-tensioned member, the concrete deforms. This causes the reinforcement to shorten with a consequent reduction in its stress. Moreover, concrete also shrinks as it hardens and flows plastically when it is placed in compression. Even the steel will creep, i.e., deform inelastically, when subjected to continuous high stress. These effects must be anticipated in determining the final desired stress in the steel. The approximate loss of pre-tension stress in the steel amounts to 20–25 per cent.

In the post-tensioning procedure, the effect of shrinkage is greatly reduced and that of initial concrete deformation is eliminated in the determination of the final stress in the steel. Plastic flow and creep, however, must be considered even though their effects may be small.

15-12. *Considerations in designing prestressed beams*

In designing a prestressed beam, the eccentric prestress load is generally applied to develop compressive stress over the entire cross section, varying from zero at the top fibers to a maximum on the bottom. The flexural stress pattern produced by the design loads is then superimposed on that caused by the prestressing load. It is common practice to limit the magnitude of the design load to a value which will reduce the intensity of the prestress compression on the lower fibers of the concrete to either zero or some small fractional part of its ultimate tensile strength (Fig. 15-20). The stress on the upper fibers, correspondingly, will be equal to the sum of the compression stresses due to the prestressing and design loads.

Because the entire concrete cross section of the beam is placed under effective resisting stresses, its gross moment of inertia may be used in computing the safe design load. It is of interest to note, too, that no cracks will form in the lower part of the beam under the application of this load.

In order to produce maximum economy in a prestressed concrete member, the steel and concrete used must be of high strength. The reinforcement is generally of high carbon or alloy steel with a maximum allowable stress up to 200,000 psi. The required concrete strength at 28 days is from 4000 to 6000 psi.

Let us now consider the actual design of a prestressed concrete beam.

Illustrative Problem 6. A rectangular concrete beam 12 in. wide, 16 in. deep, and 20 ft long, is to be pre-tensioned before assuming its design load. What uniform load per foot may it carry if the allowable $f_c = 2000$ psi and the allowable $f_s = 150,000$ psi? Allow 20 percent for the combined effects of shrinkage, compression, and creep.

SOLUTION. *Pre-tensioning analysis:* In order to produce a uniformly varying compressive stress over the cross section ranging from zero at the top fibers to a maximum at the bottom, the pre-tension load P_p applied to the end cross section must provide

$$\frac{P_p}{A} - \frac{P_p ec}{I} = 0$$

at the top. From this equation we obtain

$$\frac{P_p}{A}\left(1 - \frac{ec}{r^2}\right) = 0$$

or

$$e = \frac{r^2}{c} = \frac{I}{Ac}$$

Because

$$I = \tfrac{1}{12} \times 12 \times 16^3 = 4096 \quad \text{and} \quad A = 12 \times 16 = 192 \text{ sq in.}$$

$$e = \frac{4096}{192 \times 8} = 2.67 \text{ in.}$$

The value of P_p, the pre-tensioning force, is then computed using the 2000 psi limiting stress.

Figure 15-20

$$\frac{P_p}{192} + \frac{P_p \times 2.67 \times 8}{4096} = 2000 \qquad P_p = \frac{2000}{0.01042} = 192,000 \text{ lb}$$

If a uniform load is to be applied to the beam so as to reduce the 2000 psi compressive stress to zero, there must be applied a flexural stress pattern having a 2000 psi: tensile stress on the bottom fibers. The allowable uniform load may then be computed as follows.

$$M = \frac{w \times 20^2}{8} \times 12 = \frac{2000 \times 4096}{8}$$

$$w = 1705 \text{ lb per ft}$$
$$\text{less} \qquad \underline{200 \text{ lb per ft (weight of concrete beam)}}$$
$$1505 \text{ lb per ft (allowable uniform load)}$$

Area of steel required. The area of steel required may be obtained by dividing the required pre-tensioning force by the reduced allowable stress.

$$A = \frac{P_p}{f_s k_s} = \frac{192,000}{150,000 \times 0.80} = 1.60 \text{ sq in.}$$

It should be noted that the required pre-tensioning force will not change because of the imposed bending loads. This may be verified by considering the maximum compressive stress on the lower fibers caused by pre-tensioning to be counteracted by the equal and opposite maximum tensile stress caused by the applied loads.

$$\frac{P_p}{A} + \frac{P_p e c}{I} = \frac{M c}{I}$$

$$\frac{P_p}{A}\left(1 + \frac{ec}{r^2}\right) = \frac{M c}{A r^2}$$

$$P_p = \frac{M}{\dfrac{r^2}{c} + e} = \frac{M}{2e}$$

But
$$M = \frac{1705 \times 20^2}{8} \times 12 = 1,023,000 \text{ in.-lb}$$

Therefore
$$P_p = \frac{1,023,000}{2 \times 2.67} = 192,000 \text{ lb}$$

Extreme fiber stresses. The algebraic sum of the stresses (see Fig. 15-20) imposed by the pre-tensioning and applied loads reveals the maximum stresses at the top and bottom of the beam to be 2000 and 0 psi, respectively, with no tension appearing on the cross section.

PROBLEMS

15-22. A rectangular concrete beam, 10 in. wide, 20 in. deep, and 20 ft long is to be pre-tensioned before assuming its design load. What uniform live load may it carry if the allowable concrete and steel stresses are 2000 and 150,000 psi, respectively? Allow 20 per cent for the combined effects of shrinkage, compression, and creep.

15-23. Design the beam of Problem 15-22 assuming the reinforcement to be post-tensioned.

15-24. A water pipe of 5 ft inside diameter is intended to operate under a pressure of 50 psi. The pipe is cast of concrete 3 in. thick and then wound with $\frac{1}{4}$-in. wire under tension. If the maximum allowable unit stress in the wire is 30,000 psi, what spacing of wire must be used so that the concrete will be under a compressive stress of 100 psi when the pipe is under pressure? *Answer:* 0.818 in. on centers.

15-25. A 3 in. thick water pipe of 5 ft inside diameter is prestressed to give compression in the concrete by wrapping the concrete with $\frac{1}{4}$-in. steel wire at 2 in. centers under tension of 2500 lb. $n = 10$. (a) Compute the internal pressure intensity which would reduce compression in the concrete to 30 psi. (b) What will be the unit stress in the wire? *Answers:* (a) 41.7 psi, (b) 54,866 psi.

APPENDICES

CONTENTS

CENTER OF GRAVITY AND MOMENT OF INERTIA

CENTER OF GRAVITY

A-1. *General principles*

The method of locating the center of gravity of a mass or an area is based upon the method of determining the resultants of parallel force systems.

Should a mass or an area be divided into a large number of small, equal units, each of which is represented by one of a system of parallel vectors acting as its centroid, the resultant of the vector system would act through the center of gravity of the total mass or area. As found in Chapter 1, the resultant of a force or vector system has an effect equal to its component forces or vectors. Thus, when we find the center of gravity of a mass or of an area, we determine that point at which the entire mass or area can be considered to be concentrated.

A-2. *Center of gravity of composite areas*

Suppose the center of gravity of the area shown in Fig. A-1(a), is desired. After placing the area in the xz plane, as shown in Fig. A-1(b), subdivide the area into 1 by 1-in. squares and locate at the center of each square a vector of 1 sq in. acting perpendicular to the xz plane. The system of parallel vectors, thereby developed, can be concentrated into a resultant, the location of which will act at the center of gravity of the figure.

The magnitude of the resultant is equal to the algebraic sum of the component vectors — namely, 16 sq in. To determine its location — that is, the center of gravity — we shall make use of the fact that *the moment of the resultant of a force or vector system must equal the moment of its component forces or vectors about any axis*. Taking moments, therefore, about the z axis of the vectors and their resultant and setting them equal to one another gives us an equation whose solution will provide the perpendicular distance of the resultant from that axis. Since this distance is parallel to the x axis, it is called $\bar{x}$. A similar equation taken about the x axis provides the $\bar{z}$ which, together with the $\bar{x}$, fixes the location of the center of gravity.

A simplification of the moment equation may be made by grouping certain vectors, the location of whose resultants is obvious. For instance,

(a)

(b)

(c)

Figure A-1

the squares from 1 to 10 form a rectangle, whose resultant vector of 10 sq in. will act at its own center of gravity. Squares 11 to 14 and 15 and 16 can also be grouped to give a more simplified vector system, shown in Fig. A-1(c). The more simple the diagram can be made, the easier the solution.

Taking the moment of the vectors shown in Fig. A-1(c) about the z axis, gives the following equation:

MOMENTS OF VECTORS	MOMENT OF RESULTANT
Areas 1 to 10.............$10 \times 1 = 10$ in.^{3}	$16 \times \bar{x}$
Areas 11 to 14........... $4 \times 3 = 12$ in.^{3}	
Areas 15 to 16........... $2 \times 3 = 6$ in.^{3}	
Sum of areas............16 sq in.	
Algebraic sum of moments of	
areas.........................28 in.^{3} =	$16\,\bar{x}$

$$\bar{x} = \frac{28}{16} = 1.75 \text{ in.}$$

Now, the location of the center of gravity can be fixed in the xz plane only by another coordinate, the $\bar{z}$. This distance, which is similar in character to the $\bar{x}$, is measured parallel to the z axis. It may be obtained by taking moments about the x axis, since the coordinate to the vectors and to the resultant will be z distances.

MOMENTS OF VECTORS	MOMENT OF RESULTANT
Areas 1 to 10.............$10 \times 2.5 = 25.0$	$16 \times \bar{z}$
Areas 11 to 14........... $4 \times 1.00 = 4.0$	
Areas 15 to 16........... $2 \times 4.5 = 9.0$	
38.0 in.^{3} =	$16\,\bar{z}$

$$\bar{z} = \frac{38}{16} = 2.38 \text{ in.}$$

A-3. Advantageous selection of axes

It will be noted that the moments of the vectors and the resultant were all positive in the previous problem. Whenever possible, it is suggested that the axes be so selected that this simplification be obtained.

Should some of the moments of the component areas be positive and others minus, owing to the necessity of choosing internal axes, the location of the center of gravity will be determined by using the same principles as previously given and, of course, will be at the same place in the area.

To illustrate this point, let us choose a different set of axes, shown in Fig. A-2. Taking moments about the z axis, we obtain:

MOMENTS OF VECTORS	MOMENT OF RESULTANT
$10 \times -1.0 = -10$ in.^{3}	$16 \times \bar{x}$
$4 \times 1.0 = 4$ in.^{3}	
$2 \times 1.0 = 2$ in.^{3}	
16 sq in. $- 4$ in.^{3} =	$16\,\bar{x}$

whence

$$\bar{x} = \frac{-4}{16} = -0.25 \text{ in.}$$

Figure A-2

The moment about the x axis will be:

MOMENTS OF VECTORS	MOMENT OF RESULTANT
$10 \times \ \ \ 0.5 = \ \ \ \ 5.0$	$16 \times \bar{z}$
$2 \times \ \ \ 2.5 = \ \ \ \ 5.0$	
$4 \times -1.0 = \underline{-4.0}$	
$\ \ \ \ \ \ \ \ \ \ \ \ \ \ \ \ \ 6.0 \ \ \ \ = $	$\overline{16\,\bar{z}}$

$$\bar{z} = \frac{6}{16} = 0.38 \text{ in.}$$

It will be seen that these new $\bar{x}$ and $\bar{z}$ values locate the center of gravity at exactly the same location as found in our previous calculation.

In each of the above equations, the $\bar{x}$ and $\bar{z}$ distances were considered positive until by computation they were proven otherwise. A change in the location of the axes will make no difference in the ultimate answer, as long as the moments on one side of an axis be given a sign opposite to those on the other side.

A-4. Further development in center of gravity; areas with holes

An altogether different approach to the previous problem on center of gravity can be made if we consider its area to consist of a rectangle 4 in. wide and 5 in. long with a 2-in. square cut out of its side. If, then, in addition to the area vectors shown in Fig. A-3, we were to add two opposing area vectors at the centers of each of the four squares included in the cutout section, we would have a downward-acting-area vector system representing the complete rectangle 4 in. wide and 5 in. long, and an upward-acting-area vector system representing the area of the cut-out square. Since the opposing vectors are equal and annul one another, the moment of the

Figure A-3

downward vectors representing the cutout section and included expediently in the moment of the total rectangle is balanced by the moment of similar vectors acting in the upward direction. Stated briefly, then, the moment of the net area about any axis would be equal to the moment of the large rectangle less the moment of the square. A simplified and composite vector diagram consisting of the 20 sq-in. and 4 sq-in. vectors is shown in Fig. A-3, superimposed on the more elementary vector diagram.

It has been previously stated that the resultant of a parallel force system is equal to the algebraic sum of the component forces. Vectorially speaking, the resultant area in our problem would, therefore, be 16 sq in., which is the algebraic sum of the 20 and 4 sq-in. vectors or, in other words, the net area of the figure. Since the moment of the resultant equals the moment of its components, we may write, using the simplified diagram, the following moments about the z axis.

<table>
<tr><td>MOMENTS OF VECTORS</td><td></td><td>MOMENT OF RESULTANT</td></tr>
<tr><td>$20 \times 2 = $ 40 in.^{3}</td><td></td><td>$16 \times \bar{x}$ in.^{3}</td></tr>
<tr><td>$-4 \times 3 = -12$ in.^{3}</td><td></td><td></td></tr>
<tr><td>28 in.^{3}</td><td>=</td><td>$16\,\bar{x}$</td></tr>
</table>

$$\bar{x} = \frac{28}{16} = 1.75 \text{ in.}$$

The moments of the vectors taken about the x axis are:

<table>
<tr><td>MOMENTS OF VECTORS</td><td></td><td>MOMENT OF RESULTANT</td></tr>
<tr><td>$20 \times 2.5 = $ 50 in.^{3}</td><td></td><td>$16 \times \bar{z}$</td></tr>
<tr><td>$-4 \times 3 \ = -12$ in.^{3}</td><td></td><td></td></tr>
<tr><td>38 in.^{3}</td><td>=</td><td>$16\,\bar{z}$</td></tr>
</table>

$$\bar{z} = \frac{38}{16} = 2.38 \text{ in.}$$

A-5. Summary of center of gravity of composite areas

To summarize the procedure used in the previous problems on the center of gravity of areas, we may deduce the following general rule:

$$\text{Center of gravity coordinate (measured from moment axis)} = \frac{\text{algebraic sum of moments of component areas about axis}}{\text{algebraic sum of component areas}}$$

$$\bar{x} = \frac{\Sigma Ax}{\Sigma A} \qquad \bar{z} = \frac{\Sigma Az}{\Sigma A} \qquad\qquad (A.1)$$

TABLE 13
IMPORTANT CENTERS OF GRAVITY

	AREA	CENTER OF GRAVITY
Triangle	$A = \frac{1}{2}bh$	$\bar{y} = \frac{h}{3}$
Semicircle	$A = \frac{\pi r^2}{2}$	$\bar{y} = \frac{4r}{3\pi}$
Parabolic segment	$A = \frac{2}{3}bh$	$\bar{x} = \frac{3}{8}b, \bar{y} = \frac{2}{5}h$
Complement of above parabolic segment	$A = \frac{1}{3}bh$	$\bar{x} = \frac{1}{4}b, \bar{y} = \frac{3}{10}h$

PROBLEMS

A-1. Find the centers of gravity of the following areas shown in Fig. A-4 about the axes indicated. *Answer:* (a) $\bar{y} = 6.15$ in., $\bar{x} = 2.60$ in.; (c) $\bar{y} = 4.92$ in., $\bar{x} = 6.72$ in.; (e) $\bar{y} = 3.91$ in.; (g) $\bar{y} = 2.68$ in.

1 Pl. 10 by ½ in.
2 channels 8 in., 11.5 lb/ft
Refer to Table 17

2 L's 4 by 3½ by ⅜ in.
1 Pl. 12 by ⅜ in.
Refer to Table 18

Figure A-4

A-2. Determine the location of the center of gravity of area (a) in the previous problem about axes 2 in. to the left and below the y and x axes, respectively.

A-3. Determine the location of the center of gravity of area (f) in Problem A-1 about a horizontal axis located at the top of the figure.

MOMENT OF INERTIA OF AREAS

A-6. General principles

When in the study of strength of materials a formula is derived based on the bending or torsional resistance of a cross-sectional area, there is invariably included in that formula a term called the *moment of inertia* of the area. It has the general form of

$$\int z^2 \, dA \qquad \qquad (A.2a)$$

The magnitude of this moment of inertia term is a measure of the resistance offered by the material included within this cross-sectional area by *virtue of its shape and location.* If we should consider two prismatic beams made of the same material, but of different cross sections, that beam whose cross-sectional area had the greater moment of inertia would have the greater resistance to bending. To have a greater moment of inertia does not necessarily imply, however, a greater cross-sectional area. Less area more advantageously placed may have a greater moment of inertia.

In our discussion of the method of finding the center of gravity of areas, each area was subdivided into small elementary areas which were multiplied by their respective perpendicular distances from the reference axis. This procedure is somewhat similar for determinations of moment of inertia. The moment of inertia about the same axis would require, however, that each elementary area be multiplied by the *square* of the respective perpendicular distances from the reference axis.

Figure A-5

Let us illustrate by using Fig. A-5. Suppose we wanted to find the moment of inertia of this irregular area about the x axis. We would first consider the area to consist of many infinitesimal dA areas. Considering the dA shown, its moment of inertia about the x axis would be $z_1^2 dA$. But this product is only a minute portion of the whole moment of inertia. Each dA comprising the area, when multiplied by the square of its corresponding moment arm z and added together, will give the moment of inertia of the entire area about the x axis.

The difficulty of this integration process is largely dependent on the equation of the outline of the area and its limits. When the integration becomes too difficult or when a more simple, approximate solution is permissible, the moment of inertia may be expressed in finite terms by

$$I_x = \Sigma\, z^2\, \Delta A \qquad\qquad (A.2b)$$

The solution becomes more accurate as the size of ΔA is decreased.

Let us illustrate the approximation involved by the calculation of the moment of inertia of a rectangle about its center-of-gravity axis by the approximate method and by the exact formula derived from the calculus.

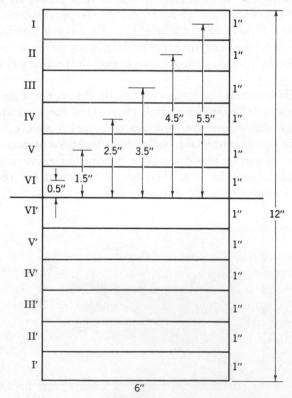

Figure A-6

Approximate method. Let us consider the elementary areas of Fig. A-6 to be 1 in. wide and 6 in. long. The use of the 6-in. length will in no way detract from the accuracy of the solution, since increasing the length of the rectangle merely adds more area similarly placed with respect to the center of gravity axis. It is the necessity of using a 1-in. width rather than one of infinitesimal width which lessens the accuracy.

	$\Delta A(in.^2)$	$y(in.)$	y^2	ΔAy^2
I............	6	5.5	30.25	181.5 in.⁴
II..........	6	4.5	20.25	121.5
III...:.....	6	3.5	12.25	73.5
IV.........	6	2.5	6.25	37.5
V..........	6	1.5	2.25	13.5
VI.........	6	0.5	0.25	1.5

$$\Sigma \Delta A\ y^2 \text{ for top of rectangle} = 429.0$$
$$\Sigma \Delta A\ y^2 \text{ for bottom of rectangle} = 429.0$$
$$\Sigma Ay^2 = 858.0 \text{ in.}^4$$

Exact method. Moment of inertia of rectangle about its center-of-gravity axis

$$= \tfrac{1}{12}bd^3$$
$$= \tfrac{1}{12} \times 6 \times 12^3 = 864 \text{ in.}^4$$

where b = width of rectangle and d = depth of rectangle.

Although the discrepancy here is less than 1 per cent of the exact moment of inertia, a still greater refinement can be made by using narrower strips.

Although the approximate method is used to great advantage in determining the moment of inertia of irregular areas, whenever the area is geometrically familiar to the extent that its center of gravity and moment of inertia are or can be ascertained from their component areas, the more exact formulas already derived from the calculus are always used. Those moment of inertia formulas of particular value are given in Table 14.

A-7. Moment of inertia of a composite area

Whenever an area can be considered as equal to a combination of other areas whose centers of gravity and moments of inertia are known, the moment of inertia of the composite area about any desired axis can be obtained by an algebraic summation of its component moments of inertia taken about the same axis. To obtain the moments of inertia of the dependent component areas, it frequently becomes necessary to use the *parallel-axis theorem*. By this theorem, one may ascertain the moment of inertia of an area about any axis parallel to a *center-of-gravity* axis, if the moment of inertia of the area about the latter axis is known. For instance, consider the case of the rectangle in Fig. A-7. Knowing the moment of inertia

Figure A-7

about its center-of-gravity axis y-y, we can obtain the moment of inertia of the rectangle about any axis parallel to the y-y axis — for instance the y'-y' axis.

Proof—parallel-axis theorem. Let the y'-y' axis be k distance from the parallel centroidal axis y-y. Consider the area to be divided into dA strips, any one of which has every portion of its area equidistant from the y'-y' axis. Select that dA area located a distance x from the y-y axis. The expression for the moment of inertia of dA about the y'-y' axis will, as previously discussed, be equal to

$$dI_{y'\text{-}y'} = (k + x)^2\, dA$$

If we were now to require the moments of inertia of the total area about the same axis, knowing that each dA had a moment of inertia similar to that given above, x being a general distance, we would merely sum up the incremental moments of inertia.

$$\int dI_{y'\text{-}y'} = \int (k + x)^2\, dA$$

Squaring the binomial, $\int dI_{y'\text{-}y'} = \int (k^2 + 2kx + x^2)\, dA$

or $\qquad\qquad I_{y'\text{-}y'} = \int k^2\, dA + \int 2kx\, dA + \int x^2\, dA \qquad\qquad$ (A.3a)

TABLE 14

MOMENTS OF INERTIA AND RADII OF GYRATION

	$I_{x\text{-}x}$	$r_{x\text{-}x}$	J_o
	$\dfrac{1}{12}bh^3$	$\dfrac{h}{\sqrt{12}}$	$\dfrac{bh}{12}(h^2 + b^2)$
	$\dfrac{1}{3}bh^3$	$\dfrac{h}{\sqrt{3}}$	$\ldots$
	$\dfrac{1}{36}bh^3$	$\dfrac{h}{\sqrt{18}}$	$\dfrac{bh}{48}(\tfrac{4}{3}h^2 + b^2)$
	$\dfrac{1}{12}bh^3$	$\dfrac{h}{\sqrt{6}}$	$\ldots$
	$\dfrac{\pi d^4}{64}$	$\dfrac{d}{4}$	$\dfrac{\pi d^4}{32}$
	$\dfrac{\pi(d^4 - d_1^4)}{64}$	$\dfrac{\sqrt{d^2 + d_1^2}}{4}$	$\dfrac{\pi}{32}(d^4 - d_1^4)$
	$r^4\left(\dfrac{\pi}{8} - \dfrac{8}{9\pi}\right)$	$\dfrac{r\sqrt{9\pi^2 - 64}}{6\pi}$	$\ldots$

c.g. distance
0.4244r

Now, k being a constant value — that is, the same for all dA's — we may write

$$\int k^2 \, dA = k^2 \int dA = Ak^2$$

and

$$\int 2kx \, dA = 2k \int x \, dA$$

But since the y-y axis is the center-of-gravity axis and the moment of the areas balance about this axis — that is, the resultant of the area acts through the y-y axis — $\int x \, dA$ must be equal to zero.

We also note that $\int x^2 \, dA$ is equal to the moment of inertia of the rectangle about the y-y axis written in general terms.

Therefore, rewriting Eq. A.3a we have

$$I_{y'\text{-}y'} = I_{y\text{-}y} + Ak^2 \qquad\qquad \text{(A.3b)}$$

which is known as the *parallel-axis theorem*.

In using the formula, care should be taken to substitute correctly. To avoid misunderstanding, the following facts should be clearly understood.

1. The y-y axis is any centroidal axis — that is, passing through the center of gravity, about which the moment of inertia is known.

2. $I_{y\text{-}y}$ is the moment of inertia of the area about the centroidal axis y-y.

3. Axis y'-y' is parallel to the centroidal axis y-y, and $I_{y'\text{-}y'}$ is the moment of inertia about the axis y'-y'.

4. Distance k is always the distance between the parallel axes — that is, the centroidal axis y-y and the new axis y'-y', about which the moment of inertia is to be determined.

On the basis of the principles given above, there may be written an even more general moment-of-inertia formula whose new terms can now be understood:

$$I_p = I_{\text{c.g.}} + Ak^2 \qquad\qquad \text{(A.4)}$$

Figure A-8

Illustrative Problem 1. Using the area in Fig. A-8, find the moment of inertia about axis x'-x'.

SOLUTION. There should immediately be located the center of gravity of the figure and an axis x-x drawn through it parallel to axis x'-x'. Then determine the distance k equal to 8 in. Now, by substituting in

$$I_p = I_{\text{c.g.}} + Ak^2$$

we obtain

$$I_{x'-x'} = \tfrac{1}{12} \times 8 \times 6^3 + 48 \times 8^2$$
$$= 144 + 3072 = 3216 \text{ in.}^4$$

(See Table 14 for moments of inertia of common areas.)

Illustrative Problem 2. Let it be desired to find the moment of inertia of the area previously used in the discussion of center of gravity (Fig. A-1) about the centroidal axes $I_{x\text{-}x}$ and $I_{y\text{-}y}$ of the net area.

Solutions. *Method I.* This area is easily divided into two rectangles and a square (Fig. A-9a and b). Locating the centroidal axes of each

Figure A-9

incremental area and the net area as found in the previous problem, we may now proceed as follows:

Areas	$I_{c.g.}$		A	k	k^2	Ak^2	$I_{c.g.} + Ak^2$
		$I_{x\text{-}x}$					
I	$\tfrac{1}{12} \times 4 \times 1^3 =$	0.33	4	2.12	4.50	18.00	18.33
II	$\tfrac{1}{12} \times 2 \times 2^3 =$	1.33	4	0.62	0.39	1.56	2.89
III	$\tfrac{1}{12} \times 4 \times 2^3 =$	2.67	8	1.38	1.90	15.20	17.87
						$I_{x\text{-}x} =$	39.09 in.^{4}
		$I_{y\text{-}y}$					
I	$\tfrac{1}{12} \times 1 \times 4^3 =$	5.33	4	0.25	0.063	0.252	5.58
II	$\tfrac{1}{12} \times 2 \times 2^3 =$	1.33	4	0.75	0.563	2.252	3.58
III	$\tfrac{1}{12} \times 2 \times 4^3 =$	10.67	8	0.25	0.063	0.505	11.18
						$I_{y\text{-}y} =$	20.34 in.^{4}

Method II. This problem may also be solved by considering the area shown to consist of a rectangle 4 in. wide by 5 in. long with a 2-in. square cut from its side (Fig. A-10a and b). By subtracting the moment of inertia of

(a)

(b)

Figure A-10

the square — which was expediently added to the irregular area — from the large 4 by 5-in. rectangle, we shall obtain the moment of inertia of the net area as shown below.

	$I_{x\text{-}x}$					
AREAS	$I_{\text{c.g.}}$	A	k	k^2	Ak^2	$I_{\text{c.g.}} + Ak^2$
I	$\frac{1}{12} \times 4 \times 5^3 = 41.67$	20	0.12	0.0144	.288	41.96
II	$\frac{1}{12} \times 2 \times 2^3 = 1.33$	4	0.62	0.384	1.536	−2.87
					$I_{x\text{-}x} =$	39.09 in.⁴
	$I_{y\text{-}y}$					
I	$\frac{1}{12} \times 5 \times 4^3 = 26.67$	20	0.25	0.0625	1.25	27.92
II	$\frac{1}{12} \times 2 \times 2^3 = 1.33$	4	1.25	1.56	6.25	−7.58
					$I_{y\text{-}y} =$	20.34 in.⁴

A-8. Radius of gyration

It has previously been stated that the moment of inertia of an area about a certain axis could be expressed in a general way as being equal to

$$I_z = \int x^2 \, dA$$

where x is the distance from the z axis to any incremental area dA. Inasmuch as x is a length and dA is a length squared, the value of I_z is expressed in terms of a length to the fourth power, such as in.⁴ or ft.⁴

If, instead of using a summation of incremental areas, we could use the total area in this equation to obtain the same moment of inertia, we would have to multiply the area by the square of a specific distance known as the *radius of gyration*. In other words, $I_z = r_z^2 A$, whence

$$r_x = \sqrt{\frac{I_z}{A}} \qquad\qquad (A.5)$$

The value of the radius of gyration should be thought of as a convenient term, closely related to the moment of inertia and often appearing in engineering formulas in which the moment of inertia would otherwise appear.

The units of radii of gyration used in strength of materials are usually expressed in inches.

Illustrative Problem 3.   Determine the radius of gyration about the centroidal axes of the figure used in Illustrative Problem 2.

SOLUTION.

$$r_y = \sqrt{\frac{I_x}{A}} = \sqrt{\frac{39.09}{16}} = \sqrt{2.44} = 1.56 \text{ in.}$$

$$r_x = \sqrt{\frac{I_y}{A}} = \sqrt{\frac{20.34}{16}} = \sqrt{1.27} = 1.13 \text{ in.}$$

PROBLEMS

A-4a, b, c, d, e, f, g, h. Determine the centroidal moments of inertia I_x and I_y of the similarly lettered area found in Problem A-1.

A-5. Determine the centroidal moments of inertia I_x and I_y and the corresponding radii of gyration of the angle section shown in Fig. A-11.

Figure A-11   Figure A-12

A-6. (a) Find the moment of inertia of the area shown in Fig. A-12 about the *x-x* axis. (b) Determine the radius of gyration about the same axis. *Answer:* $I_{x\text{-}x} = 1256$ in.[4], $r_{x\text{-}x} = 6.82$ in.

A-7. The base of a triangle is 6 in. and its altitude is 8 in. Find the moment of inertia and radius of gyration of the area of the triangle with respect to the base. *Answer:* $I = 256$ in.^{4}, $r = 3.27$ in.

A-8. Determine the moment of inertia of the area of a circle, with respect to an axis tangent to the circle, in terms of r, the radius of the circle.

POLAR MOMENT OF INERTIA

A-9. General principles

The polar moment of inertia of an area is distinguished from the moment of inertia previously described by the position of the axis about which the area is assumed to rotate. Whereas previously the axis was located in the plane of the area, the axis for the determination of a polar moment of inertia is always located perpendicular to the plane. This change, however, does not create a radical difference in the concept of the two types of moments of inertia, since the polar type is also a measure of the resistance of a material within a given area due solely to its shape and location. Its general formula is also quite similar — namely.

$$J = \int \rho^2 \, dA \qquad (A.6)$$

Figure A-13

An investigation of this general formula reveals that as dA is located further from the polar axis, the value of J, a measure of resistance, increases. (See Fig. A-13.)

Typical of the problems requiring a determination of polar moment of inertia is that of the shaft. As a shaft increases in diameter, its cross-sectional area, polar moment of inertia J, and its capacity for resisting torque also increase.

The polar moments of inertia of several common cross-sectional areas are given in Table 14.

A-10. A polar moment-of-inertia relationship

A very important relationship between the two types of moments of inertia previously described is discussed below. Familiarity with this relationship will help simplify the solution of many design problems involving irregular cross sections, and will develop a broader concept of the nature of bending and twisting resistance.

Figure A-14

Since $J = \int \rho^2 \, dA$ and, from Fig. A-14, $\rho^2 = x^2 + z^2$, we may write,

$$J = \int (x^2 + z^2) \, dA$$

or

$$J = \int x^2 \, dA + \int z^2 \, dA$$

$$J_y = I_z + I_z \tag{A.7}$$

The two latter values will be recognized as the regular moments of inertia of dA about the x and z axes. Thus, if we know the moments of inertia of an area about two mutually perpendicular intersecting axes located in the plane of the area, the polar moment of inertia about an axis perpendicular to the plane at the point of intersection of the two axes will be equal to the sum of the two.

Could J ever be smaller than either $I_{x\text{-}x}$ or $I_{y\text{-}y}$?

PROBLEMS

A-9. Find the polar moment of inertia of the angle shown in Fig. A-11 about its center of gravity.

A-10. Find the polar moment of inertia of the channel section shown in Fig. A-4(b) about the intersection of the centroidal axes.

THE PRODUCT OF INERTIA

A-11. *General principles*

The product of inertia is defined by the integral

$$I_{xy} = \int xy \, dA \tag{A.9}$$

Figure A-15

in which x and y are the distances of the differential area dA from two perpendicular reference axes (Fig. A-15). Inasmuch as these reference axes may pass through an area it is obvious that the values of x and y may be positive or negative, providing similar sign possibilities for I_{xy}. Should an area be symmetrical about one of these axes, say the x, there will be a positive y value for every similar negative y value, canceling the products $xy\, dA$ and making the product of inertia I_{xy} equal to zero. Thus, the product of inertia of a rectangle with respect to two perpendicular axes, one of which is a centroidal axis, is zero.

A-12. *Transfer theorem — product of inertia*

Figure A-16

If the product of inertia of an area is known with respect to two perpendicular axes x and y passing thru its centroid, the product of inertia with respect to any other parallel pair of axes x' and y' may be obtained easily as follows. Consider the area shown in Fig. A-16. Its product of inertia with respect to the x' and y' axes is expressed mathematically by

$$I_{x'y'} = \int x'y'\, dA \qquad (A.10)$$

But because $x' = x + a$ and $y' = y + b$, the foregoing expression may be written as

$$I_{x'y'} = \int (x + a)(y + b)\, dA$$

or
$$I_{x'y'} = \int xy\, dA + \int bx\, dA + \int ay\, dA + \int ab\, dA$$

The middle two integrals, however, equal zero since the x and y axes are centroidal axes. The equation above may therefore be expressed as

$$I_{x'y'} = \int xy\, dA + \int ab\, dA$$

or
$$I_{x'y'} = I_{\overline{xy}} + Aab \qquad (A.11)$$

in which $I_{\overline{xy}}$ is the product of inertia with respect to the centroidal axes.

Illustrative Problem 4. Determine the product of inertia of the area shown in Fig. A-17 about axes x' and y'.

Figure A-17

SOLUTION. It is obvious that the two subdivided areas I and II are symmetrical about pairs of rectangular axes. The products of inertia of these areas about their own centroidal axes are therefore zero. Because the product of inertia of the total area is equal to the products of inertia of the several parts, we may write

$$I_{x'y'} = (I_{\overline{xy}} + Aab)_I + (I_{\overline{xy}} + Aab)_{II}$$

Simplified, this expression becomes

$$\begin{aligned} I_{x'y'} &= (Aab)_I + (Aab)_{II} \\ &= (6)(-\tfrac{1}{2})(1) + (10)(2)(2.5) \\ &= -3 + 50 = 47 \text{ in.}^4 \end{aligned}$$

Had the area been subdivided in the manner shown in Fig. A-17(b), the answer would have been the same.

$$\begin{aligned} I_{x'y'} &= (Aab)_I + (Aab)_{II} \\ &= (10)(\tfrac{1}{2})(1) + (6)(2)(3\tfrac{1}{2}) \\ &= +5 + 42 = 47 \text{ in.}^4 \end{aligned}$$

PROBLEMS

A-11. Determine the product of inertia of the area shown in Fig. A-9(a) and (b) using the x and y axes shown.

A-12. Determine the product of inertia of the angle section shown in Fig. A-11 about its centroidal axes.

A-13. Determine the product of inertia of a right angle triangle about the axes coincident with its two legs.

MOMENTS OF INERTIA ABOUT
INCLINED AXES

A-13. General principles

For unsymmetrical areas, such as shown in Fig. A-1(b), moments of inertia may be arbitrarily determined with respect to axes x and y passing through their centroid. There is no guarantee, however, that either of these moments of inertia will be a maximum. On the contrary, the maximum moment of inertia for such an unsymmetrical area will invariably be found to occur about an axis inclined to the x and y axes. Because of the need for knowing the magnitude of the maximum and minimum moments of inertia and the axes on which they act in problems of unsymmetrical bending, the relationship of moments of inertia about inclined axes will now be presented.

Figure A-18

In order to express the moment of inertia about the w and z axes in terms of the moments of inertia about the x and y axes, the following distance relationships taken from Fig. A-18 will be required.

$$z = y \cos \theta - x \sin \theta \qquad m = y \sin \theta + x \cos \theta$$

Then

$$I_w = \int z^2 \, dA = \int (y^2 \cos^2 \theta - 2xy \sin \theta \cos \theta + x^2 \sin^2 \theta) \, dA \quad \text{(A.12a)}$$

$$I_z = \int m^2 \, dA = \int (y^2 \sin^2 \theta + 2xy \sin \theta \cos \theta + x^2 \cos^2 \theta) \, dA \quad \text{(A.12b)}$$

But $\quad I_x = \int y^2 \, dA \qquad I_y = \int x^2 \, dA \quad$ and $\quad I_{xy} = \int xy \, dA$

Therefore, Eq. A.12(a) becomes

$$I_w = I_x \cos^2 \theta + I_y \sin^2 \theta - I_{xy} \sin 2\theta$$

or expressing the $\cos^2 \theta$ and $\sin^2 \theta$ in double angle functions,

$$I_w = \frac{I_x + I_y}{2} + \frac{I_x - I_y}{2} \cos 2\theta - I_{xy} \sin 2\theta \qquad (A.13a)$$

Similarly, Eq. A.12(b) becomes

$$I_z = \frac{I_x + I_y}{2} - \frac{I_x - I_y}{2} \cos 2\theta + I_{xy} \sin 2\theta \qquad (A.13b)$$

Thus, if the values of I_x, I_y, and I_{xy} are known for any pair of perpendicular axes and the angle θ to any inclined pair, the value of I_z may be directly computed.

Differentiating Eqs. A.13(a) and A.13(b) with respect to θ and setting them equal to zero reveals that the maximum or minimum moments of inertia occur on planes whose

$$\tan 2\theta_{\substack{max. \\ min.}} = \frac{2I_{xy}}{I_y - I_x} \qquad (A.14)$$

If the two θ angles which obey this function are now substituted in Eqs. A.13(a) and A.13(b), the maximum and minimum moments of inertia are obtained as follows

$$I_W = \frac{I_x - I_y}{2} + \sqrt{\left(\frac{I_x - I_y}{2}\right)^2 + I_{xy}^2} \qquad (A.15)$$

$$I_Z = \frac{I_x + I_y}{2} - \sqrt{\left(\frac{I_x - I_y}{2}\right)^2 + I_{xy}^2} \qquad (A.16)$$

The similarity of Eqs. A.15 and A.16 to Eq. 12.17 reveals the applicability of Mohr's circle for combined stresses to finding moments of inertia on inclined planes, as well as their maximum and minimum values.

A further relationship. If Eqs. A.15 and A.16 are added, a further significant relationship is obtained, namely,

$$I_z + I_w = I_x + I_y \qquad (A.17)$$

Stated verbally, this equation declares that the sum of the moments of inertia with respect to any pair of rectangular axes having a common origin is a constant quantity.

Illustrative Problem 5. If the values I_x, I_y, and I_{xy} of a certain unsymmetrical section equals, respectively, 200, 1000, and -300 in.[4], determine the maximum and minimum moments of inertia and the planes on which they act.

SOLUTION. The direction of the planes requested are defined by Eq. A.14. Thus

$$\tan 2\theta = \frac{2(-300)}{1000 - 200} = \frac{-600}{800} = -0.75$$

$$2\theta = 36°52' \quad \text{or} \quad 216°52'$$

$$\theta = 18°26' \quad \text{or} \quad 108°26'$$

The maximum and minimum moments of inertia will be obtained by Eqs. A.15 and A.16.

$$I_W = \frac{I_x + I_y}{2} + \sqrt{\left(\frac{I_x - I_y}{2}\right)^2 + I^2_{xy}}$$

$$= \frac{200 + 1000}{2} + \sqrt{\left(\frac{-800}{2}\right)^2 + (-300)^2}$$

$$= 600 + 500 = 1100 \text{ in.}^4$$

$$I_Z = 600 - 500 = 100 \text{ in.}^4$$

The solution to this problem may also have been obtained by drawing a Mohr's circle as shown in Fig. A-19.

Figure A-19

PROBLEMS

A-14. If an area has I_x, I_y, and I_{xy} equal, respectively, to 300, 600, and 200 in.^{4}, determine its maximum and minimum moments of inertia. On what planes will these moments of inertia act with respect to the x and y axes used for I_x and I_y?

A-15. Solve the previous problem if I_x, I_y, and I_{xy} were, respectively, 400, 800, and -200 in.^{4}

A-16. If the maximum and minimum moments of inertia I_W and I_Z, of a certain area are, respectively, 300 and 500 in.^{4}, determine (a) the moments of inertia on planes rotated 30° clockwise with respect to the w and z axes, and (b) the maximum product of inertia.

TABLE 15

AMERICAN STANDARD BEAMS
PROPERTIES FOR DESIGNING

Nominal Size	Weight per Foot	Area	Depth	Flange		Web Thick-ness	AXIS X-X			AXIS Y-Y		
				Width	Thick-ness		I	S	r	I	S	r
In.	Lb.	In.²	In.	In.	In.	In.	In.⁴	In.³	In.	In.⁴	In.³	In.
24 x 7⅞	120.0	35.13	24.00	8.048	1.102	.798	3010.8	250.9	9.26	84.9	21.1	1.56
	105.9	30.98	24.00	7.875	1.102	.625	2811.5	234.3	9.53	78.9	20.0	1.60
24 x 7	100.0	29.25	24.00	7.247	.871	.747	2371.8	197.6	9.05	48.4	13.4	1.29
	90.0	26.30	24.00	7.124	.871	.624	2230.1	185.8	9.21	45.5	12.8	1.32
	79.9	23.33	24.00	7.000	.871	.500	2087.2	173.9	9.46	42.9	12.2	1.36
20 x 7	95.0	27.74	20.00	7.200	.916	.800	1599.7	160.0	7.59	50.5	14.0	1.35
	85.0	24.80	20.00	7.053	.916	.653	1501.7	150.2	7.78	47.0	13.3	1.38
20 x 6¼	75.0	21.90	20.00	6.391	.789	.641	1263.5	126.3	7.60	30.1	9.4	1.17
	65.4	19.08	20.00	6.250	.789	.500	1169.5	116.9	7.83	27.9	8.9	1.21
18 x 6	70.0	20.46	18.00	6.251	.691	.711	917.5	101.9	6.70	24.5	7.8	1.09
	54.7	15.94	18.00	6.000	.691	.460	795.5	88.4	7.07	21.2	7.1	1.15
15 x 5½	50.0	14.59	15.00	5.640	.622	.550	481.1	64.2	5.74	16.0	5.7	1.05
	42.9	12.49	15.00	5.500	.622	.410	441.8	58.9	5.95	14.6	5.3	1.08
12 x 5¼	50.0	14.57	12.00	5.477	.659	.687	301.6	50.3	4.55	16.0	5.8	1.05
	40.8	11.84	12.00	5.250	.659	.460	268.9	44.8	4.77	13.8	5.3	1.08
12 x 5	35.0	10.20	12.00	5.078	.544	.428	227.0	37.8	4.72	10.0	3.9	.99
	31.8	9.26	12.00	5.000	.544	.350	215.8	36.0	4.83	9.5	3.8	1.01
10 x 4⅝	35.0	10.22	10.00	4.944	.491	.594	145.8	29.2	3.78	8.5	3.4	.91
	25.4	7.38	10.00	4.660	.491	.310	122.1	24.4	4.07	6.9	3.0	.97
8 x 4	23.0	6.71	8.00	4.171	.425	441	64.2	16.0	3.09	4.4	2.1	.81
	18.4	5.34	8.00	4.000	.425	.270	56.9	14.2	3.26	3.8	1.9	.84
7 x 3⅝	20.0	5.83	7.00	3.860	.392	.450	41.9	12.0	2.68	3.1	1.6	.74
	15.3	4.43	7.00	3.660	.392	.250	36.2	10.4	2.86	2.7	1.5	.78
6 x 3⅜	17.25	5.02	6.00	3.565	.359	.465	26.0	8.7	2.28	2.3	1.3	.68
	12.5	3.61	6.00	3.330	.359	.230	21.8	7.3	2.46	1.8	1.1	.72
5 x 3	14.75	4.29	5.00	3.284	.326	.494	15.0	6.0	1.87	1.7	1.0	.63
	10.0	2.87	5.00	3.000	.326	.210	12.1	4.8	2.05	1.2	.82	.65
4 x 2⅝	9.5	2.76	4.00	2.796	.293	.326	6.7	3.3	1.56	.91	.65	.58
	7.7	2.21	4.00	2.660	.293	.190	6.0	3.0	1.64	.77	.58	.59
3 x 2⅜	7.5	2.17	3.00	2.509	.260	.349	2.9	1.9	1.15	.59	.47	.52
	5.7	1.64	3.00	2.330	.260	.170	2.5	1.7	1.23	.46	.40	.53

TABLE 16

WF SHAPES

PROPERTIES FOR DESIGNING

(SELECTED LIST)

Nominal Size	Weight per Foot	Area	Depth	Flange		Web Thickness	AXIS X-X			AXIS Y-Y		
				Width	Thickness		I	S	r	I	S	r
In.	Lb.	In.²	In.	In.	In.	In.	In.⁴	In.³	In.	In.⁴	In.³	In.
14 x 16	426	125.25	18.69	16.695	3.033	1.875	6610.3	707.4	7.26	2359.5	282.7	4.34
	264	77.63	16.50	16.025	1.938	1.205	3526.0	427.4	6.74	1331.2	166.1	4.14
	167	49.09	15.12	15.600	1.248	.780	2020.8	267.3	6.42	790.2	101.3	4.01
	158	46.47	15.00	15.550	1.188	.730	1900.6	253.4	6.40	745.0	95.8	4.00
	150	44.08	14.88	15.515	1.128	.695	1786.9	240.2	6.37	702.5	90.6	3.99
	142	41.85	14.75	15.500	1.063	.680	1672.2	226.7	6.32	660.1	85.2	3.97
14 x 14½	136	39.98	14.75	14.740	1.063	.660	1593.0	216.0	6.31	567.7	77.0	3.77
	127	37.33	14.62	14.690	.998	.610	1476.7	202.0	6.29	527.6	71.8	3.76
	119	34.99	14.50	14.650	.938	.570	1373.1	189.4	6.26	491.8	67.1	3.75
	111	32.65	14.37	14.620	.873	.540	1266.5	176.3	6.23	454.9	62.2	3.73
	103	30.26	14.25	14.575	.813	.495	1165.8	163.6	6.21	419.7	57.6	3.72
	95	27.94	14.12	14.545	.748	.465	1063.5	150.6	6.17	383.7	52.8	3.71
	87	25.56	14.00	14.500	.688	.420	966.9	138.1	6.15	349.7	48.2	3.70
14 x 12	84	24.71	14.18	12.023	.778	.451	928.4	130.9	6.13	225.5	37.5	3.02
	78	22.94	14.06	12.000	.718	.428	851.2	121.1	6.09	206.9	34.5	3.00
12 x 12	85	24.98	12.50	12.105	.796	.495	723.3	115.7	5.38	235.5	38.9	3.07
	79	23.22	12.38	12.080	.736	.470	663.0	107.1	5.34	216.4	35.8	3.05
	72	21.16	12.25	12.040	.671	.430	597.4	97.5	5.31	195.3	32.4	3.04
	65	19.11	12.12	12.000	.606	.390	533.4	88.0	5.28	174.6	29.1	3.02
12 x 10	58	17.06	12.19	10.014	.641	.359	476.1	78.1	5.28	107.4	21.4	2.51
	53	15.59	12.06	10.000	.576	.345	426.2	70.7	5.23	96.1	19.2	2.48
10 x 10	66	19.41	10.38	10.117	.748	.457	382.5	73.7	4.44	129.2	25.5	2.58
	60	17.66	10.25	10.075	.683	.415	343.7	67.1	4.41	116.5	23.1	2.57
	54	15.88	10.12	10.028	.618	.368	305.7	60.4	4.39	103.9	20.7	2.56
	49	14.40	10.00	10.000	.558	.340	272.9	54.6	4.35	93.0	18.6	2.54
10 x 8	45	13.24	10.12	8.022	.618	.350	248.6	49.1	4.33	53.2	13.3	2.00
	39	11.48	9.94	7.990	.528	.318	209.7	42.2	4.27	44.9	11.2	1.98
	33	9.71	9.75	7.964	.433	.292	170.9	35.0	4.20	36.5	9.2	1.94
8 x 8	48	14.11	8.50	8.117	.683	.405	183.7	43.2	3.61	60.9	15.0	2.08
	40	11.76	8.25	8.077	.558	.365	146.3	35.5	3.53	49.0	12.1	2.04
	35	10.30	8.12	8.027	.493	.315	126.5	31.1	3.50	42.5	10.6	2.03
	31	9.12	8.00	8.000	.433	.288	109.7	27.4	3.47	37.0	9.2	2.01
8 x 6½	28	8.23	8.06	6.540	.463	.285	97.8	24.3	3.45	21.6	6.6	1.62
	24	7.06	7.93	6.500	.398	.245	82.5	20.8	3.42	18.2	5.6	1.61

TABLE 17

AMERICAN STANDARD CHANNELS
PROPERTIES FOR DESIGNING

Nominal Size	Weight per Foot	Area	Depth	Flange		Web Thickness	AXIS X-X			AXIS Y-Y			
				Width	Average Thickness		I	S	r	I	S	r	x
In.	Lb.	In.²	In.	In.	In.	In.	In.⁴	In.³	In.	In.⁴	In.³	In.	In.
*18 x 4	58.0	16.98	18.00	4.200	.625	.700	670.7	74.5	6.29	18.5	5.6	1.04	.88
	51.9	15.18	18.00	4.100	.625	.600	622.1	69.1	6.40	17.1	5.3	1.06	.87
	45.8	13.38	18.00	4.000	.625	.500	573.5	63.7	6.55	15.8	5.1	1.09	.89
	42.7	12.48	18.00	3.950	.625	.450	549.2	61.0	6.64	15.0	4.9	1.10	.90
15 x 3⅜	50.0	14.64	15.00	3.716	.650	.716	401.4	53.6	5.24	11.2	3.8	.87	.80
	40.0	11.70	15.00	3.520	.650	.520	346.3	46.2	5.44	9.3	3.4	.89	.78
	33.9	9.90	15.00	3.400	.650	.400	312.6	41.7	5.62	8.2	3.2	.91	.79
12 x 3	30.0	8.79	12.00	3.170	.501	.510	161.2	26.9	4.28	5.2	2.1	.77	.68
	25.0	7.32	12.00	3.047	.501	.387	143.5	23.9	4.43	4.5	1.9	.79	.68
	20.7	6.03	12.00	2.940	.501	.280	128.1	21.4	4.61	3.9	1.7	.81	.70
10 x 2⅝	30.0	8.80	10.00	3.033	.436	.673	103.0	20.6	3.42	4.0	1.7	.67	.65
	25.0	7.33	10.00	2.886	.436	.526	90.7	18.1	3.52	3.4	1.5	.68	.62
	20.0	5.86	10.00	2.739	.436	.379	78.5	15.7	3.66	2.8	1.3	.70	.61
	15.3	4.47	10.00	2.600	.436	.240	66.9	13.4	3.87	2.3	1.2	.72	.64
9 x 2½	20.0	5.86	9.00	2.648	.413	.448	60.6	13.5	3.22	2.4	1.2	.65	.59
	15.0	4.39	9.00	2.485	.413	.285	50.7	11.3	3.40	1.9	1.0	.67	.59
	13.4	3.89	9.00	2.430	.413	.230	47.3	10.5	3.49	1.8	.97	.67	.61
8 x 2¼	18.75	5.49	8.00	2.527	.390	.487	43.7	10.9	2.82	2.0	1.0	.60	.57
	13.75	4.02	8.00	2.343	.390	.303	35.8	9.0	2.99	1.5	.86	.62	.56
	11.5	3.36	8.00	2.260	.390	.220	32.3	8.1	3.10	1.3	.79	.63	.58
7 x 2⅛	14.75	4.32	7.00	2.299	.366	.419	27.1	7.7	2.51	1.4	.79	.57	.53
	12.25	3.58	7.00	2.194	.366	.314	24.1	6.9	2.59	1.2	.71	.58	.53
	9.8	2.85	7.00	2.090	.366	.210	21 1	6.0	2.72	.98	.63	.59	.55
6 x 2	13.0	3.81	6.00	2.157	.343	.437	17.3	5.8	2.13	1.1	.65	.53	.52
	10.5	3.07	6.00	2.034	.343	.314	15.1	5.0	2.22	.87	.57	.53	.50
	8.2	2.39	6.00	1.920	.343	.200	13.0	4.3	2.34	.70	.50	.54	.52
5 x 1¾	9.0	2.63	5.00	1.885	.320	.325	8.8	3.5	1.83	.64	.45	.49	.48
	6.7	1.95	5.00	1.750	.320	190	7.4	3.0	1.95	.48	.38	.50	.49
4 x 1⅝	7.25	2.12	4.00	1.720	.296	.320	4.5	2.3	1.47	.44	.35	.46	.46
	5.4	1.56	4.00	1.580	.296	.180	3.8	1.9	1.56	.32	.29	.45	.46
3 x 1½	6.0	1.75	3.00	1.596	.273	.356	2.1	1.4	1.08	.31	.27	.42	.46
	5.0	1.46	3.00	1.498	.273	.258	1.8	1.2	1.12	.25	.24	.41	.44
	4.1	1.19	3.00	1.410	.273	170	1.6	1.1	1.17	.20	.21	.41	.44

*Car and Shipbuilding Channel; not an American Standard.

TABLE 18

ANGLES
UNEQUAL LEGS
PROPERTIES FOR DESIGNING
(SELECTED LIST)

Size	Thickness	Weight per Foot	Area	AXIS X-X				AXIS Y-Y				AXIS Z-Z	
				I	S	r	y	I	S	r	x	r	Tan α
In.	In.	Lb.	In.²	In.⁴	In.³	In.	In.	In.⁴	In.³	In.	In.	In.	
9 x 4	1	40.8	12.00	97.0	17.6	2.84	3.50	12.0	4.0	1.00	1.00	.83	.203
	¾	31.3	9.19	76.1		2.88	3.41	9.6	3.1	1.02	.91	.84	.212
	⁹⁄₁₆	23.8	7.00	59.1	10.4	2.91	3.33	7.6	2.4	1.04	.83	.85	.218
	½	21.3	6.25	53.2	9.3	2.92	3.31	6.9	2.2	1.05	.81	.85	.220
8 x 6	¾	33.8	9.94	63.4	11.7	2.53	2.56	30.7	6.9	1.76	1.56	1.29	.551
	⅝	28.5	8.36	54.1	9.9	2.54	2.52	26.3	5.9	1.77	1.52	1.29	.554
	⁹⁄₁₆	25.7	7.56	49.3	9.0	2.55	2.50	24.0	5.3	1.78	1.50	1.30	.556
	½	23.0	6.75	44.3	8.0	2.56	2.47	21.7	4.8	1.79	1.47	1.30	.558
	⁷⁄₁₆	20.2	5.93	39.2	7.1	2.57	2.45	19.3	4.2	1.80	1.45	1.31	.560
8 x 4	⅝	24.2	7.11	46.9	9.2	2.57	2.91	8.1	2.6	1.07	.91	.86	.262
	⁹⁄₁₆	21.9	6.43	42.8	8.4	2.58	2.88	7.4	2.4	1.07	.88	.86	.265
	½	19.6	5.75	38.5	7.5	2.59	2.86	6.7	2.2	1.08	.86	.86	.267
	⁷⁄₁₆	17.2	5.06	34.1	6.6	2.60	2.83	6.0	1.9	1.09	.83	.87	.269
7 x 4	⁹⁄₁₆	20.0	5.87	29.6	6.5	2.24	2.44	7.2	2.4	1.11	.94	.87	.332
	½	17.9	5.25	26.7	5.8	2.25	2.42	6.5	2.1	1.11	.92	.87	.335
	⁷⁄₁₆	15.8	4.62	23.7	5.1	2.26	2.39	5.8	1.9	1.12	.89	.88	.337
	⅜	13.6	3.98	20.6	4.4	2.27	2.37	5.1	1.6	1.13	.87	.88	.339
6 x 4	⁷⁄₁₆	14.3	4.18	15.5	3.8	1.92	1.96	5.6	1.9	1.16	.96	.87	.443
	⅜	12.3	3.61	13.5	3.3	1.93	1.94	4.9	1.6	1.17	.94	.88	.446
	⁵⁄₁₆	10.3	3.03	11.4	2.8	1.94	1.92	4.2	1.4	1.17	.92	.88	.449
6 x 3½	⁵⁄₁₆	9.8	2.87	10 9	2.7	1.95	2.01	2.9	1.0	1.00	.76	.77	.352
	¼	7.9	2.31	8.9	2.2	1.96	1.99	2.3	0.85	1.01	.74	.78	.355
5 x 3½	⁷⁄₁₆	12.0	3.53	8.9	2.6	1.59	1.63	3.6	1.4	1.01	.88	.76	.482
	⅜	10.4	3.05	7.8	2.3	1.60	1.61	3.2	1.2	1.02	.86	.76	.486
	⁵⁄₁₆	8.7	2.56	6.6	1.9	1.61	1.59	2.7	1.0	1.03	.84	.76	.489
	¼	7.0	2.06	5.4	1.6	1.61	1.56	2.2	.83	1.04	.81	.76	.492

TABLE 18 (*Continued*)

ANGLES
UNEQUAL LEGS.

PROPERTIES FOR DESIGNING
(SELECTED LIST)

Size	Thickness	Weight per Foot	Area	AXIS X-X				AXIS Y-Y				AXIS Z-Z	
				I	S	r	y	I	S	r	x	r	Tan α
In.	In.	Lb.	In.²	In.⁴	In.³	In.	In.	In.⁴	In.³	In.	In.	In.	
5 x 3	⅜	9.8	2.86	7.4	2.2	1.61	1.70	2.0	.89	.84	.70	.65	.364
	⁵⁄₁₆	8.2	2.40	6.3	1.9	1.61	1.68	1.8	.75	.85	.68	.66	.368
	¼	6.6	1.94	5.1	1.5	1.62	1.66	1.4	.61	.86	.66	.66	.371
4 x 3½	⁷⁄₁₆	10.6	3.09	4.8	1.7	1.24	1.23	3.4	1.4	1.05	.98	:72	.753
	⅜	9.1	2.67	4.2	1.5	1.25	1.21	3.0	1.2	1.06	.96	.73	.755
	⁵⁄₁₆	7.7	2.25	3.6	1.3	1.26	1.18	2.6	1.0	1.07	.93	.73	.757
	¼	6.2	1.81	2.9	1.0	1.27	1.16	2.1	.81	1.07	.91	.73	.759
4 x 3	⁷⁄₁₆	9.8	2.87	4.5	1.7	1.25	1.30	2.2	1.0	.87	.80	.64	.547
	⅜	8.5	2.48	4.0	1.5	1.26	1.28	1.9	.87	.88	.78	.64	.551
	⁵⁄₁₆	7.2	2.09	3.4	1.2	1.27	1.26	1.7	.73	.89	.76	.65	.554
	¼	5.8	1.69	2.8	1.0	1.28	1.24	1.4	.60	.90	.74	.65	.558
3½ x 3	⅜	7.9	2.30	2.7	1.1	1.09	1.08	1.9	.85	.90	.83	.62	.721
	⁵⁄₁₆	6.6	1.93	2.3	.95	1.10	1.06	1.6	.72	.90	.81	.63	.724
	¼	5.4	1.56	1.9	.78	1.11	1.04	1.3	.59	.91	.79	.63	.727
3½ x 2½	⁷⁄₁₆	8.3	2.43	2.9	1.3	1.09	1.18	1.2	.68	.71	.68	.54	.491
	⅜	7.2	2.11	2.6	1.1	1.10	1.16	1.1	.59	.72	.66	.54	.496
	⁵⁄₁₆	6.1	1.78	2.2	.93	1.11	1.14	.94	.50	.73	.64	.54	.501
	¼	4.9	1.44	1.8	.75	1.12	1.11	.78	.41	.74	.61	.54	.506
3 x 2½	⅜	6.6	1.92	1.7	.81	.93	.96	1.0	.58	.74	.71	.52	.676
	⁵⁄₁₆	5.6	1.62	1.4	.69	.94	.93	.90	.49	.74	.68	.53	.680
	¼	4.5	1.31	1.2	.56	.95	.91	.74	.40	.75	.66	.53	.684
3 x 2	⁵⁄₁₆	5.0	1.47	1.3	.66	.95	1.02	.47	.32	.57	.52	.43	.435
	¼	4.1	1.19	1.1	.54	.95	.99	.39	.26	.57	.49	.43	.440
	³⁄₁₆	3.07	.90	.84	.41	.97	.97	.31	.20	.58	.47	.44	.446
2½ x 2	¼	3.62	1.06	.65	.38	.78	.79	.37	.25	.59	.54	.42	.626
	⁵⁄₁₆	2.75	.81	.51	.29	.79	.76	.29	.20	.60	.51	.43	.631

TABLE 18 (*Concluded*)

Size	Thick-ness	Weight per Foot	Area	AXIS X-X				AXIS Y-Y				AXIS Z-Z	
				I	S	r	y	I	S	r	x	r	Tan α
In.	In.	Lb.	In.²	In.⁴	In.³	In.	In.	In.⁴	In.³	In.	In.	In.	In.
2½×1½	¼	3.19	.94	.59	.36	.79	.88	.16	.14	.41	.38	.32	.357
	³⁄₁₆	2.44	.72	.46	.28	.80	.85	.13	.11	.42	.35	.33	.364
2 x 1½	³⁄₁₆	2.12	.62	.25	.18	.63	.64	.12	.11	.44	.39	.32	.551
	⅛	1.44	.42	.17	.13	.64	.62	.09	.08	.45	.37	.33	.558
1¾×1¼	³⁄₁₆	1.80	.53	.16	.14	.55	.58	.07	.08	.36	.33	.27	.496
	⅛	1.23	.36	.11	.09	.56	.56	.05	.05	.37	.31	.27	.506

TABLE 19

ANGLES
EQUAL LEGS

PROPERTIES FOR DESIGNING
(SELECTED LIST)

| Size | Thickness | Weight per Foot | Area | AXIS X-X AND AXIS Y-Y | | | | AXIS Z-Z |
				I	S	r	x or y	r
In.	In.	Lb.	In.²	In.⁴	In.³	In.	In.	In.
8 x 8	¾	38.9	11.44	69.7	12.2	2.47	2.28	1.57
	⅝	32.7	9.61	59.4	10.3	2.49	2.23	1.58
	9/16	29.6	8.68	54.1	9.3	2.50	2.21	1.58
	½	26.4	7.75	48.6	8.4	2.50	2.19	1.59
6 x 6	¾	28.7	8.44	28.2	6.7	1.83	1.78	1.17
	⅝	24.2	7.11	24.2	5.7	1.84	1.73	1.18
	9/16	21.9	6.43	22.1	5.1	1.85	1.71	1.18
	½	19.6	5.75	19.9	4.6	1.86	1.68	1.18
	7/16	17.2	5.06	17.7	4.1	1.87	1.66	1.19
	⅜	14.9	4.36	15.4	3.5	1.88	1.64	1.19
	5/16	12.5	3.66	13.0	3.0	1.89	1.61	1.19
5 x 5	½	16.2	4.75	11.3	3.2	1.54	1.43	.98
	7/16	14.3	4.18	10.0	2.8	1.55	1.41	.98
	⅜	12.3	3.61	8.7	2.4	1.56	1.39	.99
	5/16	10.3	3.03	7.4	2.0	1.57	1.37	.99
4 x 4	7/16	11.3	3.31	5.0	1.8	1.23	1.16	.78
	⅜	9.8	2.86	4.4	1.5	1.23	1.14	.79
	5/16	8.2	2.40	3.7	1.3	1.24	1.12	.79
	¼	6.6	1.94	3.0	1.1	1.25	1.09	.80
3½ x 3½	5/16	7.2	2.09	2.5	.98	1.08	.99	.69
	¼	5.8	1.69	2.0	.79	1.09	.97	.69
3 x 3	5/16	6.1	1.78	1.5	.71	.92	.87	.59
	¼	4.9	1.44	1.2	.58	.93	.84	.59
	3/16	3.71	1.09	.96	.44	.94	.82	.59
2½ x 2½	¼	4.1	1.19	.70	.39	.77	.72	.49
	3/16	3.07	.90	.55	.30	.78	.69	.49
2 x 2	¼	3.19	.94	.35	.25	.61	.59	.39
	3/16	2.44	.71	.27	.19	.62	.57	.39
	⅛	1.65	.48	.19	.13	.63	.55	.40
1¾ x 1¾	3/16	2.12	.62	.18	.14	.54	.51	.34
	⅛	1.44	.42	.13	.10	.55	.48	.35

TABLE 19 (*Concluded*)

Size	Thickness	Weight per Foot	Area	AXIS X-X AND AXIS Y-Y				AXIS Z-Z
				I	S	r	x or y	r
In.	In.	Lb.	In.^{2}	In.^{4}	In.^{3}	In.	In.	In.
1½ x 1½	3/16	1.80	.53	.11	.10	.46	.44	.29
	1/8	1.23	.36	.08	.07	.47	.42	.30
1¼ x 1¼	3/16	1.48	.43	.06	.07	.38	.38	.24
	1/8	1.01	.30	.04	.05	.38	.36	.25
1 x 1	3/16	1.16	.34	.03	.04	.30	.32	.19
	1/8	.80	.23	.02	.03	.30	.30	.20

T able 20

TIMBER
AMERICAN STANDARD SIZES
PROPERTIES FOR DESIGNING
NATIONAL LUMBER MANUFACTURERS ASSOCIATION

Nominal Size	American Standard Dressed Size	Area of Section	Weight per Foot	Moment of Inertia	Section Modulus
In.	In.	In.²	Lb.	In.⁴	In.³
2 x 4	1⅝x3⅝	5.89	1.64	6.45	3.56
6	5⅝	9.14	2.54	24.1	8.57
8	7½	12.2	3.39	57.1	15.3
10	9½	15.4	4.29	116	24.4
12	11½	18.7	5.19	206	35.8
14	13½	21.9	6.09	333	49.4
16	15½	25.2	6.99	504	65.1
18	17½	28.4	7.90	726	82.9
3 x 4	2⅝x3⅝	9.52	2.64	10.4	5.75
6	5⅝	14.8	4.10	38.9	13.8
8	7½	19.7	5.47	92.3	24.6
10	9½	24.9	6.93	188	39.5
12	11½	30.2	8.39	333	57.9
14	13½	35.4	9.84	538	79.7
16	15½	40.7	11.3	815	105
18	17½	45.9	12.8	1172	134
4 x 4	3⅝x3⅝	13.1	3.65	14.4	7.94
6	5⅝	20.4	5.66	53.8	19.1
8	7½	27.2	7.55	127	34.0
10	9½	34.4	9.57	259	54.5
12	11½	41.7	11.6	459	79.9
14	13½	48.9	13.6	743	110
16	15½	56.2	15.6	1125	145
18	17½	63.4	17.6	1619	185
6 x 6	5½x5½	30.3	8.40	76.3	27.7
8	7½	41.3	11.4	193	51.6
10	9½	52.3	14.5	393	82.7
12	11½	63.3	17.5	697	121
14	13½	74.3	20.6	1128	167
16	15½	85.3	23.6	1707	220
18	17½	96.3	26.7	2456	281
20	19½	107.3	29.8	3398	349
8 x 8	7½x7½	56.3	15.6	264	70.3
10	9½	71.3	19.8	536	113
12	11½	86.3	23.9	951	165
14	13½	101.3	28.0	1538	228
16	15½	116.3	32.0	2327	300
18	17½	131.3	36.4	3350	383
20	19½	146.3	40.6	4634	475
22	21½	161.3	44.8	6211	578

Nominal Size	American Standard Dressed Size	Area of Section	Weight per Foot	Moment of Inertia	Section Modulus
In.	In.	In.²	Lb.	In.⁴	In.³
10x10	9½x9½	90.3	25.0	679	143
12	11½	109	30.3	1204	209
14	13½	128	35.6	1948	289
16	15½	147	40.9	2948	380
18	17½	166	46.1	4243	485
20	19½	185	51.4	5870	602
22	21½	204	56.7	7868	732
24	23½	223	62.0	10274	874
12x12	11½x11½	132	36.7	1458	253
14	13½	155	43.1	2358	349
16	15½	178	49.5	3569	460
18	17½	201	55.9	5136	587
20	19½	224	62.3	7106	729
22	21½	247	68.7	9524	886
24	23½	270	75.0	12437	1058
14x14	13½x13½	182	50.6	2768	410
16	15½	209	58.1	4189	541
18	17½	236	65.6	6029	689
20	19½	263	73.1	8342	856
22	21½	290	80.6	11181	1040
24	23½	317	88.1	14600	1243
16x16	15½x15½	240	66.7	4810	621
18	17½	271	75.3	6923	791
20	19½	302	83.9	9578	982
22	21½	333	92.5	12837	1194
24	23½	364	101	16763	1427
18x18	17½x17½	306	85.0	7816	893
20	19½	341	94.8	10813	1109
22	21½	376	105	14493	1348
24	23½	411	114	18926	1611
26	25½	446	124	24181	1897
20x20	19½x19½	380	106	12049	1236
22	21½	419	116	16150	1502
24	23½	458	127	21089	1795
26	25½	497	138	26945	2113
28	27½	536	149	33795	2458
24x24	23½x23½	552	153	25415	2163
26	25½	599	166	32472	2547
28	27½	646	180	40727	2962
30	29½	693	193	50275	3408

All properties and weights given are for dressed size only.
The weights given above are based on assumed average weight of 40 pounds per cubic foot.

Tables 15 through 20 reproduced by permission of American Institute of Steel Construction, Inc.

BIBLIOGRAPHY

Texts and articles which explain in greater detail the more advanced material of this text.

The Procurement of Experimental Data:
Davis, H. E., Troxell, G.E., and Wiskocil, C. T., *Testing and Inspection of Engineering Materials.* McGraw-Hill Book Co., 1941.
Marin, J., *Mechanical Properties of Materials and Design.* McGraw-Hill Book Co., 1942.

Stresses in Riveted & Welded Joints:
Davis, Woodruff and Davis, "Tension Tests of Large Riveted Joints." *Trans. ASCE,* **105,** 1193, 1243 (1940).
Baron, F., and Larson, E. W., "Comparative Behavior of Bolted and Riveted Joints." *Proc. ASCE,* **80,** Separate No. 470, August 1954.
American Institute of Steel Construction, "Structural Shop Drafting," Vols. 1 and 2.
Churchill, H. D., and Austin, J. B., *Weld Design.* Prentice-Hall, Inc., 1949.

General — Advanced Mechanics of Materials:
Seely, F. B., *Advanced Mechanics of Materials.* John Wiley & Sons, Inc., 1932.
Murray, G., *Advanced Mechanics of Materials*, McGraw-Hill Book Co., Inc., 1946.

The Plastic Theory:
Van den Broek, J. A., "Theory of Limit Design." *Trans. ASCE,* **105,** 638 (1940).
Beedle, L. S., "Plastic Strength of Steel Frames," *Proc. ASCE,* **81,** Paper No. 764, August 1955.

Membrane Analogy:
Marin, J., "Evaluating Torsional Stresses by Membrane Analogy," *Machine Design,* **15,** 118-123 (1943).
Mindlin, R. D., and Salvadori, M. G., "Analogies" in *Handbook of Experimental Stress Analysis* (M. Hetenyi, ed.), Chapter 16, p. 700. John Wiley & Sons, Inc., 1950

Electric Strain Gages:
Perry, C. C. and Lissner, H. R., *The Strain Gage Primer*, McGraw-Hill Book Co., Inc., 1955.
Baldwin-Lima-Hamilton Co., Bulletins on Strain Gages.

Photo Elasticity:
Frocht, M., *Photoelasticity.* John Wiley & Sons, Inc., 1941.

General — Experimental Stress Analysis:
Lee, G. H., *Air Introduction to Experimental Stress Analysis*, John Wiley & Sons, Inc., 1950.
Hetenyi, M., *Handbook of Experimental Stress Analysis*, John Wiley & Sons, Inc., 1950.

Prestressed Concrete:
Lin, T. Y., *Design of Prestressed Concrete Structures.* John Wiley & Sons, Inc., 1956.

INDEX

A

Allowable stress, 61, 62
American Institute of Steel Construction
    Code, 80, 101, 197, 366, 368
    riveted construction, 80
    welded construction, 101
American Railway Engineering Association
    Code, 80
American Railway Engineering Association
    Code, 80
American Welding Society, 100
Angle of twist in shafts, 124
Angles:
    elements of equal leg, 526
    elements of unequal leg, 523
Axially loaded members:
    effect of changing cross section, 43
    statically determinate, 14
    statically indeterminate, 38

B

Beams, 145
    American standard, 519
    cantilever, 146
    continuous, 146, 295
    curved, 469–474
    deflection of, 222–260
    design of, 177–221
    effect of couples on, 173
    effect of lateral buckling in, 197
    internal resistance of, 147
    maximum shearing stress in rectangular,
        209
    non-homogeneous, 474–479
    non-rectangular cross section, 186
    on three supports, 286
    overhanging, 146
    partially restrained, 283
    plastic design of, 309
    radius of curvature, 222
    reinforced concrete, 481

Beams (cont'd.):
    relationship of vertical and horizontal
        shear, 209
    restrained, 146, 261, 271
    sections having two axes of symmetry, 187
    shearing stresses in, 204
    simple, 146
    statically indeterminate, 261–313
    with varying section modulus, 199
Bearing unit stress, 78, 84
Bending moment, 145
    algebraic expressions for, 161
    definition of, 157
    during yield, 204
    maximum, 162, 171
    signs for, 153
Bending-moment diagram, 156, 171
    composite form of, 271
    definition of, 156
    for continuous beams, 288, 296
    for statically indeterminate beams, 265,
        271
    point of inflection, 163
    separated, 254
    shear area method of constructing, 166
Brittle lacquer:
    for principal planes, 433
    for stress concentrations, 447
Buckling action, 345
Butt welds, 97

C

Carry-over factor, 305
Castigliano's theorem, 455
    solution of statically indeterminate mem-
        bers by, 459
Center of gravity, 496–501
    table of important centers of gravity, 501
C frames, 323
Channels, properties of, 521
Chicago Building Code formula, 361
Coefficient of linear expansion, 34
Cold working, effect of, 55

531